2-8-62

*The
Kirtland's
Warbler*

The Kirtland's Warbler

by

Harold Mayfield

CRANBROOK INSTITUTE *of* SCIENCE

Dedicated
to the memory of

Josselyn Van Tyne

friend, field companion, and dedicated scientist
who for half a lifetime had hoped
to write this book

Publisher's Preface

THE KIRTLAND'S WARBLER, or the "Jack-Pine Warbler," as it is often known in Michigan, holds interest well out of proportion to its small population and negligible economic importance. The present confinement of the warbler to Michigan in the nesting season, and its restriction within our State to but part of the range of the jack-pine forests, have led many persons to study it, and at the same time have made study easier because the range is so concentrated. This same concentration has made the Kirtland's Warbler particularly vulnerable to parasitism by the cowbird, and thus a study of the populations has particular biological interest and significance. The winter range has been another matter, for, although these birds are apparently confined to the Bahama Islands at that season, there have been almost no sighting records of them in recent years.

Foremost among the students of the Kirtland's Warbler was the late Josselyn Van Tyne, Curator of Birds at the Museum of Zoology, University of Michigan. Each nesting season for many years he went north to the jack-pine plains to study them, and one winter he sought the birds in the Bahamas. For more than half of those years his field companion was Harold Mayfield of Toledo. Together they learned more about this warbler than, it is believed, has been learned about all but a few passerine birds. Dr. Van Tyne had published a few short accounts of the Kirtland's Warbler, and had intended to write a full report, but after his untimely death in 1957 there could be found only his card records and a few scattered notes. It was fitting that these were turned over to his colleague, Mr. Mayfield, and that he should prepare the final report. Because of Dr. Van Tyne's close association with Cranbrook Institute of Science, where he was a Trustee from 1934 to 1957 and Chairman of its Publications Committee from 1940, we sought the privilege of publishing this book.

We are proud to present this life history of the Kirtland's Warbler which resulted from the long and fruitful collaboration in the field of Van Tyne and Mayfield. To Harold Mayfield we are grateful not only for his scholarly analysis and treatment, but also for the labor of love that brought this book into being.

Dr. and Mrs. H. Lewis Batts, Jr. and Mr. Clarence B. Randall have made substantial financial contributions toward the manufacture of this book, and the Edwin S. George Publication Fund of the Institute, by additional subsidy, made possible our undertaking the project.

The book was designed by William A. Bostick. William Brudon drew the maps. The manuscript was prepared for publication by Dorothy L. Tyler. The color frontispiece, by Roger Tory Peterson, was produced by Barton-Cotton, Inc., of Baltimore, by gracious permission of the present owner of the original painting, Mr. Cyrus Mark. The manufacture of the book was by Kingsport Press, Inc.

R. T. H.

Author's Preface

MORE THAN expression of thanks is needed to acknowledge the part the late Josselyn Van Tyne played in this work. For many years it was *his* study. In 1930 he paid his first visit to the nesting ground of the Kirtland's Warbler, and soon thereafter decided to make a life history study of the species. In twenty-two of the succeeding years—all but four in the period 1930 to 1956—he returned for from one to twenty-five days' further work on the project.

During this time, it was widely known that he was undertaking the study, and information from many sources therefore funneled in to his office at the University of Michigan Museum of Zoology. This was especially appropriate, because his predecessor as Curator of Birds, Norman A. Wood, had been the discoverer of the first nest and had left files on this subject dating back to 1903.

Over a period of years Van Tyne had maintained a fairly complete list of published references to the Kirtland's Warbler. These works, many of them not cited in the body of this report, are included in the bibliography at the end.

On his trips to the nesting ground, Van Tyne usually had one or more companions. I was one of them in 1944, and continued to be closely associated with him until his death on January 30, 1957. Our many trips together included a five-week sojourn in the Bahama Islands in an unsuccessful attempt to find the Kirtland's Warbler on its wintering grounds.

For many years Van Tyne had looked forward to the time when he would write a full account of this bird, but pressing demands of editing, teaching, and curatorship always intervened. His only publications on this topic were short papers for Peterson's *Field Guide* (1947:202–203), for the *Proceedings* of the Tenth International Ornithological Congress (1952:537–544), for Bent's *Life Histories* (1953:417–428, but written in 1946), and for Griscom and Sprunt's *Warblers of North America* (1957:178–181). Also he spoke on various phases of this study at meetings of the American Ornithologists' Union and the Wilson Ornithological Society, but he did so from brief pencilled notes. Consequently, he seems never to have started his general report nor to have drawn a plan for it.

After his untimely death, his widow, Helen Bates Van Tyne, turned over to me the accumulated files on the Kirtland's Warbler. These consisted chiefly of card records, correspondence, and pocket field notes, much of the material handwritten, and some of it cryptic. In interpreting this material I was fortunate in having been a collaborator in much of the field work, well acquainted with the areas visited and the people who participated.

This is truly a cooperative study. Until I began analyzing the records I did not fully realize how many people had made important contributions. It is not possible to name here all who helped gather data. But special mention should be made of the following: Verne Dockham, State Conservation Officer in the nesting region, who has felt a proprietary interest in the well-being of the species for more than 25 years; Lawrence H. Walkinshaw, who began banding and nest studies simultaneously with Van Tyne, and who shared his notes fully and curtailed his own work on the species to avoid duplication; Andrew J. Berger, who helped in field work in the most fruitful years of the study, coordinating his efforts with Van Tyne's and mine so that we could extend the total period of observation, and who shared generously his detailed notes on Kirtland's Warblers reared in his aviary. There were many others who helped in field work at various times, particularly Dr. and Mrs. W. Powell Cottrille, A. William Dyer, Mr. and Mrs. Frederick Hamerstrom, Walter Hastings, Fenn M. Holden, Irene Jorae, Douglas Middleton, Milton B. Trautman, and Mr. and Mrs. Dale Zimmerman.

James L. Baillie helped obtain information on a number of questions pertaining to Ontario, and David K. Wetherbee supplied an analysis of the prenatal down on two specimens. The work of the photographers is acknowledged under each picture: Harry W. Hann, Lawrence D. Hiett, Roger Tory Peterson, Edwin Way Teale, Josselyn Van Tyne, and Lawrence H. Walkinshaw.

From a number of paintings and color photographs of the Kirtland's Warbler, we selected our favorite, Peterson's painting of a family group, for the frontispiece of this book.

Valued suggestions were received from Andrew J. Berger, Robert W. Storer, and Harrison B. Tordoff, who read the entire manuscript; from David E. Davis and Herbert Friedmann, who read the chapters on Cowbird, and Reproduction and Mortality; from

Dale A. Zimmerman, who read the chapters on Nesting Ground, and Mating and Territorial Behavior; from Frank Preston and Donald Borror, who read early drafts of the sections on Cowbird and Song, respectively; from Harrison B. Tordoff and Norman L. Ford, who assisted greatly in checking the bibliography; from Pierce Brodkorb, who was helpful on some questions about the geologic history of the Bahama Islands; and from John Rapparlie, who advised on certain statistical questions.

It was the interest and faith in this work by Robert T. Hatt, Director of the Cranbrook Institute of Science, that brought it to publication, and the painstaking editorship of Dorothy L. Tyler that put it in final form for the reader.

Finally, but not least, I am grateful to Estelle Thomas for the meticulous typing and retyping of this manuscript, much of it from difficult script.

Table of Contents

I

Introduction

The Kirtland's Warbler as a Subject for Study

The Kirtland's Warbler is a bird of unusual interest.

It has great scientific interest because it is a rare and perhaps vanishing species. In this age, when the expansion of man and his works is altering the face of the earth as never before, when one species after another is pressed to the brink of extinction, we have an increasing need to understand the problems of survival in all forms of life, including our own. These problems come into sharpest focus in a species recognized to be in a precarious position.

Also, the Kirtland's Warbler is a fruitful subject for study because it is a member of one of the largest families (the wood warblers, Parulidae) of the largest order of birds. Hence, knowledge of it tends to throw light on all songbirds.

In addition, the Kirtland's Warbler holds much human interest. It is an attractive member of an attractive family. With its bright plumage, spirited song, and trusting manner, it has engendered affection in everyone who has come to know it in the field. The nesting habitat, too—desolate reaches of fire-scarred land covered with little pine trees—has an austere charm of its own, as well as moments of beauty when the dew sparkles on the fresh leaves and the ground is sprinkled with the blossoms of shadbush, bird's-foot violet, harebell, wood lily, and puccoon.

The regional interest in this species is remarkable for a songbird so few people have seen. There are less than 1,000 Kirtland's Warblers. In winter they are probably scattered among the many islands of the Bahamas, where they are unlikely to be seen by anyone. In migration, when hundreds of millions of other warblers are passing through the United States, they are virtually lost in the throng. But in summer all of them nest in a few suitable locations in northern Lower Michigan, where they are regular and conspicuous. So they are regarded as Michigan's special bird. From time to time there have been proposals to make this recognition official, by naming it the

Michigan State Bird. Many years ago its name was given to the bulletin of the Michigan Audubon Society, *The Jack-Pine Warbler*.

Why Is the Kirtland's Warbler So Rare?

Through a study of this kind we should like to be able to explain the rarity of this species. We cannot yet answer that question with complete finality, but our tentative conclusions follow.

The Kirtland's Warbler is a relict species, possibly much more numerous a few thousand years ago when the jack-pine plant association was abundant far south of its present range "on the great expanses of sandy moraines and outwash plains left in the wake of the retreating Wisconsin glaciers" (Zimmerman, 1956:233). From that time until about 1895, the population of Kirtland's Warblers was probably limited by its requirement of a specialized nesting habitat, which has existed in a slowly shrinking amount. At the same time, the nonnomadic character of the bird—that is, its excellent homing abilities—and its tendency to nest in colonies, have stood in the way of its exploiting new areas at any considerable distance from its homeland.

Presumably it has not been able to compete with other birds in more common types of habitats but has found a way of survival in the comparative sanctuary of habitats that are marginal for most other birds and mammals. It spends the greater part of the year in the West Indies, but only on the smaller and more barren islands, the Bahamas. On its nesting ground, too, it finds an "island." Here, in the barrens created by fire, for a brief interval while the pines are small, it finds a niche where enemies are few and bird competitors are, perhaps without exception, an overflow from more favorable habitats. With better control of forest fires in recent years, the burned-over tracts are smaller; and although much land acceptable to the bird exists, in these areas the bird shares the land with the richer animal life of the unburned areas nearby, and thus has less of that sanctuary from predators and competitors which is most favorable to its success. Hence, by better control of forest fires man may have reduced the success of the Kirtland's Warbler, even though the total acreage of the right plant association still seems ample.

And now, probably since 1895, a new factor has become important in the life of the Kirtland's Warbler. That factor is the Brown-headed Cowbird, a native of the Western plains, which was probably not present here until the forests were cleared for farming up to the nesting ground of the Kirtland's Warbler. This social parasite, which removes warbler eggs and places its own eggs in the warbler nest, takes a heavy toll of the reproductive potential of the warbler, already marginal.

These ideas will be developed more fully in the sections to follow.

Methods of This Study

This study presented many difficulties. The nesting area of the Kirtland's Warbler lies a considerable distance from the homes of all who have done the detailed work, and none of us has been able to stay with the birds throughout a nesting season. This fact, along with the usual difficulty of finding concealed nests of small songbirds, has given us our evidence in fragments, and in regrettably small quantities for the effort expended. For example, I have information on 250 nests, but no one person has seen half of them, and very few nests were observed from start to finish. I have therefore been obliged to use some unconventional means of piecing together the bits of evidence.

Five areas received intensive study at various times. Two of these were studied until the trees became too large for the Kirtland's Warbler and the colonies of nesting birds had dwindled to nothing. Much but not all the information of this report was gathered from these areas.

Over a period of 26 years, beginning in 1932, but mostly in the years 1951–57, 112 adults and 222 nestlings were banded. Every captured bird was given a Government aluminum band, serially numbered, adults on the right leg and nestlings on the left leg. In addition, birds on study areas were given colored plastic bands so that they could be identified again on sight.

Most females were captured by dropping a butterfly net over the nest. Some of the more wary ones, and nearly all the males, were captured with a bow net, which could be covered with leaves at the nest and jerked over it with a long string. None of the birds were injured in capture nor visibly inconvenienced by the bands on their legs. One male, banded as an adult in 1941, was on the nesting ground in 1949, having completed eight round-trip migrations with a band on each leg.

In general, the methods of this study involved watching the wild birds, with little interference in their lives. Few experimental techniques were used.

Style Details

I have used the common names of birds throughout, and at the end of the report have listed them alphabetically with their scientific names.

Time on the nesting ground (longitude, about 84°) is Eastern Standard Time.

Capitalized names of colors are from Ridgway (1912).

In the Bibliography titles are given as published, even though some names are no longer spelled as shown—"Dendroeca" and "kirtlandi," for example.

2

History

Discovery of the Species

The Kirtland's Warbler first became known to science when Spencer F. Baird (1852:217) published a description of a male taken "near Cleveland, Ohio," on May 13, 1851. The precise location was near Kirtland's farm, Rockport, on the shore of Lake Erie, five miles west of the center of Cleveland (Christy, 1936:89). The collector, Charles Pease, gave it to his father-in-law, Dr. Jared P. Kirtland. A few days later, Baird, returning to the Smithsonian Institution in Washington from a scientific meeting in Cincinnati, stopped in Cleveland to visit with his friend Kirtland, and was given the specimen (Dall, 1915:264). Baird named the new warbler *Sylvicola kirtlandii* in honor of "a gentleman to whom, more than [to] any one living, we are indebted for a knowledge of the Natural History of the Mississippi Valley." Indeed, Kirtland was deserving of recognition. Physician, teacher, horticulturist, naturalist, he was the author of the first lists of birds, fishes, mammals, reptiles, and amphibians for Ohio, and also had a species each of mollusk, snake, and fossil plant named in his honor.

An element of drama enters this history from the curious circumstance that a specimen, taken ten years earlier, would lie unnoticed in museum drawers until 1865. In the second week of October, 1841, Samuel Cabot, Jr. collected a bird of this species on shipboard "between Abaco and Cuba." At this time he and John L. Stephens were on their way to Yucatan. Then, and subsequently, he was "so preoccupied with his studies of the spectacular tropical birds of a country then entirely untouched by ornithologists that the little Bahaman warbler skin, brought back to Boston and deposited in his collection, remained unnoticed. . . ." (Van Tyne *in* Bent, 1953:417 and Baird, 1865:207.)

Discovery of the Winter Home

After the taking of the first Kirtland's Warbler in 1851, five more spring migrants (four in Ohio and one in southern Michigan) were collected before the first bird was found in winter. Charles B. Cory (1879:118) collected it on Andros Island, Bahamas, on January 9, 1879. Subsequently, other collectors found the bird on nearly all the major islands of the Bahamas, and took at least 71 specimens there, mostly between 1884 and 1897. The bird has never been found outside the Bahamas in winter.

Discovery of the Nesting Ground

The Kirtland's Warbler was known for more than 50 years before its nesting ground was found. Meanwhile, there was much speculation about its location, with guesses placing it from Cuba to the Arctic. The mystery was solved in 1903. E. H. Frothingham, of the University of Michigan Museum of Zoology, and a friend, T. G. Gale, were trout fishing on the Au Sable River in western Oscoda County. On June 13, Frothingham, an experienced ornithologist, heard a bird song he did not recognize on the jack-pine plains north of the river. There were several singing birds present, and Gale shot one to have it identified. The men returned to Ann Arbor, and Norman A. Wood identified the specimen as the rare Kirtland's Warbler (Frothingham, 1903:61).

Wood promptly set out to find the nest. He took a train to Roscommon and there hired a rowboat to drift some 60 miles down the winding stream. After two long days on the river, he reached his destination, Butler Bridge (now Parmalee Bridge), in western Oscoda County. He took lodging at a house near the bridge.

The next day, July 2, he walked north about a quarter mile and then west a mile. Here he heard his first Kirtland's Warbler song. During the next five days he located four singing males and saw one female, but could not find a nest. Two of these males were in the first location, and the others were two miles farther west. Wood described the small groups as "colonies."

On July 8 he decided to visit the jack-pine plains farther west. He set out in a horse-drawn buggy driven by James Parmalee, who had been with Gale when he took the specimen in June. The wagon trail followed the second terrace above the river for some miles westward. Near the Crawford County line, on the plains some distance away from the river, he examined a tract of several hundred acres, swept by fire about six years before, and now covered with jack pines three to ten feet tall.

The excitement of the discovery is conveyed by Wood's jottings in a pocket notebook carried during the days of search:

"Leaving the river bottom I climbed to the top of the first plain and walked slowly along, seeing the junco, song sparrow, and grass finch [Vesper Sparrow] . . . suddenly I heard a new song, so rich, loud, and clear, I knew it must be the one I was in search of. I followed it around and heard it sing many times. I tried to get sight of the singer but failed on account of his keeping low down in the bushes, acting much like the Maryland Yellowthroat in this respect. After a long time I saw him alight in a low bush and sing. . . . I shall be disappointed if I do not find the nest low down (in a jack pine probably) or maybe on the ground. Its song, the most beautiful of any warbler, is so wild and clear and has such a ringing, liquid quality, I feel well repaid for my trip by this one experience. I had hoped by watching the birds to find the nest, but found [it] hard even to see the bird after locating it by the song. . . . I have just found a pair of Kirtland's Warblers and, as I write, the female is 3 feet away, fluttering her wings, and seems very anxious. I am near a small heap of brush and logs and maybe the nest is here. . . . As I go around on my hands and knees, I see she keeps very near. . . . The male is on top of a dead stub 20 feet high. . . . Near the top of the stub is a small hole, and it may be the nest is there, although I have not seen the female go there. . . . [Then at the moment of discovery] I saw him go down and went over there. I saw him come to the stub, and he had a worm in his mouth. . . . Down into the jack pine he went. . . . No bird and no nest! I watched a few minutes longer and saw the female in the low jack pines. I watched her and she seemed very uneasy [having just been flushed from the nest]. I began looking carefully on the ground, as I had made up my mind it would be found there. Suddenly I saw the nest! . . . . In the nest were 2 young birds a few days old, and, as luck would have it, one beautiful egg . . . pinkish white, thinly sprinkled with chocolate brown spots gathered in a wreath at the larger end."

By painstaking study of Wood's handwritten notes and sketch maps, by talks with old residents about the historic wagon trails, and by examination of the area on foot, Fenn M. Holden concluded in 1959 that the first nest was located in the western part of Section 31, T27N, R1E, Oscoda County; that is, less than half a mile from the Crawford County line. Every nest since the first has been found within 60 miles of this spot.

After Wood's discovery of the nesting ground of the Kirtland's Warbler, there was still some confusion about "firsts." In the following summer Edward Arnold went to the site of Wood's discovery.

On June 29, 1904, he took "the first full sets . . . known to science," and published information on this "type set." In fact, he published it three times (Arnold, 1904a:67–68; 1904b:171; 1905:1–3). However, Wood had arranged for a local resident, Parmalee, his companion of the previous summer, to collect a full set for him. Parmalee did so on June 6, 1904. Two years later, needing money because of illness in the family, Wood sold this "first" nest with complete set of eggs to Frank M. Chapman at the American Museum of Natural History in New York for $25. Since Parmalee did not have a collector's permit, and Wood did not want to expose him to possible arrest, Wood did not publish mention of this nest until 1926, and then without mentioning the personal circumstances (Wood, 1926:12).

Summary

The Kirtland's Warbler was first made known from a specimen taken on May 13, 1851, near Cleveland, Ohio, and turned over by J. P. Kirtland to Spencer F. Baird, who described it. An earlier specimen had been taken by Samuel Cabot, Jr. on shipboard "between Abaco and Cuba" in October, 1841, but lay unnoticed for 24 years.

The winter home of the bird was found to be in the Bahama Islands by Charles B. Cory in 1879.

The nesting ground was discovered in northern Lower Michigan in July, 1903, by Norman A. Wood.

3

The Nesting Ground

Nesting Range and Population

The Kirtland's Warbler has been found nesting in scattered locations in the northern part of the Lower Peninsula of Michigan, and nowhere else. The distance from the northernmost to the southernmost nest on record is less than 85 miles (136 km.), and from the easternmost to the westernmost, less than 100 miles (160 km.). The nesting range extends north to the southern edge of Presque Isle County, west to Kalkaska County (six or seven miles southwest of the town of Kalkaska), south to the northwest corner of Clare County, and east to within two miles of Lake Huron in Iosco County.

In 1951, 32 people cooperated with me in an attempt to count all the singing males of the species (Mayfield, 1953:17–20). The total count of males was 432, suggesting, with allowances for birds possibly missed, that the total adult population was under 1,000. All these birds were found in 91 surveyor's sections (square miles), roughly one per cent of the sections within the known nesting range. But even in these sections only a small part of the land was occupied. On much of it the habitat was unsuitable, and much that appeared to human eyes to be suitable was not occupied by Kirtland's Warblers. Nowhere was the available habitat filled. The most favorable part of the range was in the drainage of the Au Sable River, where fully nine-tenths of all nesting Kirtland's Warblers in history have been found. Here, in several tracts in Crawford County, Douglas Middleton and his associates found one male for each eight acres of suitable land; and in several tracts in Oscoda County, I found one male for each 23 acres. At the northern edge of the range, outside the Au Sable drainage, Richard Olsen and his associates found one male for each 63 acres. These densities are rough approximations, because jack-pine growths usually merge gradually into deciduous scrub or grasslands, and opinions differ in estimating the amount of land "suitable."

Under natural conditions the Kirtland's Warbler is limited to lands forested with jack pines. Zimmerman (1956:8–31) has estimated 470,000 acres (190,000 hectares) of natural growth of jack pine in the Lower Peninsula of Michigan, with 21 counties each possessing 1,000 acres or more. Inclusion of plantings raises the total to about 600,000 acres. However, the Kirtland's Warbler has been found nesting in only 12 counties, and not in more than nine at one time, near the center of greatest abundance of jack pine. These 12 counties are listed in Table 1. The most extensive stands of jack pine

Table 1

Occurrence of Kirtland's Warbler in 12 Michigan Counties
(1951)

County	Townships (N)	Sections (N)	Singing males counted (N)	Natural growth of jack pines in 1956 (acres)
Crawford	7	19	142	90,000
Oscoda	6	19	103	85,000
Iosco	8	20	74	40,000
Montmorency	2	11	43	35,000
Presque Isle	2	13	34	8,000
Kalkaska	1	6	28	25,000
Roscommon	1	2	4	25,000
Alcona	1	1	4	6,000
Ogemaw	0	0	0	30,000
Clare	0	0	0	10,000
Alpena	0	0	0	2,000
Otsego	0	0	0	3,000
Total	28	91	432	359,000

to be found in the state are in the first four counties listed, where the greatest number of Kirtland's Warblers were found in the 1951 census. The other counties are closely adjoining. Nests of the Kirtland's Warbler have been found in all the counties listed except Alcona, where nesting is assumed from the existence of a colony of several birds.

Some of the counties lying well within the range of the Kirtland's Warbler, particularly Alpena and Alcona counties, have little suitable land because of swamps and areas of heavier soil with hardwood forest.

Only three occurrences of the Kirtland's Warbler in nesting season have been reported outside the 12 counties listed.

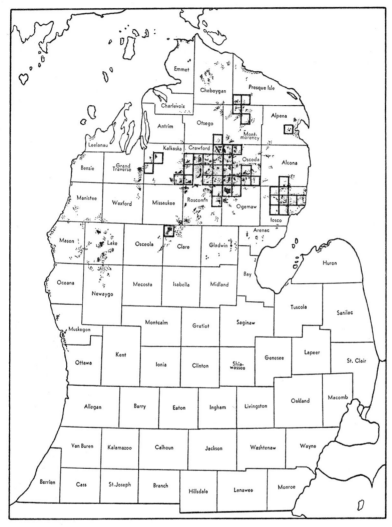

FIGURE 1

Michigan townships (six-mile squares) where Kirtland's Warbler has been known to nest, 1903–1959, small squares. Natural stands of jack pine in northern Lower Michigan dotted (Zimmerman, 1956:265).

In June, 1932, Walter Hastings (letter, July 20, 1933) saw a singing male about five miles north of Manton, in the northwest corner of Wexford County. However, he was unable to find it again on later visits. It was within 15 miles of the location of a colony reported in Kalkaska County. Van Tyne included Wexford County in the nesting range (in Bent, 1953:428, and A.O.U. Checklist, 1957:502). However, I have omitted Wexford County from the list of known breeding areas because no nest was found there and the circumstances suggest an isolated unmated male.

A singing male, probably without a mate, was found in 1958 in Ontario, just across Lake Huron, about 100 miles from the nesting region. It was found on June 8 by George Moore and Crawford Skelton, and was seen later by several persons. It was in an area of small jack pines on rocky soil, in St. Edmund's Township, near the tip of Bruce Peninsula.

Harrington (1939:95–97) reported Kirtland's Warblers in 1916 and 1939 among small jack pines at Petawawa Camp near Pembroke, Ontario, but he did not find a nest. Others have searched the area without finding Kirtland's Warblers there.

Climate

The climate of northern Lower Michigan in nesting season is notable for extremes, although the average temperature and rainfall are moderate.

The average July temperature here is about 68° F. (20° C.), but there is no month in which the Michigan jack-pine plains have not at some time had frost. In late May, when the warblers are on the nesting ground, temperatures as low as 20° F. (−7° C.) have been recorded during field work, and snow has fallen in early June after nesting has started. However, if the sun is shining, the temperature may rise 45° F. (25° C.) from morning to afternoon of the same day. Summer temperatures up to 112° F. (44° C.) have been recorded in Oscoda County.

The growing season, from the last killing frost of the spring to the first killing frost of the fall, is probably less than 90 days in most Kirtland's Warbler areas. For example, at Mio in Oscoda County, near the center of the Kirtland's Warbler range, the average growing season is 97 days, from June 6 to September 11. But in the early mornings of June the sandy pinelands often have frost when none is visible in towns and cultivated areas and near lakes, where weather observers are likely to be located.

Rain occurs frequently in the nesting season (annual average about 30 inches, 76 cm.), but the soil is so porous and lightly vegetated that the surface can return to desertlike aridity in a few hours.

Soil of the Region

The soils of this region are podsols, formed, presumably, under a cool, moist climate, from the decomposition of pine needles into acid products, which percolate down into the surface, leaching out the alkalis and leaving the acid-resisting silica.

Nests of the Kirtland's Warbler, perhaps without exception, have been found on land of one podsol type, Grayling Sand. This soil is characterized by looseness and perviousness to a depth of one or two meters or more. The humus layer is 2–4 cm. thick at most, and is entirely lacking in many places. The surface soil is acidic, lacking in organic matter, lime, phosphoric acid, and potash. At lower levels it is pale-yellowish in color and coarser in texture, allowing water to penetrate rapidly. Poor soil originally, it has been further impoverished by forest fires.

The region generally is level or gently rolling, with fewer lakes and swamps than found ordinarily in northern coniferous forests. For example, Oscoda County has only 5 per cent swampland; Crawford County has 9 per cent. The principal river system within the nesting range of the Kirtland's Warbler is that of the Au Sable, appropriately, "The Sandy."

The nature of the soil is significant to the Kirtland's Warbler in two ways: (1) it produces the vegetation required for the nesting habitat, and (2) it absorbs water so rapidly that rain seldom floods the nests, although they are usually indented into the ground.

Jack Pine and Other Trees

One of the most remarkable facts about the Kirtland's Warbler is its restriction to a narrow and distinctive habitat during the nesting season—extensive tracts densely covered with small jack pines, *Pinus banksiana*. The early settlers called these areas "jack-pine plains" or "barrens." (In recent years men have simulated these natural conditions with plantings of other conifers, as will be noted later.) The unique character of this habitat was apparent to the naturalists who discovered the nesting ground, and was recognized even by less observant people living in the region, who called the warbler the "Jack-pine Bird."

Under natural conditions (where other pines have not been planted by man), the Kirtland's Warbler is never found in a tract of land unless the dominant tree is the jack pine. However, the bird will tolerate a sprinkling of other trees.

Among the jack pines in Kirtland's Warbler areas we find a few scattered spires of the red pine, *Pinus resinosa*, and white pine, *Pinus strobus*. But most of the other tall, woody plants are deciduous, more often occurring as tall shrubs than trees. The most common are, in order of abundance: scrub oak, *Quercus ellipsoidalis* or *Q. coccinea*; quaking aspen, *Populus tremuloides*; fire cherry, *Prunus pennsylvanica*; and June berries or shadbush, *Amelanchier* spp. (Zimmerman, 1956:209–220). If any of these deciduous trees or shrubs begin to approach the jack pines in numbers, the area is not used by the Kirtland's Warbler. Many of the jack-pine stands in Lower Michigan, particularly those at the periphery, have too many deciduous trees and shrubs to be acceptable to the Kirtland's Warbler.

Typically, the warblers first appear when the tallest trees of the young growth are about as tall as a man (Christmas-tree size), with trunks one to two inches in diameter at the base. And the warblers no longer use an area when most of the trees become 16 to 20 feet tall, with trunks four to six inches in diameter at the base. However, if the new growth is exceptionally dense ("as thick as timothy hay"), the warblers may appear when the trees are only waist high; and years later, if there are ample openings, the warblers may remain even though many trees have become larger than the usual limit.

The crucial requirement appears to be, not the *height* of the trees, but the presence of living pine-branch *thickets* near the ground. Trees are not big enough to produce such thickets until adjacent trees touch each other, and they are too big when the lower limbs die, opening a gap between the foliage and the ground cover. It is characteristic of jack pines that the lower limbs die when shaded; thus large jack pines close together have no foliage near the ground.

I suspect this configuration is favorable to the success of the Kirtland's Warbler. The female, particularly, stays in the thickets. She usually moves from tree to tree at the level where the foliage is most dense, and here meets the male. Although the male frequently moves about and sings in exposed locations, he too spends most of the time in the midst of twigs and needles. If the pine branches reach down to the ground cover, the adults can approach the nest without leaving concealment, and the fledglings can make their way from the shelter of the ground cover to the shelter of the trees with a minimum of exposure.

The time required for jack pines to become suitable for Kirtland's Warblers depends upon the fertility of the soil as well as the density of the stand. In naturally seeded growths, the age of the trees may be guessed from the date of the fire that produced them. In five such areas, warblers first appeared 6 to 13 years (average, 8 years) after fire.

Where jack pines have been planted by foresters, warblers appear more slowly—in four tracts in 7 to 10 years (average, 8½ years) after the planting. But pines grown artificially are started in nurseries as seedlings and transplanted to forests when about two years old; thus the trees in plantings are usually about 10 to 11 years old when warblers first appear; that is, two to three years older than in natural growths. I believe this difference occurs because normal planting practice spaces the rows about six feet apart, and, although the trees are close together in the rows, they do not produce suitable thickets until they are mostly 6 to 7 feet tall and 1½ to 3 inches in diameter at the base.

Thus plantings are slower than natural growths to become suitable for Kirtland's Warblers because they are not so dense, and they become unsuitable more quickly because they become dense more quickly. This paradox is explainable as follows: In natural growths there are frequent openings interspersed with dense thickets, whereas in plantings the openings are likely to be few and small. As the branches begin to bridge the openings in a planting, the lower limbs begin dying and the warblers tend to disappear from the interior of the plantation. This, I believe, explains why openings are so notable a feature of the habitat of the Kirtland's Warbler.

In natural growth, on the other hand, innumerable clearings allow the sunlight to penetrate, keeping alive the low branches even when the trees have become fairly large, and providing exposed edges where new ground-hugging pines will sprout for many years. Hence, the life of a Kirtland's Warbler tract is variable; it may be as few as six years or as many as 19, with a typical life of 10 to 12 years.

To attract nesting warblers, a tract must be much larger than would be supposed from the size of the territories defended by the males. Tracts smaller than 80 acres (32 hectares) will seldom be occupied; an 80-acre tract is equivalent to a rectangle ¼ x ½ mile. To illustrate how selective the warblers may be, I mention one planted strip 150 yards wide, paralleling a road for 1½ miles in Oscoda County, one of the most favorable portions of the range. It appeared suitable in all respects except breadth, but it had no warblers. The smallest area ever found with nesting Kirtland's Warblers was 32 acres. It held three singing males and at least one nest in 1952, ten years after the fire that created it. But the life of the colony was short; it was possibly disrupted by workmen laying a pipeline, and was not resumed thereafter.

So, in summary, the Kirtland's Warbler is likely to be found in fairly homogeneous and extensive stands (more than 80 acres) of jack pines between 6 and 18 feet tall, and 8 to 20 years old.

Within the range of this bird the only pine growing naturally in dense stands over extensive tracts is the jack pine. Consequently it was long believed that the Kirtland's Warbler would accept no other tree on its nesting grounds. But in recent years the national and state foresters have planted other species of pine successfully in this region, particularly the red or Norway pine, *Pinus resinosa*. This pine, under natural conditions, never grows in dense, homogeneous, uniform stands, but it forms such stands in plantings. Here, while the trees are small, they produce the conditions required by the Kirtland's Warbler—dense coniferous foliage with living branches near the ground.

In 1948 we found a nest in a planting of red pines for the first time, but there were jack pines nearby. Then, in the course of the census of the Kirtland's Warbler in 1951, we found several colonies of nesting Kirtland's Warblers in red-pine plantations where there were few if any jack pines. It seems probable that plantings of other needle-bearing trees might be equally acceptable to the warbler. As Odum (1945:197) has pointed out about birds in general, the requirement of the Kirtland's Warbler probably is a certain "life form," not a species of plant.

Ground Cover

Viewed from above, the distinctive feature of the jack-pine plains is the wide spacing of the trees and tree clumps. Close up, the lower plants also are more widely spaced than in richer soil, and an unusual amount of ground is bare. There is no turf. The plants are those that can survive fire, drought, and a short growing season. Most of them are low shrubs or deep-rooted perennials. Although the land gives a general impression of unproductiveness, here, as McAtee (1920:187) points out ". . . some plants reach their very acme of development."

The "intermediate layer" (more than one foot, 30 cm., in height) consists mostly of shrubs and bracken fern, *Pteridium aquilinum.* Among the common shrubs are shadbushes, *Amelanchier* spp.; cherry, especially the northern dwarf cherry, *Prunus pumila;* and sweetfern, *Comptonia peregrina.* In late summer some grasses and other herbs grow to a height of a meter or more, but these taller growths seem of little consequence to the Kirtland's Warbler, either for nest concealment or foraging.

Of much greater significance is the ground layer of vegetation (mostly less than one foot, 30 cm., high). Here the most common genera, in order of abundance, are: bluestem grass, *Andropogon* (*A. scoparius* and *A. gerardii*); sedge, *Carex;* wild oat grass, *Danthonia* (*D. spicata*); goldenrod, *Solidago;* blueberry, *Vaccinium;* reindeer moss, *Cladonia* (*C. rangiferina*); bearberry, *Arctostophylos* (*A. uva-ursi*); cherry, *Prunus* (chiefly *P. pumila*); blackberry, *Rubus* (Zimmerman, 1956:216).

The Kirtland's Warbler on its nesting ground shows a preference for areas with heavy ground cover. Individual nests are found occasionally where the cover is poor, but they are exceptional. Usually the territory of a pair of warblers has innumerable sites where the nest could be concealed. A favorite location, as will be described later in connection with the nest, is under a tussock of dead grass, where last year's leaves have curled over to form a natural arch. Often, woody stems of the blueberry push up through the grass and support the arches under which the nest is concealed.

The ground cover has other uses as well. It provides concealment to the female when she approaches the nest along the ground, as she sometimes does. Both sexes forage through low shrubbery, bathing in the dew and gathering food. The fledglings spend most of their first two weeks out of the nest under the ground cover.

However, we have not been able to isolate any characteristic of the ground cover that explains why warblers are found in some jackpine tracts and not in others. The bird utilizes cover provided by a variety of plants in different proportions as they are available, and most of these plants are found throughout the fire-scarred lands where jack pine grows.

Food and Water for the Warblers

On first considering a rare and restricted species of bird, one is likely to wonder if there is not some special food requirement. If it is so with the Kirtland's Warbler, we have not been able to discover the secret. The bird seems to be an opportunist, eating whatever animal matter is available and sampling many other items (ants, pine needles, twigs, grass, pitch, and automobile grease—these to be mentioned again under Behavior), some rejected as though unpalatable, others eaten though of doubtful nutritional value. During the summer, food does not appear to be a problem to the adult warblers. They seem able to fulfill their needs in a small part of the daylight hours.

Entomologist J. Speed Rogers spent three hours in a blind in Oscoda County on June 26, 1947, watching adult warblers carry food to two five-day-old cowbirds. He identified the following invertebrates:

> Limp green larvae (sawfly?) about 15 mm. long (3 times)
> Cecidomyids (3 times)
> Whitish moth
> Caterpillar (geometrid or sawfly)
> Small adult sawfly or diptera
> Small green grasshopper nymph
> Small brownish caterpillar
> Large battered, soft-bodied fly or adult sawfly

At the time of the discovery of the first nest, Wood (1904:10) noted that the birds were feeding on spanworms, deer flies, and a spanworm moth, *Diastictis inceptata*. On June 8, 1953, Van Tyne recovered a female cicada, *Okanagana rimosa* (identified by I. J. Cantrall) from a male Kirtland's Warbler 1½ miles north of Clear Lake in Montmorency County.

Everyone who has watched the adult Kirtland's Warbler carry food to young birds has noted green and brown caterpillars. Winged insects reported fed to young birds include adult ant lions, damsel flies, white and cream-colored moths, tabanid flies, and beelike insects. Probably most of this food is gathered in small jack pines, especially in the terminal clusters of twigs. But some is gathered on the ground and in the high limbs of large trees nearby, and some, a smaller portion, by flycatching on the wing.

Ants are abundant on the nesting ground, but though the adults seem to eat the ants they pick off their own nestlings, they do not seek ants for food. Berger observed that captive fledglings discriminated between ants and other small insects, frequently picking up ants but discarding them.

When the blueberries ripen early in August, the Kirtland's Warbler feeds extensively on them, selecting only the ripe, soft fruit. At this time of year there is no shortage of animal food. In winter, in the Bahama Islands, Chapman (1908:224) noted the birds "feeding on the berries of low 'sage' bushes."

No one has seen a Kirtland's Warbler drink water in the wild. Adult birds have ignored water in a pan placed by the nest. Presumably they get enough moisture from their food, and possibly from droplets of dew on the foliage. There is no standing water on Kirtland's Warbler areas, except briefly after a rain. However, Berger has found that captive Kirtland's Warblers drink water from a saucer, like other birds.

Associated Species of Birds

To an ornithologist the birds seen in an area are a revealing indication of its character. The jack-pine plains bring together an interesting assemblage of birds, all of which, except for the Kirtland's Warbler, are probably better suited to some other habitat. Here the birds of the grasslands are on the verge of being crowded out by the young forest growth; the birds of the forest barely gain a foothold; the birds of the brush find the shrubbery rather sparse; and most of the cavity-nesting birds are here solely through the circumstance of rotting, fire-killed stubs.

For example, the Vesper Sparrow, which Norman A. Wood (1904:5) considered the most common bird of the jack-pine plains, is typically a bird of open grasslands. The two birds that come nearest to being limited in Michigan to the same habitat as the Kirtland's Warbler are the Prairie Warbler and the Clay-colored Sparrow, both of which favor areas of more deciduous shrubbery.

Barrows (1912:9) says, "It is a singular fact that the Jack Pine Plains proper have no single species of warbler which is at all characteristic, with the exception of the rare Kirtland. . . . the typical Jack Pine Plains are marked by the complete absence of warblers."

Referring perhaps to the earlier years after a forest fire, he says this of the burnt-over lands: "One may ride for hours through these desolate solitudes and see hardly more than a dozen species of birds. . . ."

Such impressions have caused the jack-pine lands to be called "barrens." Indeed, their flora and fauna, including bird life, are not rich. After mid-July, when most species have stopped singing, the small jack pines seem almost devoid of birds. However, three years' censusing in nesting season on one Kirtland's Warbler area revealed a population lower than in most forests, but comparable to that of dry, brushy fields in this climate—which do not occur except after fire or clearing of the land by man.

On this Kirtland's Warbler area, in Sec. 19, T25N, R4E, Oscoda County, the population of breeding birds of all species was 178, 137, and 106 (average, 140) pairs per 100 acres (40 hectares) in three consecutive years. Here the bird population probably was larger than in many Kirtland's Warbler areas, because the pines were rather large and there were a number of deciduous trees nearby, somewhat enriching the bird population. Table 2 compares censuses in ten northern forest types of the United States.

Kendeigh (1948:101–114) found low bird populations also in several different plant communities in northern Lower Michigan, near Douglas Lake, about 35 miles northwest of the northern limit of the Kirtland's Warbler range. He attributed these low populations to the infertility of the soil, later finding densities roughly twice as great in various forest types on better soil in Minnesota (1956:103). His findings in Michigan were as follows:

	Breeding Pairs per 100 Acres
Grassland	56
Aspen-red maple	59
Pine-aspen	112
Cedar-aspen	139
Cedar-balsam	146
Beech-maple-pine	155

Lack (1951:173–179) in England found bird populations in 26-year-old pine plantations "very low compared with most woods of other types (about 90 pairs per 100 acres) but about three times the usual density on heathlands."

Table 2

Bird Populations in 10 Northern Forest Types: Comparative Censuses

Forest type	State	Years (N)	Pairs per 100 acres	Authority
Jack-pine plains	Michigan	3	140	Van Tyne *et al.*, 1942:30; 1943:23; 1944:23
Brushy fields with deciduous shrubs	Michigan	10	115	Walkinshaw, 1947:215
Scrub oak, burned 10 years before first census	Michigan	4	196	Walkinshaw *et al.*, 1944: 18; 1945:61; 1946:134; 1947:198
Young oak–hickory forest	Michigan	3	293	Snyder, 1949:261; 1950: 297; 1951:321
Upland oak forest	Minnesota	6	220	Breckenridge, 1955:408–412
White cedar–tamarack bog	Minnesota	4	211	Breckenridge, 1955:408–412
White-pine–hemlock forest, partly opened by hurricane damage	Vermont	17	263	Smith, 1934–1953
Climax red and white spruce forest with a clearing	Maine	15	272	Cruickshank *et al.*, 1936–1954
Partially cutover northern hardwood slope	New Hampshire	14	325	Wallace, 1943–1956
* Climax beech–maple forest with some hemlock	Ohio	16	215	Williams, 1947:205–210

* Climax forest in the Kirtland's Warbler range is also beech-maple.

So the jack-pine plains, although not rich in bird life and probably not ideal for any species except the Kirtland's Warbler, share in enough elements of the grasslands, forest, and deciduous scrub to have a total bird population comparable with that of many other types of forest on poor soil. Mackenzie (1950), studying a sandy area planted to pine in England, found that three species of tits (Great, Blue, and Coal) would nest there if cavities were provided, but they suffered higher mortality of nestlings than in normal areas. He speculated that the poverty of the soil might bring a deficiency in some trace elements or a shortage of food at some crucial time.

To determine the typical birds associated with the Kirtland's Warbler on its nesting ground, I have used lists of birds seen on 10 areas in different years from 1903 to 1957.

It will be recognized at once that there is nothing very remarkable about this list of birds. These are the birds of the roadside in northern Michigan—a hodgepodge of the birds of grasslands, scrub, and forest. Some of them are present, not because of any attraction provided by the small jack pines, but because of habitat available in the forest fringing the Kirtland's Warbler areas. In part, therefore, these lists reflect the nature of adjoining areas. Also, there is an interesting difference between the natural and the planted areas, the former having many more cavity-nesting species because of the presence of fire-killed stubs.

Birds nesting on Kirtland's Warbler areas and found on at least 8 out of 10 such areas are:

Common Nighthawk	Robin
Yellow-shafted Flicker	Hermit Thrush
Eastern Kingbird	Eastern Bluebird
Blue Jay	Brown-headed Cowbird
Common Crow	Vesper Sparrow
Black-capped Chickadee	Slate-colored Junco
Brown Thrasher	Chipping Sparrow

Birds nesting on Kirtland's Warbler areas and found on at least 3 out of 10 such areas are:

Upland Plover	Myrtle Warbler
Mourning Dove	Pine Warbler
Tree Swallow	Prairie Warbler
House Wren	Ovenbird
Black-billed Cuckoo	Rufous-sided Towhee
Black-and-white Warbler	Clay-colored Sparrow
Nashville Warbler	Field Sparrow

Birds we have not found nesting in a Kirtland's Warbler area but have seen on at least 3 out of 10 such areas are:

Red-tailed Hawk	Rose-breasted Grosbeak
Marsh Hawk	Indigo Bunting
Eastern Wood Pewee	Purple Finch
Cedar Waxwing	American Goldfinch
Red-eyed Vireo	Song Sparrow
Black-throated Green Warbler	

Other birds as well wander into Kirtland's Warbler areas, and a few others even nest there occasionally.

Forest Fire

Under natural conditions, the habitat of the Kirtland's Warbler is produced only by forest fire. This bird is therefore unusual among living creatures in being dependent upon fire. This chain of circumstances was not understood by Wood (1926:12), who suggested that fire might be the worst enemy of the bird. Actually, fires could endanger the birds only during the nesting season, and fires are more likely to occur later in the summer or in the fall, when the ground cover has become dry and crisp.

Van Tyne (1951:539) suggested that tornadoes might have leveled portions of the original forest, making way for young jack pines and eventually for the Kirtland's Warbler habitat. I believe this to be unlikely for three reasons: (1) tornadoes rarely clear out strips of the forest wide enough for the warbler; (2) tornadoes usually leave many living, though broken, trees; and (3) tornadoes would not produce the soil and temperature conditions that would cause the jack pine to become dominant in the regrowth. It is significant that Kirtland's Warblers have never been known to come into an area opened by lumbering.

Jack-pine cones enclose the seeds in tight, resinous jackets, which neither rot nor open easily. The cones may lie on the ground dormant or cling to branches tightly closed for several years, but fire helps them to pop open and release their seeds. Thus fire helps the seeds germinate and at the same time reduces competition from other plants. The other species of pine in the region, red pine and white pine, do not have this ability to survive fire or to propagate themselves in soil with so little organic matter and water-holding capacity.

The oaks in the region also owe their prominence to fire, but they survive because of their ability to spring up again from the roots after the stems above ground have been killed—usually as a dwarfed clump rather than a standing tree.

Before the coming of the white man, fires were started by lightning, and perhaps by Indians. Such fires raged through the pine country until rains put them out, or the winds changed, or the fires reached a dead end against a lake, swamp, or arm of deciduous forest.

History of the Jack-pine Plains

The jack pine probably entered Michigan from the south between 6,000 and 8,000 years ago. Since it is a hardy, pioneer species —even now extending farther north than any other eastern pine— it may have followed the retreating glaciers rather closely. Many of the other plants of the jack-pine plains are prairie species that probably came into Michigan from the southwest during the Xerothermic period, considerably later.

Zimmerman (1956:222–226), from whom many of the foregoing views are drawn, also says: "The jack pine plains represent a relict plant association in Lower Michigan. This is indicated by (1) its former known presence in southern Michigan where it does not occur today, (2) the relatively small area it now occupies in this peninsula, (3) evidence indicating the association's probable former abundance on the great expanses of sandy moraines and outwash plains left in the wake of the retreating Wisconsin glaciers."

Thus, the jack-pine plains in Michigan have a recent origin in geologic time—almost certainly more recent than the Kirtland's Warbler. It is more likely that the warbler came north with the jack pine than that it developed its specialized nesting habit in the last 6,000 years.

For centuries before the coming of the white man, the condition of this region must have been fairly constant. The forests grew and succeeded one another, only to be interrupted sooner or later by fire, infrequent but of vast extent, returning a portion of the land once again to its starting point and a new crop of jack pine. The Indians made little use of the comparatively barren pinelands, and there were no permanent Indian villages in the Kirtland's Warbler region.

Zimmerman estimated the total area of Lower Michigan jack-pine lands in the 1950's to be less than 500,000 acres, and believed the area was less in recent prehistory. It would be sheer guesswork to say how much of this forest was in the stage of growth required by the Kirtland's Warbler at all times, but I would suggest it might have been of the order of 10 per cent, or 50,000 acres. The fires of the prehistoric period were doubtless fewer but much more extensive than today, and more often caused vast "barrens."

Essentially primeval conditions existed in this region until about 1870. The first white settlement in the range of the Kirtland's Warbler was at Tawas City on Lake Huron in 1854, and was made there for the purpose of cutting the white pine. But for the next 20 years lumbering was mostly on a small scale, and limited to the vicinity of large streams. Then railroads were pushed into the region, making all of it accessible to the loggers. Lumbering was at its height from about 1875 to 1900, and was virtually over by 1900. Only the white pine and red pine were cut, the jack pine being considered worthless.

The slash from cutting operations was scattered on the ground. It was expected that this waste would be burned sooner or later, intentionally to clear the land, if not accidentally. There was neither means nor desire to stop fires in "the bush" unless they threatened camps or settlements. The damage to humus and game was not recognized at the time. The fire season began in midsummer and lasted until the fall rains. For many years the odor of burning wood and reddened sunsets from smoke were a normal feature of the region during the hot, dry months (Davis, 1936:316–318).

Without doubt the area in the stage of growth required by the Kirtland's Warbler was at its peak in that period. It seems reasonable to suppose that the area may have amounted to 200,000 acres, most of it in large tracts; that is, at least four times the minimum amount of prehistoric times.

It appears significant that the period of most active lumbering, and of forest fires, occurring before the cowbird had become a serious factor in the range, coincides with the period of greatest abundance of the Kirtland's Warbler, as indicated by wintering and migration records. This was in the 1880's and 1890's. Van Tyne (1951:542) noted that all the migration records outside the normal route (as well as the greatest number of records on the wintering ground) occurred between 1885 and 1900. Five of these occurred west of the present range (in Missouri, Illinois, and Minnesota); one, north of the present range (at the Straits of Mackinac); and two, east (in Ontario and Virginia). From these records he concluded that the range must then have included areas farther north and west than at present. But I would suggest that a very much higher population within the present range also would have sent an unusual number of strays west, north, and east of the range.

After the active period of lumbering, many of the jack-pine plains, known locally as "commons," were burned deliberately again and again to encourage the blueberry crop. As late as 1913–27, fires in the Huron National Forest burned an average of more than 5,000 acres per year (Dockham, November 2, 1958, letter). Since the Huron National Forest lies entirely within the range of the Kirtland's Warbler, but occupies less than one-fourth of it, we may suppose that about 20,000 acres burned per year in the entire area. If only half of this came back in jack pine, and was not burned again within 20 years, this burning rate would provide about 100,000 acres at all times in the 10-year span of growth suitable for the warblers. Since the 1920's the number of fires probably has increased (because of more hunters and tourists), but the fire-fighting means have improved; so the total acreage ravaged by fire has declined, and the fires have more often been confined to small tracts, many of them too small for Kirtland's Warblers. However, the reduction in fire-caused jack-pine growth has been offset by forest planting, and for this reason the area in young jack pines has probably been greater at all times in this century than in most years of recent prehistoric times. But the proportion of land in tracts of sufficient size to attract the Kirtland's Warbler is probably smaller now than ever before.

And, perhaps more important to the Kirtland's Warbler, many of the tracts used today, bordered closely by other forest types—that is, not occurring in vast barrens—do not provide the sanctuary from competitors and predators that may be needed for its best success.

There is no exact information to tell us how the population of Kirtland's Warblers has varied since the discovery of the nesting ground in 1903. For the time prior to 1951 we have only the casual impressions of men who had seen a few areas each. On one point all these observers agree: at no time since the discovery of its nesting ground has the Kirtland's Warbler occupied more than a fraction of the habitat that appeared suitable. Wood (1904:10) said, "It is not, however, every jack pine plain that is the home of a colony, as I examined hundreds of acres where the conditions seemed all right, and found none." Within the present century available nesting habitat has not been the factor limiting the population of this bird.

Dr. Max Peet found Kirtland's Warblers near Luzerne, Oscoda County, in 1913 and 1914. His impressions of their numbers, related in conversation, suggest that the warblers were more abundant in that time and place than anywhere we have seen them in recent years. Milton Trautman (letter, July 11, 1951) found the warblers more numerous along the road from Roscommon to Luzerne in 1926 than we have found them anywhere since that time. In 1934 and 1935 he revisited several areas within the region and believed the birds were then much less common. J. Stokely Ligon (letter, January 12, 1939), on the other hand, found the bird "rare" in 1924 and 1925, adding that their range seemed to center about Grayling. However, these opinions, even if accurate for the areas seen, are based on examination only of segments of the range.

We have a few early attempts to estimate the total population of Kirtland's Warblers. Walter B. Barrows, in a letter to Frank M. Chapman at the American Museum of Natural History, dated October 29, 1920, estimated the Michigan population at 18,000 birds. He based it on an estimate of five million acres of jack pine (ten times too high), and then proceeded with calculations we could endorse today, guessing that one-tenth of the jack-pine country was suitable and that warblers averaged one pair to each 32 acres in suitable areas.

Wood (1926:13) estimated 5,000 to 6,000 pairs "for all known colonies," but shakes our confidence in his opinion by basing it on "a conservative estimate of one pair per acre." Others besides Wood have walked through a Kirtland's Warbler colony, with birds singing all around and moving about, and have casually suggested there might be "a pair per acre." But Wood's own published observations reveal a much lower density. For example, at the site of the first nest, he tramped over "several hundred acres" and counted 13 males. At the same place in the following year R. A. Brown (letter, June 25, 1904) told Wood he found 18 males. This is about what we would expect today on such a tract, and very far indeed from a density of one pair per acre.

Later, Wing (1933:72) expressed the opinion it was "doubtful if more than four or five thousand individuals are in existence."

It is apparent that the Kirtland's Warbler has existed only in small numbers since its nesting ground was discovered. At most, there have been a few thousand birds. It is probable that the population was several times larger in the period 1885 to 1900, and considerably below the maximum in an earlier time, although larger than today.

Future Prospects of the Habitat

Since the required habitat for the Kirtland's Warbler is entirely dependent upon forest fires and forestry plantings, the future of the habitat is uncertain. Better control of forest fires may reduce the amount of habitat created by burning. In fact, there are jack-pine plains in Wisconsin and Minnesota that may have been suitable for the Kirtland's Warbler at one time but, as a result of fire control, do not appear to be so any longer. Planting activities of state and national forest agencies are also subject to major changes, according to economic conditions and land-use policies.

At present there is no immediate cause for alarm. Fires are still occurring, and forestry plantings are still being made. Furthermore, the cutting of jack pine for pulpwood has brought a new kind of lumbering which cuts the entire stand almost completely; it remains to be seen whether the resulting growth is suitable for Kirtland's Warblers.

Nevertheless, with a view to providing a permanent refuge for the bird, the Michigan Conservation Commission in 1957 voted to set aside certain state forest lands for this purpose. Three tracts were chosen, one each in Crawford, Oscoda, and Ogemaw counties. These lands are to be managed specifically for the benefit of the Kirtland's Warbler, with cutting, burning, and planting, if necessary, to maintain optimal conditions. These tracts alone probably would not be sufficient to maintain the species if no other areas were available, but they will provide land where the bird may be given special encouragement in the years ahead.

Why This Limited Nesting Range?

It is interesting to speculate about why the Kirtland's Warbler has such a small and specialized nesting range. In offering some tentative explanations, I shall consider the larger question in two parts: Why is the warbler restricted to areas of small jack pines? Why is it restricted to the jack pines of one small part of Michigan?

The family of wood warblers probably originated in the New World Tropics, and this particular species perhaps originated in the West Indies. Here, on a group of small and barren islands, it still spends the greater part of the year. By good powers of flight and navigation, it attains the comparative sanctuary of its wintering ground. Here, doubtless, it escapes some of the competition and dangers faced by its continental relatives.

On its nesting ground, likewise, it finds an "island." Here, in the barrens created by fire, for a brief interval while the pines are small, it finds a niche where enemies are few and where nearly all other birds are an overflow from more favorable habitats. In this sheltered niche it can reproduce in spite of the certain disadvantage of an incubation period one or two days longer than that of most other open-nesting songbirds, and in spite of the possible disadvantage of behavior lacking in the degree of wariness usually found in small birds. (It may be argued that this lack of wariness comes from slight experience with large predators.)

Within the racial history of this bird, the species must have experimented many times with nestings in the mature forests, swamps, and open grasslands available in its range. Presumably, the Kirtland's Warbler was not successful in these attempts. Hence, we find it reproducing only in a narrowly specialized niche. Lack (1944:278) says, ". . . purely psychological factors restrict each bird to its specific habitat . . . [but] when a bird . . . breeds outside its normal habitat, it will usually meet with failure in the long run. . . ."

From its restricted nesting and winter range, Amadon (1953:461–469) concluded that the Kirtland's Warbler is a relict species, with present distribution less than in the past. He further observes that "birds with a relict type of distribution will be especially susceptible to persecution or to man-made ecological changes and hence will require more than the ordinary degree of protection."

Now, let us consider why the Kirtland's Warbler is restricted to so small a part of the jack-pine range. This tree grows east and west over almost the entire width of northern Canada, and north from central Michigan almost to tree line; yet only in one small region at the southern limit of its range does it harbor the Kirtland's Warbler.

The answer, I believe, lies in three interrelated factors: (1) porous soils, (2) suitable ground cover, and (3) large tracts of young jack pine available at all times as a result of an extensive area with an unimpeded sweep of forest fires.

The practice of the Kirtland's Warbler in placing its nest on flat ground and depressing it below ground level would be fatal in any soil that held surface water. It also effectively excludes this bird from bogs, where other ground-nesting birds use the sides of slopes and hummocks to place their nests above water level. Many such boggy areas have dense growths of small conifers that otherwise would seem acceptable to the Kirtland's Warbler. As we go farther north in the jack-pine range, the underfooting usually becomes wetter in early summer when the birds are nesting, or, if dry, is sparsely vegetated. Within its range, the Kirtland's Warbler has never been

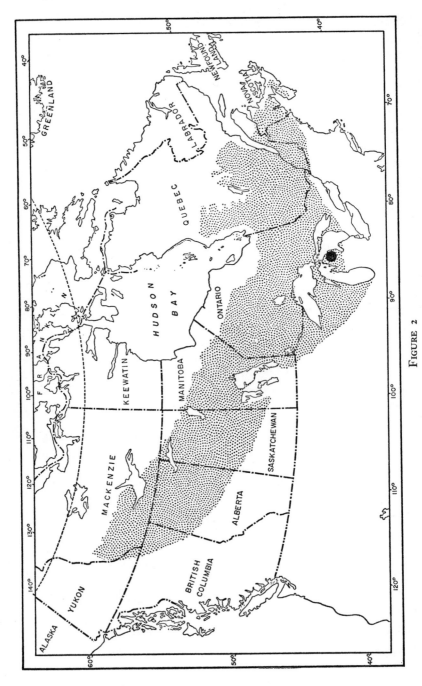

FIGURE 2

Range of the jack pine in North America (Munns, 1938), dotted, and nesting range of Kirtland's Warbler, large dot.

times, because the smaller tracts are exposed to an influx of competitors and predators from the surrounding forest, and thus may not provide the sanctuary needed for the best success of this species.

The future prospects of the habitat are uncertain but not immediately alarming.

I suggest that the Kirtland's Warbler is restricted to one small part of the vast range of the jack pine by a combination of three factors found uniquely in northern Lower Michigan: (1) porous soils, (2) ample ground cover, and (3) unimpeded sweep of forest fires.

In summary, the nesting requirements of the Kirtland's Warbler may be described as follows: extensive stands of small coniferous trees, growing thickly enough for the branches to interlace, but interspersed with generous openings; the trees must have live foliage reaching down to the ground cover; the ground cover must be short but, at least in places, fairly thick; and the soil must be dry and porous.

4

Wintering Ground and Migration

Winter Behavior and Habitat

As with other migrant songbirds, nearly everything known about the Kirtland's Warbler has been learned on its nesting ground, and yet it spends the greater part of each year in another region and in another phase of its life. A number of collectors took specimens of the Kirtland's Warbler in the Bahama Islands, especially in the period 1884 to 1897, but few of them commented about its behavior or habitat. The best statement on the subject is C. J. Maynard's account (1896:594), based on his experiences in 1884:

"Kirtland's Warblers are shy birds of solitary habits, for never in any case did I find two together. They inhabit the low scrub, preferring that which is only three or four feet high, but retire at night to roost in the higher, more dense shrubbery near the spots which they frequent during the day. Those taken were, with one or two exceptions, found in an exceedingly limited area, within a mile or two of the city [Nassau], and always in old fields grown up to low shrubbery. I have never heard Kirtland's Warblers sing, the only note that they uttered was a harsh chirp, with which they greeted me when alarmed at my approach. When one was not secured at first sight, it generally retreated into the bushes and silently disappeared. The thick and tangled character of the scrub rendered any quiet or swift pursuit impossible, thus a retreating bird was never seen again that day, and a number seen escaped in this way. [He took 26 specimens that year.]

"As with many shy birds, however, these warblers presented strange exceptions to the usual rule; twice at least as I was making my way through the thickets in search of the Greater Yellow-throat, I was confronted by a Kirtland's Warbler. In both instances the birds appeared from out of the thicket within a yard of my path, remained a few seconds then darted off into the scrub."

Cory (1879:118), who collected the first winter specimen (on Andros), said it behaved like a Myrtle Warbler and seemed to prefer thick brush.

On first seeing the sparse pinelands of New Providence Island, one is likely to be struck by a superficial resemblance to the forest in the summer range of the Kirtland's Warbler. But Maynard's account shows that he found the warbler not in pines but in broad-leaf scrub, which is abundant on all the islands. It is pertinent also that pines are missing on many of the islands of the Bahamas, including Eleuthera, where a number of Kirtland's Warblers have been taken.

In January and February, 1949, Van Tyne and I spent 59 man-days on New Providence and at Hatchet Bay, Eleuthera, without finding the Kirtland's Warbler. We searched various habitats systematically—large scrub, small scrub, pine woods, grasslands, and mangrove thickets.

Twomey (1936:127, 131) has suggested that average temperature and humidity conditions in the Bahamas during the period December through April, as shown by a climograph, are similar to those in the Kirtland's Warbler range in Michigan during the nesting season. However, winter temperatures in the Bahamas are equable, usually between 60° and 80° F. (16° to 27° C.), whereas on its nesting ground the warbler may encounter temperatures from 20° to 112° F. (−7° to 44° C.).

Winter Records

By search of museum collections and literature, Van Tyne in 1950 was able to learn of 71 specimens collected during the winter in the Bahama Islands. The earliest bird on the wintering ground was taken on November 13 (1891, Eleuthera) and the latest on April 25 (1887, New Providence). The distribution of specimens by islands is shown in Table 3.

In addition, Van Tyne admitted records from two islands on the basis of sight records. These were Cat Cay, April 28, 1907 (Chapman, 1908:224; field journal) and Inagua, March 8, between 1935 and 1940 (exact year not recorded), by James Bond.

Grouping the winter specimens by decades, we have the following distribution:

1870–79	1
1880–89	44
1890–99	22
1900–09	2
1910–19	2
Total	71

Table 3

Winter Records of Kirtland's Warbler in Bahama Islands

Island	Number taken	Collector	Year
Andros	1	C. B. Cory	1879
Berry	3	C. S. Winch	1891
Caicos	2	C. B. Cory	1891
Cat	1	J. P. Moore	1891
Eleuthera	2	C. J. Maynard	1884
Eleuthera	5	C. S. Winch	1891
Eleuthera	3	C. J. Maynard	1897
Great Abaco	1	C. S. Winch	1891
Green Cay	2	Robert Ridgway	1886
Little Abaco	1	J. L. Bonhote	1902
New Providence	24	C. J. Maynard	1884
New Providence	4	C. B. Cory	1884
New Providence	8	A. H. Jennings	1887
New Providence	2	C. J. Maynard	1893
* New Providence	5	C. J. Maynard	1897
New Providence	1	J. L. Bonhote	1902
New Providence	1	C. J. Maynard	1913
New Providence	1	C. J. Maynard	1915
Watlings	4	Robert Ridgway	1886
Total	71		

* Includes one on Athol.

Although collecting efforts in these islands were not distributed evenly over the decades of the last hundred years, there was considerable field work before and after the period shown. For example, Henry Bryant spent four months (January to May) on these islands in 1859, and a shorter period in 1866, without finding the Kirtland's Warbler. In the more than 40 years since the last specimen was taken (in 1915), several ornithologists have worked in the islands, including Van Tyne and Mayfield, 59 man-days, and James Bond, about 100 days. (Bond saw one Kirtland's Warbler.) These circumstances, along with the fact that collectors of those days called the bird "fairly numerous" or "not uncommon," lead us to believe that the Kirtland's Warbler reached a peak in the 1880's and 1890's.

The Wintering Ground as a Limitation on the Species

It is possible that there have been factors on the wintering ground tending to limit the population of this rare species. But it is difficult to speculate about them when we know so little about the bird's requirements or behavior in winter. The only factor to be considered here, therefore, is the land area in the Bahama Islands.

This portion of the earth's crust has been stable since the Cretaceous (Eardley, 1951:574); so for many millions of years changes in land area of the Bahamas have come about chiefly from changes in sea level as the glaciers have advanced and retreated. The islands are so low and the surrounding waters mostly so shallow that some major changes have occurred. For example, the Wisconsin glacial stage began about 25,000 years ago and came to a close about 8,000 years ago (Horberg, 1955:281), and in the early portion of it, perhaps 20,000 years ago, the sea dropped 10 fathoms, exposing the Great Bahama Bank and uniting many of the existing islands into a land mass approaching to within ten miles of the shore of Cuba. At that time the bird life was much richer, with perhaps 40 per cent more species than now, a number comparable to that on Cuba or Hispaniola (Brodkorb, 1959:368). However, as discussed in the section on Nesting Ground, there is some doubt whether a richer avifauna would be more favorable to the Kirtland's Warbler. Also, when we go back so far, remembering that the breeding range may have been much larger and displaced several hundreds of miles southward, we are far from certain that the wintering range was located exactly where it is now.

As the Wisconsin glacier receded, the ocean rose and the islands in the Bahamas shrank to approximately their present size. Subsequently, the sea level has been fairly stable. The only significant change in "postglacial" time was a rise of 6 to 8 feet some 4,000 to 6,000 years ago. This Silver Bluff time in geology is also recognizable from botanical evidence. In Michigan it was a warm, dry period, during which a number of Western plants are believed to have become a part of the jack-pine association which we now regard as part of the typical Kirtland's Warbler breeding habitat. The present sea level is thought to be merely a retreat from the Silver Bluff level (MacNeil, 1950:104). Consequently, even though there has been erosion of shores by wave action in some places, it does not appear that the land area in the Bahamas has been greatly larger or smaller during the 6,000 to 8,000 years that the Kirtland's Warbler has probably been nesting in Michigan; that is, the islands have not been so large as to have had a significantly different fauna or so small as to have crowded the birds unduly in "postglacial" times.

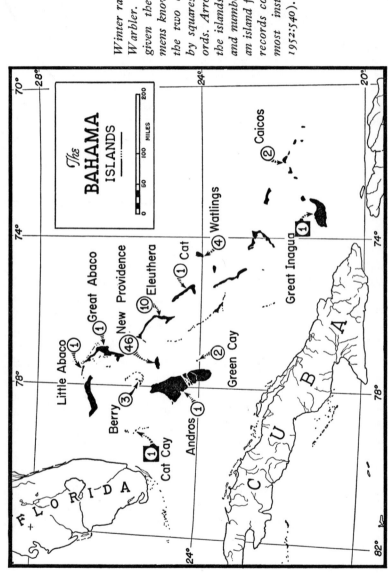

FIGURE 3

Winter range of the Kirtland's Warbler. In the circles are given the numbers of specimens known from each island; the two circles circumscribed by squares represent sight records. Arrows simply designate the islands to which the names and numbers refer—the part of an island from which the given records come is not known in most instances (Van Tyne, 1952:540).

Fall Migration

Verne Dockham, who has lived in the nesting region of the Kirtland's Warbler for many years, finds that they begin to disappear in late August; that the majority leave in the first week of September; and that they become rare after the middle of September, although an occasional straggler may remain until late in the month. The latest record from the nesting range was September 28, 1919 (specimen by Max M. Peet). There are no fall records in Michigan south of the jack-pine country. The latest fall specimen in the United States was recorded on October 29 (1903, South Carolina).

Fall migration records for the species are few in number. All occur in Ontario, Ohio, or the South Atlantic states—that is, in the general direction of the Bahama Islands from central Michigan. The records are shown in the following tabulation.

FALL MIGRATION RECORDS OF THE KIRTLAND'S WARBLER

Point Pelee, Ontario, October 2, 1915 (specimen by W. E. Saunders, letter, December 10, 1934)

Toledo, Ohio, September 22, 1929 (seen by Louis W. Campbell and Edward S. Thomas, 1940:146)

Oberlin, Ohio, August 28, 1902 (Lynds Jones, 1903a:104, incorrectly given by Dawson, 1903:164)

Cleveland, Ohio, October 14, 1886 ("found [dead] under electric light mast," Davies, 1906:118)

Fort Myer, Virginia, September 25, 1887 (specimen by Hugh M. Smith and William Palmer; and another seen October 2 of the same year; 1888:147–148)

Rocky Mount, North Carolina, September 2, 1936, September 22, 1938, September 23, 1941 (seen by Francis H. Craighill, 1942:25–26)

Mt. Pleasant, South Carolina, October 29, 1903 (specimen by A. T. Wayne, 1904:83–84)

Christ Church Parish, South Carolina, October 4, 1910 (seen by A. T. Wayne, 1911:116)

East Goose Creek, Florida, September 9, 1919 (seen by Ludlow Griscom and John T. Nichols, letter, May 15, 1950)

Off the coast of Florida, second week of October, 1841 (specimen taken on shipboard "between Abaco and Cuba" by Samuel Cabot, Jr., Baird, 1865:207)

The fall ocean flight takes place in the hurricane season. Milton Trautman has suggested that these storms might decimate the population of Kirtland's Warblers if they caught many birds in flight or resting on low islets. He believed the period 1927 to 1932 brought

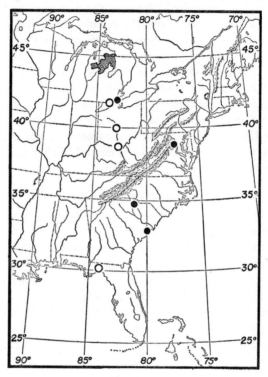

FIGURE 4

Fall migration of the Kirtland's Warbler. Solid black dots represent specimen records; open circles represent accepted sight records (Van Tyne, 1952:543).

September and October hurricanes of unusual intensity in the migration lane and, from his field work in Michigan, suspected the population of nesting warblers dropped sharply in the same period.

Spring Migration

There are many more records of spring migrants than fall migrants of the Kirtland's Warbler. This fact is not surprising, for the males sing during spring migration, the leaves offer less concealment in early May than in September, and there are more observers afield in spring.

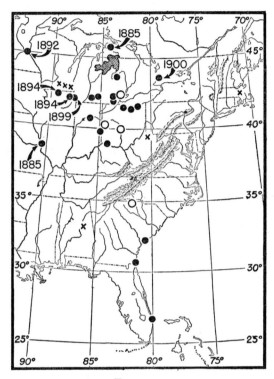

FIGURE 5

Spring migration of the Kirtland's Warbler. Solid black dots indicate one or more specimen records; open circles represent accepted sight records; crosses represent published reports open to doubt (Van Tyne, 1952:542). The dated records fall outside the normal migration route, and all of them occurred in the period 1885 to 1900, when these birds are believed to have been more numerous than before or since.

The earliest spring date for a migrant in the United States was April 12 at Cumberland Island on the coast of Georgia. Van Tyne (1951:541) says: "Other dates for southern states range from April

27 to May 5. To the north, in Ohio and Indiana, the dates range from May 1 to 28; in southern Michigan, from May 6 to 30."

The most dramatic modern record was provided by a specimen collected when a migrant female was killed by flying against the lighted Perry Monument on South Bass Island, Ohio, in Lake Erie. The episode happened at 9:45 p.m., May 24, 1954, and the falling bird struck Milton Trautman, who was gathering bird casualties at the base of the tall stone spire. Another modern record of unusual interest was that of a bird captured in a mist net at Point Pelee, Ontario, on May 10, 1959. It appeared to be a first-year male. It was singing in low, open brush at the edge of a cattail marsh. It was weighed, measured, banded, and released by five members of the Ontario Bird Banders' Association (Woodford, 1959:234).

The first Kirtland's Warblers arrive on the nesting grounds as early as May 3 in some years and as late as May 20 in others, with an average date of May 12. In 1956, when Van Tyne observed the appearance of the first birds of the spring, they arrived under conditions that typically bring a wave of migrants of many species; that is, during a northward flow of air accompanying a barometric low-pressure system. Arrival dates for 23 years, not consecutive, are shown in the following tabulation.

ARRIVAL DATES OF KIRTLAND'S WARBLER BY YEARS

1904	May 3	1944	May 12
1906	May 12	1947	May 18
1929	May 11	1948	May 15
1930	May 14	1949	May 14
1935	May 12	1950	May 13
1936	May 10	1951	May 11
1937	May 13	1952	May 11
1938	May 13	1953	May 6
1939	May 14	1955	May 5
1940	May 20	1956	May 12
1941	May 9	1958	May 12
1942	May 8		

Mean, median, and modal date for 23 years: May 12.

In spring migration, as on the wintering ground, the Kirtland's Warbler prefers low elevations and brushy situations. In describing locations where they have seen the birds, observers have said:

"thicket," "plum thicket," "ash second-growth thicket," "plum trees," "in bushes and briars," "lower limbs of elm," and "scrub willow."

Summary

Little is known about the life of the Kirtland's Warbler except during the nesting season. Scant notes by collectors in the 19th century suggest that the bird is a quiet inhabitant of deciduous brush throughout the Bahama Islands.

Specimens have been collected on most of the principal islands of this group, particularly in the '80s and '90s of the last century. No specimen has been taken there since 1915.

We know too little about the bird's requirements and behavior in winter to consider adequately the factors that may have tended to limit the population on the wintering ground. One variable that may have been important is the extent of land area in the Bahamas. This area was very much larger about 20,000 years ago than at present. At that time it also had a much richer bird life, a condition that may have been unfavorable to the Kirtland's Warbler. However, the land area in the Bahamas seems to have been not significantly different from that of today during the 6,000 to 8,000 years that the Kirtland's Warbler has been nesting in Michigan.

The Kirtland's Warbler begins its fall migration in late August, and nearly all the birds have left the nesting ground by September 15. Spring migrants begin entering the United States in April, and the first birds reach the nesting grounds between May 3 and May 20, with an average date of May 12.

5

Mating and Territorial Behavior

Pair Formation

Information is scant about the first few days on the nesting grounds. What we know is based mostly on the impressions of Dockham, who has been interested in determining the time of arrival for many years, and those of Van Tyne, who was present for just two days after the first warblers arrived in 1956.

The first Kirtland's Warblers to arrive in the spring are males. They are already singing in migration and sing immediately on the nesting ground, weather permitting, but perhaps not as persistently as they do a few days later when settled on territories. The number of males builds up during the ensuing days, and probably all are on the nesting grounds within two weeks after the first arrivals.

The females begin arriving soon after the first males, and females therefore arrive simultaneously with the later males. Thus, very early in the season females are to be found on the nesting grounds with the males. Probably this circumstance misled Dockham, who was quoted by Van Tyne in Bent (1953:418), into believing the sexes arrived together, already paired. Later, however, Dockham concluded the "very first males" were not accompanied by females, and this conclusion was confirmed by Van Tyne's impression in 1956. For example, Van Tyne (and Holden in the adjacent county) noted the arrival of the first males on May 12 at five separate nesting areas. On this day and the next he looked in vain for females. But on May 15, three days after the arrival of the first males, Dockham found females on two areas. Actually, it is difficult to be sure females are not present, for the males are singing and perching conspicuously, while the females may escape notice by remaining quietly in dense cover.

Immediately on arrival the males show some signs of territorial behavior. They chase other small birds that fly near them and sing at intervals. However, for a day or two they range over a wider than normal territory, sometimes taking flights of 200 or 300 meters. In this stage they are hard to follow. But within about three days some of the males give evidence that they have taken possession of the territory they will hold until the end of the nesting season.

From these circumstances and from the behavior of other warblers, I suspect that the Kirtland's Warblers are not paired before arrival, that the male establishes his territory without a mate, and that the female chooses the territory (or male) where she is to nest. Since, typically, the first males arrive about May 12, and the first nests are started about May 26, this prenesting time lasts about two weeks—perhaps a little less for the female, since she may arrive later than her mate.

Territory Defense

The male Kirtland's Warbler, in typical songbird fashion, selects a territory before he is joined by the female. He defends this territory against other males of the species. He sings from all parts of the territory, and does not leave it until the nesting season is over, or he is feeding young birds out of the nest, and even then he tends to stay on or near it.

When another male Kirtland's Warbler appears on the territory, the owner chases him until he departs. Conflict is most severe early in the season. Often the action is too rapid for the human eye to follow the details. But sometimes the males pause together in mid-air, fluttering violently, head to head, rising or descending vertically, as though neither one is able to press the other back. In these struggles there are rapid snapping sounds, presumably from the bills of the contenders. Once, on May 24, hearing two males singing from the same spot, I penetrated the pines and found a female with two males in attendance. The two males joined in aerial conflict and fluttered to the ground almost at my feet. Their mandibles were interlocked deeply, and they lay on the ground motionless, with wings outspread. One was on its back and the other pressed down on it, pinning it there. Their intensity and gleaming eyes conveyed an impression of surprising ferocity. The birds seemed quite oblivious to me until I reached down hesitantly to pick them up. Then they broke free and flew rapidly out of sight.

Just prior to this fight both males had been singing full-throated songs. Sometimes males near one another give "whisper songs." Also, males often utter a harsh "tzit" several times a second during the crisis of pursuit, as the birds twist and turn through the trees.

No instance of injury to a male in territory defense has come to our attention, but even if it occurred it would not be likely to be noticed. The severity of their encounters causes us to believe that injury, or even death, could occur in the conflicts of the Kirtland's Warbler. Such deaths have been reported a few times for other songbirds.

Display between males is not often seen. Van Tyne described one instance in his notes, as follows: "A female was found near a singing male. Then another male appeared, and there began a series of rapidly repeated incomplete songs back and forth between the two males about 25 feet apart. Some were song starts. Others were a low *chrrr, chrrr,* so much like a Purple Martin that I looked overhead. Then through an opening I saw a male displaying. He stood stiffly on a nearly horizontal branch with tail cocked up at a 30° angle, back arched, head pointed stiffly upward, bill open but moving slightly, wings considerably drooped, quivering. He turned slowly back and forth, rotating through 180° or more. In a few minutes, he did it again. Then I lost sight of him and there were brief sounds as though of conflict. The songs resumed and gradually became more complete as the birds moved off."

Freeman (1950:521) noted a rare instance of display by one male Ovenbird toward another; in this case also the aggressive bird elevated its tail and lowered its wings. Stewart (1953:105) noted flickering movements of the wing and tail by male Yellow-throats in territorial encounters that suggested some of the gestures of courtship.

As the season progresses the amount of conflict lessens, and the resident male spends very little time and energy chasing encroaching males. Usually the intruding male offers little resistance and, when chased, flies away. Late in the season territorial barriers seem to relax somewhat, even though the resident male is still singing. In late July, the day after nestlings had fledged, an adult male was observed ignoring the neighboring male when it perched in a tree five meters from the empty nest. One August 4 I saw two males within one meter of a young cowbird one of them was feeding—without conflict. Males feeding young sometimes encroach on the territories of other males without challenge. Whether this becomes possible because the impulse to defend territory has declined in the resident male, or because the encroaching bird now acts "unmalelike," I do not know.

The song of another Kirtland's Warbler male within the territory brings instant response. I was able to see this reaction in detail with the aid of a tape-recorded song played through a loud-speaker. On May 31, 1957, W. W. H. Gunn and Donald J. Borror used their portable recording and play-back equipment on the territory of a male warbler, about 100 meters from the nest, which was in the first day of incubation. The loud-speaker was placed on a pine limb two meters from the ground. When the recorded song was played, the defending male approached, singing. He paused about 10 meters away, sang a few times, and then flew directly toward the loud-speaker, passing above it to a point three meters beyond. Then he turned and flew back past the loud-speaker. Again and again he flew past, over, under, or to one side of the loud-speaker, but never alighting on it. Occasionally he alighted within about one meter of it, in spite of the presence of five men nearby. The male gave his usual song in a normal manner, but also gave a number of "whisper" songs and "chips."

By use of recorded songs, Weeden and Falls (1959:351) concluded that Ovenbirds distinguished between near neighbors and others, and reacted more vigorously to the songs of strangers.

The male sometimes chases other species of small birds, though, I believe, only when the male sees swift, low-level flight—not when the other bird flies above the trees, feeds, or sings from a perch. Nor does it invariably occur when other species of birds fly nearby. The Kirtland's Warbler is not notably pugnacious or intolerant of other species. The birds chased include many of the small songbirds of the area, such as the Vesper Sparrow, Slate-colored Junco, Chipping Sparrow, Nashville Warbler, Prairie Warbler, Myrtle Warbler, and even the Scarlet Tanager. It may be significant that four of these seven species show a flash of white in the tail, superficially like that of a Kirtland's Warbler.

Once I had the opportunity to observe closely the interaction between a resident male and a female entering from a neighboring territory. It was on June 27, the day after her young had fledged. When she had entered about seven meters into the adjacent territory, the resident male approached to within half a meter. She gave no sign of awareness until he came very close. Then she darted at him with outthrust bill, and he flew away.

We have never found a mated male an appreciable distance outside his territory except when he is feeding fledglings. But I have one observation suggesting that unmated males may become restless and do some exploring as the season advances. One June 13 I had been watching an unmated male from 5:30 to 7:30 a.m. He sang frequently and behaved like a normal territorial male. At 11:30 a.m., as I was driving away from the area, I heard a Kirtland's Warbler song in an unfamiliar place, and there found the banded male I had been watching earlier in the morning. He was 1.2 miles (2 km.) from his original territory. By June 15, however, he was back in the first location.

Territory Size

I doubt if the female is aware of the male's territory limits. She leaves the territory without hesitation when feeding fledglings. However, during nest building, incubation, and the nestling period, she rarely goes more than 100 meters from the nest, and usually gathers food much nearer. Consequently, her habits probably would hold her within the territory limits without any other influence. The male frequently joins the female when she moves, and his attentions may help keep her near. The female chases small birds and mammals that come within a meter or two of the nest, but her "defended area" does not comprise an appreciable part of the area she ranges.

The nest may be anywhere in the territory, but it is often in the central portion. When the nest is near the extreme edge, the boundary is always found to be ecological (open fields or large trees), not another Kirtland's Warbler territory. Whether the behavior of the males tends to steer the females to central locations for their nests, or whether some males readjust their territories after the nest is started, I do not know, for we have never mapped a territory before and after nesting has started. However, nests of neighboring pairs are usually more than 200 meters apart, rarely less than 150, and never less than about 100. This wide spacing does not come about by chance alone. Stenger and Falls (1959:128) found there was sometimes a shift in the Ovenbird's territory after the arrival of the female and also variation in the size of the territory during the breeding season.

The territory is usually roughly circular, but it may be a long oval or have irregularities caused by habitat limits. The extent of a territory has been estimated by marking the most distant points reached by the singing male. Thus the area includes the entire defended territory, regardless of any unutilized portions within it; that is, it is identical with the "maximum territory" of Odum and Kuenzler

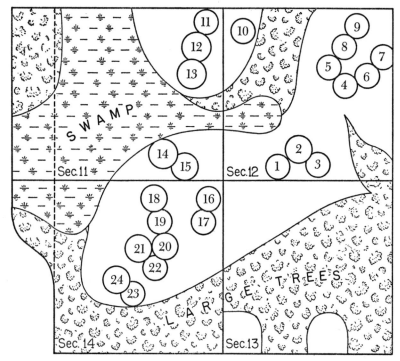

FIGURE 6

Kirtland's Warblers nesting at near maximum abundance on four square miles in T27N, R1E, Oscoda County, Michigan, in June, 1946. Circles show approximate territories of the males. Twenty-four pairs are found here on about 1,000 acres of suitable habitat.

(1955:129). All these birds were on study areas where, over a period of days, the observer acquired a general familiarity with the range of each male; in no instance, however, were sustained and precise studies made of the movements of each bird. More observations undoubtedly would have somewhat increased the total area, and these areas should therefore be regarded as rough approximations.

Twelve territories measured over a period of 20 years had areas as follows: 1.5, 3.0, 4.1, 6.7, 7.0, 8.5, 8.8, 8.9, 11.6, 12.8, 13.0, and 16.5 acres (average 8.4 acres, or 3.4 hectares). This area is more than twice the size of the usual area for North American warblers, as shown in Table 4.

Among Kirtland's Warblers the territories seem to be larger where

Table 4

Size of Territory of North American Warblers

Species	Size of Territory (acres)		Authority
	Range	Average	
Kirtland's Warbler (*Dendroica kirtlandii*)	1.5–16.5	8.4	This work
Ovenbird (*Seiurus aurocapillus*)	2.5–4.5	3.0	Hann, 1937
"	0.8–4.3	2.3	Stenger & Falls, 1959
Northern Waterthrush (*S. noveboracensis*)	2.0–3.7	2.5	Eaton, 1957
Prairie Warbler (*Dendroica discolor*)	1.2–6.0	3.0	Nolan, letter, Dec. 31, 1958
Prothonotary Warbler (*Protonotaria citrea*)	1.9–6.38	3.66	Walkinshaw, 1953
American Redstart (*Setophaga ruticilla*)	......	0.19	Sturm, 1945
"	......	0.5–1.0	Hickey, 1940
Yellowthroat (*Geothlypis trichas*)	0.8–1.8	1.26	Stewart, 1953
"	......	2.0	Hofslund, letter, Dec. 19, 1958
Yellow Warbler (*Dendroica petechia*)	......	0.4	Kendeigh, 1941
"	0.15–0.94	0.42	Brewer, 1955
Tennessee Warbler (*Vermivora peregrina*)	0.4–1.7	0.68	Kendeigh, 1947
Nashville Warbler (*V. ruficapilla*)	1.2–6.0	2.7	"
Magnolia Warbler (*Dendroica magnolia*)	1.0–1.6	1.4	"
Cape May Warbler (*D. tigrina*)	0.4–2.4	1.1	"
Black-throated Green Warbler (*D. virens*)	0.8–2.1	1.2	"
Blackburnian Warbler (*D. fusca*)	2.0–2.2	2.1	"
Bay-breasted Warbler (*D. castanea*)	0.1–1.2	0.37	"

the tree growth is more open, and smaller if hemmed in closely by neighboring territories. Perhaps these two factors may also help to explain why Kirtland's Warbler territories are larger than territories of closely related species; that is, there is less vegetation in Kirtland's Warbler areas than in most forests inhabited by warblers, and there is plenty of habitat available to all without crowding. However, the total amount of vegetation in an area does not seem to give any clue to the small territories of the Yellow Warbler in brush, of the Redstart in forest, or of the Yellowthroat in an open expanse of marshland.

Stenger (1958:335–346) found that the territory of the Ovenbird, which feeds almost entirely on the ground, was smaller where the weight of invertebrates in the leaf litter was higher per unit area. This suggests that availability of food may help determine territory size in that species. However, if food availability is a factor in the size of the Kirtland's Warbler territory, I think it is a minor one. By the time the young have hatched and food needs are greatest, food seems extremely easy to get, and the female, particularly, gathers much of her food within 10 meters of the nest or in equally small feeding areas a short distance away—that is, within a very small part of the territory. Then, when the young have fledged, the family groups wander beyond the territorial boundaries but still seem to utilize only a small fraction of the area available. Lack (1943:100) similarly had the impression that food in the territory was far in excess of the needs of European Robins and their young during an ordinary summer.

By studying birds on small islands, Beer *et al.* (1956:200–209) found that the species studied were able to raise their young on territories "much smaller when the boundaries are strictly physical barriers rather than invisible lines determined by intraspecific conflict"—in some cases less than one-tenth the minimum area supposedly required on the mainland.

For the Kirtland's Warbler I believe the territory must be large enough to provide insulation from other adults of the species. Unless there is some freedom from the distractions of competition and conflict, I suspect certain delicately poised activities of the mating sequence cannot proceed successfully. These may include nest searching and building, when the female is easily deterred, and meetings of the pair, including copulation, which takes place only in concealment. The fact that many wild birds do not breed in captivity suggests that the requirements may be subtle and precise. Denser vegetation, providing the desired amount of seclusion in a smaller area, would of course also provide a higher concentration of food supply.

Colonies

Norman Wood, the discoverer of the nesting ground of the Kirtland's Warbler, recognized in his first few days of observation that the bird occurred in "colonies." He said (1904:10), "It is not, however, every jack pine plain that is the home of a colony, as I examined hundreds of acres where the conditions seemed all right, and found none." So the nesting pairs are not distributed evenly or randomly over the available areas, but occur in groups or clusters. When we examine a suitable area, we ordinarily find either none at all or several pairs—almost never an isolated pair.

These are not colonies in the usual sense, where birds nest in compact groups and go elsewhere for food, but rather a loose assembly of pairs, each with an exclusive territory of ample size for all the needs of the pair during courtship and nesting. However, since the term "colony" has been used by field students of the Kirtland's Warbler for more than fifty years, I use it here, even though a new term may be needed.

This tendency of songbirds to locate near others of their kind— like human settlers who want plenty of elbow room and yet choose land near one another rather than in remote empty spaces—has been recognized in several species, and may occur unnoticed in many more. For example, Nice (1943:86) remarked that male Song Sparrows attempted to locate where there were already others, instead of on unoccupied ground a little distance away. Davis (1959:74) says of Least Flycatchers: "The birds formed a definite colony in the study area. Searches in nearby areas revealed no birds, even in apparently suitable vegetation." Bent (1953:139, 339) uses the word "colony" to describe assemblies of pairs of the Parula and Blackburnian warblers, but does not make clear whether it is a social phenomenon or merely a habitat limitation.

In the Kirtland's Warbler the grouping of pairs is very loose. Territories are rarely touched by others on more than one or two sides, and sometimes adjacent territories do not touch at all. Yet I feel justified in calling such a group a colony, for each male (and female) is in touch with at least one other male by hearing and sight. Colonies often have 6 to 12 pairs, occasionally as few as two or three, and rarely as many as 30. Occasionally isolated males have been reported, but in only three such instances have females been found. In one, both adults of the pair had fine speckling on the breast, a possible mark of immaturity. This female incubated a clutch of five eggs for at least 20 days, and then disappeared. The eggs, when opened, showed no evidence of development.

Isolated males sometimes have been found to be survivors of former colonies, clinging to their territories although the habitat is no longer suitable, or pioneers in new or marginal areas. In two colonies followed to the end, the next-to-last year brought several males but few females, and the last year in each brought a lone, unmated male. In new areas, singing males are sometimes present a year ahead of the first females. Once a male was found singing on half an acre of suitable habitat, a tract far smaller than any used by a nesting pair.

These circumstances suggest that there may be a surplus of males. An additional inkling was supplied by midsummer field work in 1956. On a good area virtually all the males were banded in June, but by July 22, after most of the pairs were feeding young and the territories were only slightly defended, if at all, six new males were singing regularly, but without mates, so far as I could determine.

It is possible that the clustering of pairs in a few chosen areas is a result of some attractive habitat features not recognized by us. However, I believe that it is instead a result of a gregarious drive, only partly suppressed by the temporary demand for territorial exclusiveness. It may confer some benefit upon the species. For example, a group of males on territory may be more easily found by the females; lost mates may be more easily replaced; and exposure to almost continuous song and other aspects of breeding behavior by several nearby males may be stimulating to the reproductive drive of males or females.

Darling (1938:76, 108) has suggested that the cumulative effect of courtship all about in a colony may help in the "synchronization of the breeding cycle" of the nesting pair, and that nests in very small colonies may therefore be less successful than those in large colonies. Some of his views have been challenged, but there can scarcely be a doubt that, in some species of birds, nesting in a colony confers an advantage.

Mates and Locations in Successive Years

The male Kirtland's Warbler usually returns almost exactly to the territory he defended in the previous year. Sometimes he moves a little, and occasionally as much as the width of two territories. If he were to move a mile or more (2 km.), he would probably not be found again; but the high recorded survival rate of adults of this species makes it unlikely that many move far enough to escape notice. I have 18 instances (9 males) in which distances between nests were measured for consecutive years. Twelve showed movements of less than 180 meters, and only three moved 360 meters or more; that is, the majority returned to essentially the same territory, and less than one-fourth moved more than the width of two territories. The mean movement was 200 meters, the minimum was 27, and the maximum was 1,000.

The females showed less tendency to return to the same spot in successive years. In 23 instances (14 females), the distances between nests in consecutive years was less than 180 meters in 10 cases, and more than 360 in 13; that is, more than half moved at least the width of two territories. The mean movement was 426 meters, the minimum was 4, and the maximum was 1,350. These figures do not include one female that moved 19 miles (31 km.). (She was banded at her nest in Sec. 12, T27N, R1E, on June 14, 1945, and captured at her nest in Sec. 19, T25N, R4E, on June 18, 1946.)

Occasionally we have found the remains of old nests near nests in use, but we know of no instance in which a female built a nest on a site used previously by herself or another bird. A search of favorable sites often uncovers remnants of former nests which could be attributed to any of a number of ground-nesting species, particularly the Slate-colored Junco, Nashville Warbler, Black-and-White Warbler, Hermit Thrush, and Vesper Sparrow.

There is some tendency for a female Kirtland's Warbler to return to the same mate (or territory) in successive years. I have 12 instances in which I knew the matings of both members of a pair in consecutive years. In five instances they kept the same mates, and in seven instances they changed mates. This finding is similar to the frequency of rematings in some other small samples of migratory songbirds on this continent: House Wrens, 11 rematings out of 26 opportunities (Kendeigh, 1941:56); Song Sparrows, 8 out of 30 (Nice, 1943:182–183); nine species, 6 out of 17 (Brackbill, 1959:123).

The number of cases is too small to warrant any conclusion, but the circumstances suggest that the female may return to the territory rather than to the male. In only one of the five cases in which the same individuals paired again in the following year did the female rejoin her former mate in a new territory—in that instance the new location was about the width of two territories away from the location of the previous year; in the other four cases the females paired again with their mates of the previous year *on the same territory*. In five of the seven cases in which the females chose different mates the next year, the former mates had moved to new locations at least the width of one territory away. However, in all cases in which the females chose different mates they moved to different territories, usually in a different part of the colony, not next door. It is reasonable to suppose that some females return to the familiar territory, find it pre-empted by another female, and move on to another.

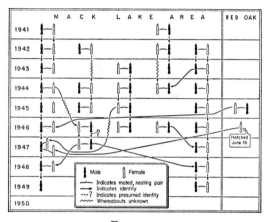

FIGURE 7

Chart (Van Tyne) showing interrelationships of pairs of Kirtland's Warbler within a colony, 1941–1949.

Some of the interrelationships of the pairs within a colony are shown here on a chart (Figure 7) prepared by Van Tyne. It illustrates a number of phenomena discussed elsewhere: females re-mating with the same males in some successive years and failing to do so in others, females missed in one year and found in later years, a female changing mates and then returning to a former mate after four years, and the recruitment of two females—one a first-year bird and one an older bird—from another colony 19 miles (30 km.) distant. However, the chart does not attempt to portray all the birds present in the colony for any year except 1949, the last year of the colony's existence.

Courtship

"Attentiveness" seems the best word to describe most of the actions of the male Kirtland's Warbler toward the female throughout the time of the pairing bond. The male accompanies the female as she moves, "socializing" (that is, twittering and approaching closely without actually touching her, usually in the concealment of encircling foliage), and gives her food. We have not detected any elaborate display or ritual. At times there is pursuit that seems to have no purpose except courtship or play.

We have little information about the behavior of these birds in the earliest stages of pair formation, except that when the male is located by his song the female usually can be found nearby.

While the female travels the territory, "searching," just prior to nest building, the male stays in close attendance. Sometimes he hops along the ground with her, sometimes he travels through the branches of trees nearby, and occasionally he hovers momentarily over her. Once we saw a male slant with fluttering wings down over the female from a height of two meters, as though in display. He sings during this period, but not as often, I think, as when unmated or when the female is sitting on the nest. At intervals she chips and he joins her, "socializing."

During nest building any movement of the female spurs the male to attention and song. When she perches quietly he may wander off to another part of this territory, feeding. But when she resumes activity he reappears promptly and sings. As she works intermittently, it seems that his song unfailingly announces her resumption of work.

I have witnessed coition only three times, and each time it took place before incubation began, and probably before the first egg was laid. Once it occurred on June 23, after a nest had been destroyed, and three days before the first egg of the new set was laid. The female was perched in a cluster of pine branches, about one meter from the ground, silhouetted through an opening. The male flew in from a distance of about ten meters and alighted on her back for an instant. I did not see any warning from him or invitation from her. The action was so rapid that I doubted whether the act was complete. Immediately they moved apart, he singing.

On two other occasions I saw the complete act. In view of the dates, May 22 and May 24, and the behavior of the females, I judged that incubation had not yet begun and perhaps egg laying had not yet started, but I was not successful in finding these nests. In both instances the female chipped vigorously and, as the male approached, assumed a rigid posture, with bill and tail vertical, her body sway-backed. (Nero (1956:32) describes a similar precopulatory posture by the female Red-winged Blackbird.) The male settled on her, maintaining his balance with the aid of fluttering wings. I think he also grasped her head or beak with his bill, but I was positive only that he was clinging to her with his mandibles as he fell away. Both times she was perched in the middle branches of small pines. One act occurred at 9:30 a.m. and the other at 11 a.m.

The earliest in the nesting cycle I have seen the male feed his mate was two days before the first egg was laid, that is, about halfway through the nest-building period. However, this feeding took place away from the nest. Also, I have seen the male feed the female on and off the nest during the egg-laying period before incubation started. Feeding occurs frequently during incubation. In a typical instance, when the male approaches the nest the incubating female rises, quivers half-spread wings like a young bird "begging," and flies up into a nearby tree, twittering. The male follows and feeds her. Then she moves off, foraging for her own food. The female that leaves a nest where she has been incubating eggs or brooding young is often joined by the male, with or without food, and they move into dense cover together, twittering and "socializing."

Lack (1940:169–172) suggests that courtship feeding does not have food as its primary object but serves rather to maintain the bond between the pair. He points out also that courtship feeding is found mainly in birds in which both sexes care for the young.

Polygamy

Ordinarily the male or female Kirtland's Warbler has only one mate. We have never found a female attended by two males, and only once a male with two females nesting on his territory. This polygamous male had been banded as an adult six years before, and therefore was at least seven years old. He had returned each year to his original territory. This year his territory was more than usually elongated. In the central part of one lobe of the territory the first nest was found in the early morning of June 14. A few minutes after it was found, the last egg in a set of five was laid. The female had been banded as an adult three years earlier, but had not been seen in the intervening years. She incubated these eggs for at least 21 days, and then abandoned the nest.

The nest of his second mate was found in the afternoon of the same day, about 150 meters from the first nest. She had been banded as a nestling the previous June at another colony, 30 kilometers away. This nest held four eggs when found, but when next visited, two days later, held only three and was abandoned. On June 23 she completed a second set of four eggs, all of which hatched. Many times we have found more males than females on an area, but this was our only experience of an apparent surplus of females.

Polygamy has been reported in rare instances among at least four other species of warblers. Hann (1937:155) twice found male Ovenbirds with two mates each, and once found a female with two males (1940:69–72); Eaton (1957:12) found a male Northern Waterthrush with two nesting females on his territory. Stewart (1953:105) found a male Yellow-throat with two females, each on separate territories; and Nolan (unpublished) observed a similar situation in the Prairie Warbler.

Nice (1937:88–90) noted four instances in which male Song Sparrows had two mates each, and believed that in every case the female on the adjacent territory had lost her mate after nesting had started and took the neighboring male as a replacement.

We have no cases in which Kirtland's Warblers changed mates during a nesting season.

Summary

The first males arrive on the nesting ground slightly, perhaps only about three days, ahead of the first females. Almost immediately the males begin establishing territories and are joined by the females.

The male stays within and defends his territory against trespassing males of the same species throughout the breeding season, but gradually relaxes his defense after the young birds leave the nest.

The nest is usually located in the central part of the territory. The average size of the Kirtland's Warbler territory is about eight acres, more than twice the size of the territory reported for any other North American warbler.

The Kirtland's Warbler tends to nest in "colonies"—that is, assemblies of pairs, each pair with its own exclusive territory, but grouped together, leaving much suitable habitat empty.

The male usually returns almost exactly to the same territory in succeeding years. The female returns to the same general area, but settles on the same territory in less than half the instances. In 12 instances observed in this study both members of a pair returned the following year, and five of these remated.

Courtship seems to consist mostly of "attentiveness" by the male to the female, with little ritual or display. Coition, as far as known, takes place only before incubation begins. Feeding of the female by the male begins as early as the nest-building phase, before the first egg is laid.

We have only one instance of polygamy—a male with two females nesting on his territory, but the eggs of one of these females did not hatch, although incubated far beyond the normal period. The mating bond lasts throughout the nesting season; we have no examples of new mates being acquired during the course of the season.

6

Miscellaneous Notes on Behavior

Tameness

One of the notable characteristics of the Kirtland's Warbler on its nesting ground is its tameness. Compared to other birds in the same area, and compared to wood warblers generally, it is less easily frightened and more easily approached by a human observer. When feeding, it pays little attention to a moving person ten steps away, and approaches almost within arm's length of a person sitting quietly.

At the nest the warbler often behaves boldly. Sometimes a male will approach, singing, and carry food to the female or young in the nest with an observer watching openly two steps away. The greatest extremes of tameness have been exhibited by certain females. In the report of the discovery of the first nest, Wood (1904:10) told of a female alighting on the toe of his companion's shoe. Walkinshaw and Van Tyne had female Kirtland's Warblers alight on them—on their boots, hats, and shoulders—and hop along their bodies as they lay or crouched before the nest. At such times the warblers showed no great agitation, but seemed merely curious. Walkinshaw found a female that took food from his hand, and Leopold (1924:54), a male that perched on his shoe and on his thigh, and ate 17 flies from his fingers!

The females sit tightly while incubating eggs or brooding young, and most of them are caught for banding by dropping a butterfly net over the nest. A few females have been caught by hand on the nest or have been plucked from a nearby twig, but these were unusual incidents.

Ordinarily the warblers recover quickly from a fright. Sometimes an incubating female, after being netted and banded, will be back on her nest in five minutes. A male that has been banded often will resume feeding and singing almost immediately. This remarkable tolerance for disturbance causes the Kirtland's Warbler to continue nests when birds of many species would desert. Nearly all birds become more strongly attached to their nests as incubation progresses, and especially after the young hatch; but the Kirtland's Warbler often shows little tendency to desert even in the early days of incubation. It has happened that a person stepped accidentally on a nest, breaking three of four eggs, and the female removed the fragments and continued incubating the remaining egg. A female has been known to return and incubate one egg in the nest, while the others were removed for measuring. Although desertion of nests occurs, I have seldom considered it attributable to human interference.

Except for the singing of the male, this warbler is quiet and inconspicuous. The adults rarely scold or make other sounds. Sometimes a person can flush a female off her nest and examine the contents without hearing a sound from either adult, although the female usually chips softly at such times.

Yet in all these respects there are great individual variations. Some females are extremely wary, approaching their nests hesitantly even when the observer is quite a distance away. Most of these warblers ignore a person in a blind after it is in place a few hours, although their manner of peering into the eyehole slits suggests that they may be aware of the observer. But one female with nestlings brought food only seven times in a total of five hours' observation during five days, and chipped constantly whenever a person was in the blind; in this same period the male carried food 37 times and showed no sign of alarm. It is interesting also that alarm does not seem to be communicated readily from one individual to another in this species. Scolding by one bird of a pair is not automatically joined by the other, and alarm notes by other species nearby do not usually arouse emotion or curiosity in the Kirtland's Warbler. While an excitable warbler shows agitation, its mate often carries on its normal activities undisturbed. Sometimes a male will continue to sing and otherwise behave normally in the presence of great danger—as when his mate is captured and is being held for banding.

Even in this tame species, however, there is a limit to tolerance of disturbance. A good many nests are deserted for reasons unknown. Presumably some experience caused the warblers to abandon such a nest, although the contents were unharmed. On one occasion, as I led a group of about 20 people toward a singing male, the bird, ordinarily undisturbed by the approach of one or two persons, flew away at high altitude, and far beyond the limits of its territory.

In several instances I have suspected that the female returns to her nest with less hesitation in the presence of the male. I have noticed this in attempting to follow the female to her nest; sometimes she hesitates for long periods until the male appears, and then goes rapidly to the nest. If this impression is valid, the behavior may benefit the species, for the more conspicuous manner of the male tends to divert attention to him while the female slips quietly onto the nest.

The tameness of the Kirtland's Warbler in the presence of human beings probably indicates that the bird has had little experience with large mammals in summer or winter. Such nesting associates as the Nashville Warbler and the Prairie Warbler, with different and more extensive winter ranges, are much more wary than the Kirtland's Warbler on the nesting ground.

At first glance, tameness would seem to be a disadvantage. It would appear to make the warblers easy to capture by predators, and yet losses of adults on the nesting ground are very low. Although tameness on the part of the female often seems to make nest finding easier for the human observer than it would be otherwise, the quietness and directness of the bird sometimes have the opposite effect. A female that rarely makes a sound and proceeds directly to the nest through heavy shrubbery may be surprisingly difficult to discover and follow.

Lack (1943:160, 80) has commented similarly on the tameness of the European Robin and the ease with which observers stumble on some nests, and on the difficulty, nevertheless, of finding the nest of all the pairs in an area.

The reluctance of the Kirtland's Warbler to desert its nest probably makes the bird more vulnerable to the depredations of the cowbird than are species that desert on slight provocation and build again.

Reactions to Danger

In the face of danger to itself or the nest, the Kirtland's Warbler has several possible courses of action, depending on the circumstances. These alternative courses are:

1. *Flight.* In a situation involving danger—not complicated by the need to defend territory, nest, or young—the Kirtland's Warbler usually flees soundlessly. It has excellent powers of flight and perception, and seems fully capable of escaping the enemies in its familiar habitat.

2. *Attack* (*threat*). When small animals or small birds approach the nest or fledglings, the female sometimes attacks (the action might be described more accurately as a *threat*, since there is usually no contact and the bird has little capacity for doing harm). Some examples are given under *Care and Defense of Nestlings*. Although we have records of cowbirds and small mammals repulsed near the nest, our best opportunities to observe the method have come in those infrequent instances when females have attacked us. Usually the attack has consisted of short rushes along the ground, with noisy wing motion and snapping bill. In a few cases females have flown explosively toward our faces as we stooped over their nests. Rarely, they have pecked our hands or shoes, but noisy wing motion seems to be the main feature of the attack. One persistent female pursued me when I retreated and withdrew when I advanced. Although the male Kirtland's Warbler chases other birds at times, we have never known him to chase any creature that held any element of danger for him. Armstrong (1956:650) suggested that birds have developed no special defenses against man. Rather, they respond according to the manner of his approach. If he approaches like a predator, in a slinking, purposefully aggressive manner, they give distraction display; if he approaches like an ungulate, in a plodding, heavy-footed manner, they simulate attack.

3. *Freezing*. When danger is at a distance, the Kirtland's Warbler sometimes freezes. Females on the nest regularly do so; once a female sat motionless on a perch 1½ meters above her nest while a group of Common Crows and Blue Jays called noisily 50 meters away. Leopold (1924:53) tells of a male, frightened by the presence of several people, assuming "absolute rigidity as birds often do when they sight a hawk." Once a male stood rigidly on the lip of the nest for almost 15 minutes while I erected a blind three meters away. On another occasion, a male, under observation from a blind as he brought food to young in the nest, paused motionless for four minutes while two people moved about in the vicinity. In every such instance there were young birds in the nests, and in most of them the nestlings were nearly ready to leave.

4. *Distraction Display* (*injury feigning*). In the presence of overwhelming danger to the nest or to fledglings under parental care, the Kirtland's Warbler sometimes gives elaborate displays.

The act is performed by either sex, and occasionally by both members of a pair at once. The female often gives a brief display when flushed from her eggs or young, even in the earliest stages of incubation, but the most intense performances take place when the young have just left the nest. On the other hand, some females may be frightened from nests with young without any demonstration. One male displayed at the nest in the absence of the female in the first or second day of incubation.

Ordinarily the display begins with the bird running away from the intruder on the ground, like a mouse—a "rodent run." The rapid feet seem to move alternately, quite unlike the usual hopping gait of the bird, and make a noisy rustling in dead leaves. After a few feet, the bird slows enough so that its posture may be discerned. Its head and tail are low, "humped over," and its wings are lowered and quivering. The mouth opens wide and closes slowly, with a faint quavering note. Then the head is raised and bent backward, and the tail, which has been held unspread against the ground, rises to an angle of almost 45°, while the body crouches low. In this position the bird turns its body, presenting one side and then the other to the intruder. Sometimes the tail may be spread, showing the white spots prominently. The bird may travel three to ten meters in one rush. One display lasted three minutes. When Van Tyne followed a displaying female, she led him about 50 meters before "recovering" and flying up into the trees.

An analysis of this display without a slow-motion film is difficult. Superficially, the first part of the "rodent run," as the female leaves the nest and darts under nearby vegetation, suggests escape. The quivering wings and the voice suggest a young bird or a female begging food. At times the body postures suggest a female's invitation to copulation. Once, when a female Kirtland's Warbler near a fledgling assumed the display posture, quivering with uplifted bill and tail, her mate approached closely, as though to mount her, and was repulsed. Armstrong (1956:645) has stated that in some species an intruder at the nest may elicit sexual behavior, including copulation.

Some writers have suggested that this display arises from involuntary partial paralysis. But if the warbler is partially paralyzed or otherwise incapacitated during this display, it recovers in an instant when pursued and takes flight readily to avoid capture. Armstrong (1949:180) remarked that displaying birds are seldom captured, but seem to keep a "watchful eye" on the intruder and "choose their route with care."

Doubtless the display sometimes distracts the attention of a predator and thus gives some protection to the nest and young. Skutch (1955:138) pointed out: "Some birds steal unobtrusively from the nest while man is a long way off; others wait until he is almost within arm's length. . . . Both of these modes of departure are strategically sound; but any intermediate course needlessly exposes the nest to detection."

Gregariousness

The Kirtland's Warbler does not occur in tightly-knit flocks at any time, and yet there are evidences of gregariousness.

1. *Colony nesting.* The males establish nesting-season territories near one another, rather than scattered at random over the suitable habitat.

2. *Nonterritorial groups.* Family groups in late summer tend to concentrate in a few small areas, leaving the rest of the former colony area devoid of warblers. As noted earlier, Maynard (1896:594) called the birds "solitary," but later described circumstances that seemed to contradict the idea, when he said that nearly all the Kirtland's Warblers he took in winter on New Providence Island were "found in an exceedingly limited area."

3. *Location call note.* When a Kirtland's Warbler moves through the trees, especially after the nesting season, it frequently utters a location note, "zeet." Answering notes usually reveal that there are others near, although unseen. Often this call is uttered in flight. It is similar to the high-pitched note of other warblers, heard especially in fall migration as they feed concealed among the trees or pass overhead in flight at night.

4. *Chasing.* As mentioned under the heading "Play," Kirtland's Warblers sometimes fly in pursuit of one another for reasons other than conflict, courtship, or food seeking.

5. *Tail signals.* Nice (1943:86) has pointed out that some small sparrows, the juncos and longspurs, for example, which are highly gregarious, have a flight note and a flash of white in the tail. The pipits, gregarious birds in another family, have these signals, and also tail wagging. The Kirtland's Warbler has all three signals—call note, tail flash, and tail wagging—although the call note is not as loud and the white flash not as prominent as in the other birds named.

Tail Wagging

One of the field marks of the Kirtland's Warbler is its habit of jerking or bobbing its tail. This movement has been called tail "wagging," but that term implies a sidewise movement, while the tail actually moves up and down. Watched closely, the tail seems to be jerked downward and then allowed to return to position more slowly. Tail bobbing occurs more rapidly when the bird is agitated, but it is noticeable at almost all times—as will be attested by any photographer who has tried to get a portrait of the bird without tail movement. Both sexes perform it.

It is interesting that the three species of warblers best known for this mannerism—Kirtland's, Prairie, and Palm—all nest in brushy, semi-open country, and spend the winter, at least in part, in the brushy, semi-open lands of the West Indies. It is reasonable to suppose that this tail movement serves as a recognition signal of particular value to birds that see one another frequently through narrow, horizontal vistas.

Hopping on the Ground

There are several published statements to the effect that the Kirtland's Warbler progresses on the ground by "walking" (Forbush and May, 1939:438; Henshaw and Allen, 1937:203; Howell, 1932:407; Henninger, 1906:57). Although the bird is capable of moving its feet alternately, and seems to do so in the "rodent run" of its distraction display, normally it travels on the ground by hopping, like most other small songbirds.

Bill Wiping

After eating food or feeding young, the Kirtland's Warbler often wipes its bill on a branch. In the Song Sparrow, Nice believed bill wiping to be a sign of distaste for food eaten, but in the Kirtland's Warbler I believe it signifies only an attempt to clean moisture or debris from the mandibles, especially when the food morsels are large and juicy. When the warbler catches a big caterpillar, it works with its prey for some time, killing it and reducing it to suitable size. When carrying food to large nestlings, the warbler often carries several caterpillars in a bundle, pinched in the middle and bulging from both sides of the bill. In these activities it is evident that food particles adhere to the sides of the mandibles and that bill wiping is required.

Anting

The Kirtland's Warbler has never been seen anting in the wild, although ants of several kinds are plentiful on the nesting areas and the warbler frequently visits the ground. This activity, in which a bird crushes ants and rubs them on its plumage, has been noted in many other species of songbirds, including several wood warblers, and Berger witnessed it in a captive Kirtland's Warbler.

Play

Some of the chasing of one bird by another seems to be play. It is particularly noticeable among family groups of young birds more than three weeks old. These birds, now able to maneuver well, often chase one another in flights of 100 meters or more, twisting and curving among the trees, and perhaps returning to their starting point. In these flights there is no begging or other sign that they are seeking food from one another. Rather, the behavior suggests the chasing of males during territory defense or the chasing of females by males during courtship.

I have seen a female (intermittently attending a widely ranging cowbird at least 30 days old) chase another Kirtland's Warbler for no apparent reason on August 15, after territory defense and courtship had ceased for the year.

Bathing and Basking

In the early morning the Kirtland's Warbler sometimes bathes in the dew. It places itself in a cluster of dripping leaves and fluffs out its plumage, preens and shakes its wings and tail vigorously, and throws droplets all about. Then it moves to a fresh perch and repeats the performance. The process sometimes takes place in the middle levels of jack pine, but more often in the heavier dew on the low leaves of oak and blueberry. The male usually sings while bathing. Berger saw a captive Kirtland's Warbler take a bath in a shallow puddle on the floor of the aviary when it was about 19 days old. It dipped its breast feathers into the water, fluttering its wings all the while, and repeated the act several times. However, he noted that captives also preferred to bathe in wet leaves.

Abbott (1954:163) described similar leaf bathing in the Mockingbird, and Miller (1942:232) noted in the Rufous-sided Towhee that a pan of water was "not so stimulating of the bathing reaction as the natural supply of water" on dripping trees and bushes.

Haverschmidt (1953:369–370) described Yellow Warblers on the wintering ground bathing in rain and rubbing against wet leaves.

Bathing in water probably serves to dress the plumage, not to clean it.

Sometimes on bright days the warbler seeks a sunny perch, or an open spot on the ground, and sunbathes. It fluffs its feathers, raises its tail, and slightly spreads its wings. In this posture the bird may sit for periods of a minute or so, alternated with periods of preening and foraging. The male may sing intermittently, or be silent. Berger noted sunbathing in a captive bird as early as age 17 days. It crouched on the floor with tail raised and wings drooping, feathers on head erected, and sometimes with bill open. On some occasions it faced the sun; on others, away from the sun.

Sleeping

The female, while incubating eggs or brooding young, sleeps on the nest at night with her head turned back among her scapular feathers. This is her posture when a flashlight beam is thrown on the nest in the dark. In the daytime she usually dozes on the nest with her head straight forward.

We have never seen the male on a night roost.

Berger noticed that a captive bird, at this time about 19 days old, did not maintain a continuous grasp on the perch while sleeping. At intervals of 10 to 30 seconds, at most one minute, the bird lifted one foot, flexed it, extended the toes, and replaced it on the perch. Sometimes a foot was raised only for an instant. Sometimes the same foot was raised several times consecutively; sometimes the feet were relaxed alternately.

Eating

The Kirtland's Warbler gathers most of its food by foraging among pine branches and in the deciduous foliage of trees, shrubs, and ground cover. The terminal clusters of pine branches offer a rich supply of insect food, and the warblers sometimes gather it by hovering at the twig tips. A few flying insects are gathered on the wing.

If a larva is too large to be swallowed whole, the warbler beats it on a branch and passes it back and forth between its mandibles until it is limp and easily dismembered. Ripe blueberries also are mashed thoroughly and the hard parts discarded before the pulp and skin are swallowed.

Sometimes they eat matter that has little or no nutritive value. Several times I have seen them eat pine needles and pieces of rotten wood, and chew on pine needles, grass, and twigs, perhaps without swallowing them. Sometimes they pick small globules of pitch off the twigs of jack pine. Once, as Van Tyne was taking photographs at a nest, he used some lubricating grease to darken the end of a broken stem. To his surprise, the female warbler ate the grease, returning several times for more.

Head-scratching Movements

Several times Kirtland's Warblers have been seen scratching their heads by reaching the claw up over the wing. This movement has been considered distinctive for certain groups of birds, but Nice and Schrantz (1959:339–342) have shown that there is more variability within groups and between individuals than was formerly supposed.

Anticipatory Food-bringing

Skutch (1953) suggested that the male brings food to the nest in anticipation of nestlings that may not yet have arrived, and that by means of such visits he discovers the young when they hatch. Nolan (1958) presented a number of instances in the Prairie Warbler and discussed the few reports of males, of other species of wood warblers, bringing food to females or nests before the hatching of eggs.

I can throw little light on the relation between courtship feeding and anticipatory food-bringing in the Kirtland's Warbler. On several occasions I have seen males bring food to the nest when the incubating female was away, but perhaps he was bringing it to her. Even before incubation begins the female "begs" like a young bird and is sometimes fed where she is, away from the nest. At a nest with young birds the male sometimes gives the food to the female, which feeds the young. On the other hand, sometimes a male will shoulder by a female to give food to the young directly, as though his drive to feed them was stronger than the drive to feed her.

Once on June 15, Van Tyne saw a *female* bring food to a nest in the tenth day of incubation, and chip for 15 seconds, as though to arouse the young, before eating the food and settling onto the eggs.

Summary

Compared to most other wood warblers, the Kirtland's Warbler is quite tame, but individuals vary greatly in this respect.

In the face of danger the Kirtland's Warbler according to circumstances (1) flees, (2) attacks, (3) freezes, or (4) gives distraction display.

The Kirtland's Warbler gives various evidences of gregariousness with its own species, although it does not occur in flocks.

It is a tail-wagging species, and like the other dendroicas with this habit lives in brushy, semi-open country in both summer and winter.

It normally progresses on the ground by hopping, in spite of references in the literature to its "walking."

The bird frequently wipes its bill on a branch after eating, but this act seems to have no significance except to remove food particles.

The Kirtland's Warbler lives in the presence of many ants, but has not been seen anting in the wild.

Some of the chasing by adults and fledglings seems to have no other purpose than play.

This bird sometimes bathes in dew, and also sunbathes.

The female on the nest dozes in daytime with her head pointing forward, but at night tucks her head back among her scapular feathers.

The bird gleans most of its food among leaves and branches, beating and mashing large objects before swallowing them. Occasionally it samples non-food items of little or no nutritive value.

The male brings food to the female on and off the nest before the eggs have hatched. Some of these actions may be interpreted as courtship, some as anticipation of young. It was clearly anticipation of young in a female that brought food to her eggs.

7

The Nest

Searching

Before she starts building the nest, the female warbler spends much time roaming over the ground of the territory. She moves deliberately, penetrating into the densest ground cover, where she turns this way and that, as though looking under the canopies and fitting her body into them. She seems to explore every square foot over considerable areas. The possible nest sites seem innumerable.

She feeds as she moves, and pauses at times for as long as fifteen minutes to preen or doze. Since the female moves about on the ground not only during searching but also during and after the nesting period, it is not easy to recognize the searching stage. Her behavior is distinctive at this time only in that she spends more time on the ground, keeps on the move more continuously, and travels over a larger area than in her ordinary feeding activities during incubation or the care of nestlings.

When the female is moving, and especially when she flies, the male is much in evidence. He sings nearby, ranging from the ground to the tops of the trees. Sometimes he comes near her, but usually he keeps at a sufficient distance and high enough in the vegetation so that a person may watch him for a considerable time without noticing the female on the ground. At times he too drops down and moves through the low vegetation, but this act is normal for him at other times also. When the female stops to preen or doze, the male may fly for brief periods to distant parts of his territory. But if she moves, he reappears so promptly that one concludes he must be very much aware of her location almost all the time.

The female gives little sign that she is aware of the male's presence. Sometimes near the edge of the territory conflict with a neighboring male may occur, and the melee may involve all three birds in action too fast for the eye. And yet, she does not leave the territory, and usually she builds her nest in the central portion of it. So I suspect her mate exercises some influence on her, even though she moves usually in the lead and he does not deter her by any obviously aggressive or attractive gesture. Yet if she flies any distance, he is always right after her. And at intervals they chip to each other and approach closely, twittering and "socializing." So there may be a considerable force of attraction that holds them together while he is anchored to his territory.

Searching is conducted most actively in the morning. Later in the day the female spends most of her time perching quietly or feeding among the trees. At the start of the nesting season the female may spend portions of several days in searching. But in renesting after loss of a nest, the female spends only one or two days in this activity.

Nest Building

The female Kirtland's Warbler builds the nest, carrying all material in her bill. Though in replacing a lost nest, the building period usually covers only four days, the building period for the first nest of the year may sometimes be longer, especially if cold weather intervenes. I have three instances in which at least eight days passed between the start of nest building and the laying of the first egg, all occurring early in the season. For example, at one nest the female was completing the nest on May 31, but the first egg was not laid until June 8. This was at a time of cold weather, with snow on June 3.

Once we were able to watch the process of building from the very start. Van Tyne had been watching the pair two days earlier and had concluded the nest had not yet been started. Early on June 10, 1945, we were watching this pair closely. It seemed to us that the female was centering her attentions on a particular clump of grass; so we waited there, even though the warblers disappeared for more than half an hour. When the female reappeared, she held nesting material in her bill—her first building trip, we were sure. We drove our truck to within 24 paces of the nest, and for 2½ days watched the nest from the cab; then we set up a blind three paces from the nest for closer observation.

Examining the nest at the end of the second day of building, we judged it to be nearly complete. The third and fourth days may be little more than a time of waiting for the first egg, during which the female gives the nest a few final but insignificant touches.

At first the female brought coarse material—strands of sedge or grass, a part of a tree leaf, and several pieces of crumbling wood from a jack-pine log. Even so, after 50 trips we could scarcely make out the site; after 120 trips, it was obvious and well-shaped; after 200 trips it appeared nearly complete, with lining. As the nest progressed she added finer material. Toward the end she brought small wisps of grass that were sometimes difficult to see in her bill.

She gathered material at distances from 3 to 30 meters. At first she traveled in various directions for material, but after about 30 or 40 trips she worked faster and concentrated on a few sources.

During much of the first two days there was rain or mist. She continued to build during light rain but ceased during heavy rain.

When resuming work after a period of absence, she usually remained at the nest 1½ to 2 minutes on the first trip. On later trips she sometimes remained as little as 6 or 8 seconds. On the third day she paid four visits to the nest before her first trip with material, but her behavior at this time may not have been normal, since a cowbird egg was laid in the nest early in the morning.

Although the female sometimes pecked at the nest, she seemed to shape it mostly with her body. She dropped grass into the nest and pressed her breast against it, snuggling low and turning her body through several rotations. In shaping the nest with her body, she spread her wings slightly and flattened her tail over the rim.

The male sang vigorously during each nest-building session. Often his first in a new series of songs came at the moment she arrived at the nest with a load of material. This "announcement" was frequently helpful to us, alerting us to the approach of the female. The male never came to the nest, nor did he follow the female closely; yet most of his singing occurred in the quadrant where she gathered material.

In another instance a nest was largely built between 7 a.m. on June 11 and 12:15 p.m. on June 12. This period is similar to that of the Song Sparrow, whose "nest is usually pretty well completed in two days and lined on the third and perhaps fourth" (Nice, 1943:210). That species also normally lays its first egg on the fifth day.

We have never seen a male pick up nesting material or help in building the nest, but at nest 45–1 (Table 5), judged in its third day of building, the male twice put his head into the nest.

Table 5 summarizes observations on building work at two nests.

Description of the Nest

Often the nest is embedded in the ground. However, we have never seen the female excavating with bill or feet. Probably the rotat-

Table 5
Building of Two Nests of Kirtland's Warbler

Day	Time of trip		Work periods					Trips		
	First	Last	N	Long-est	Short-est	Total	Aver-age	N	Maxi-mum	Aver-age
						(minutes)			(per work period)	

Nest 45–2

Day	First	Last	N	Longest	Shortest	Total	Average	N	Maximum	Average
	a.m.	*p.m.*								
First day (June 10)	6:28	3:37	8	38	3	160	20	143	40	18
Second day (June 11)	5:13	3:15	11	28	2	142	13	59	10	5
		a.m.								
Third day (June 12)	7:50	10:18	7	5	1	15	2	7	1	1
Fourth day (June 13)	7:33	10:45	6	3	1	12	2	6	1	1
Totals						329 minutes		215 trips		

Nest 45–1

Day	First	Last	N	Longest	Shortest	Total	Average	N	Maximum	Average
Third day (May 30)	...	11:29 a.m.	11	9	1	52	5	24	5	2

NOTES. *Nest 45–2:* Each work period was timed from the arrival of the female at the nest until her departure without an immediate return. The time between work periods on the first day ranged from 10 to 91 minutes, with an average of 46 minutes; on the second day, from 11 to 106 minutes, with an average of 40 minutes. The first egg was laid at 6:18 a.m. on the fifth day, June 14. *Nest 45–1:* Observations began at 6:59 a.m. When discovered, the nest was considered almost complete, and was therefore judged to be in its third day of building. The first egg (delayed by cold weather) was laid on June 8.

ing of her body in loose sand hollows out a shallow cup as she presses the strands into place.

The inside cavity of the nest is almost circular. William E. Southern (MS.) found that 27 nests were out-of-round from 0 to 9 mm. each, with long and short axes differing an average of about 4 mm. Sometimes it is difficult to measure more than one axis in the field without disturbing the nest cover unduly. I have therefore treated the nests as though circular, measuring the diameter or taking the average of two axes, if these measurements were available. Twenty-three nests with eggs—that is, not yet subject to stretching and flattening from the wear and tear of young birds—had an average diameter of 58 mm., and ranged from 49 to 66 mm.; 24 such nests had an average inside depth of 38 mm., and ranged from 29 to 48 mm.

The weights and outside dimensions of these nests cannot be given with precise accuracy, because of uncertainties about the inclusion of extraneous materials already at the site, and losses and compacting through handling. Southern found that 23 nests ranged from 7 to 25 grams, with an average weight of 13 grams; 27 nests had an average outside diameter of about 100 mm. and an average outside depth of about 50 mm.

The warbler does not construct a roof over the nest like the Ovenbird, but often chooses a site where overarching grass or other plants provide a natural canopy. Such nests usually are entered from one direction only. Occasionally the vegetation near the nest provides a tunnel entrance. In 87 nests where the direction of the entrance was recorded, 21 faced north; 21, east; 33, south; and 12, west. Thus it is clear that the nest may face in any direction. The seeming preference for south and avoidance of west may be a matter of chance, from the arrangement of tree-planting ridges on study areas; it may be a choice of a site warmed by the heat of the sun during the chill hours when building is most active (for even the north quadrant gets the sun in the earliest hours); or it may be a result of the way the vegetation grows and is bent on the wind. On hillsides, nests always face downhill; on the edge of thickets, they usually face toward the clearings.

The outer part of the nest is usually made of dead leaves of sedge, particularly *Carex pensylvanica*, and grass. The lining is made of various fine strands available on the territory—deer hair, moss sporophytes, grass, and other vegetable fibers. In former days, when horses traveled the sand trails of the region, horsehair was often noted in the lining. Sometimes the lining is white, sometimes almost black. The color, not in itself important, may be determined by the kind of fine material available.

Dale Zimmerman (letter) made a detailed analysis of a nest found in 1951 in an Oscoda County red-pine plantation. His analysis is shown in Table 6. This nest, it should be noted, differed from most

Table 6

Analysis of Materials in a Kirtland's Warbler Nest
(After Zimmerman)

Material	Per Cent *
Exterior	
Leaves and fibrous leaf bases of the sedge *Carex pensylvanica* (most of the nest rim of this material)	50
Needles of *Pinus resinosa* (red pine)	30
Needles of *Pinus banksiana* (jack pine)	5
Fine branchlets of *Vaccinium angustifolium* (low blueberry)	5
Dry leaves of *Vaccinium angustifolium* and *Salix humilis*	1
Unidentified rootlets	1
Stems of various grasses (some *Danthonia*, but mostly *Andropogon* sp.)	8
Lining	
Grass remains (mostly pieces of culms of *Agrostis scabra* and *Andropogon scoparius; Danthonia spicata* and *Andropogon gerardii* possibly represented)	20
Unidentified rootlets (very fine)	20
White deer hair (?)	10
Stalks of the moss *Polytrichum piliferum*	10
Panicles of the grass *Agrostis scabra*	30
Pieces of *Andropogon scoparius* inflorescences (including fruits)	5
Needles of *Pinus banksiana* (jack pine)	5

* Percentage refers to number of pieces of material, not weight.

in containing the long needles of red pine (*Pinus resinosa*), which would not be available to the Kirtland's Warbler in most of its locations.

William E. Southern (MS.) identified the materials used in 25 nests and dismantled 20 to weigh the proportions of each material. The results are shown in Table 7. The materials listed are typical sweepings from the floor of forest and savanna. There appears to be nothing special about them to account for the nesting preferences of the Kirtland's Warbler.

Nests are frequently placed at the base of trees, particularly where the trees are small. Among larger trees, nests are likely to be out farther from the trunk, where the branches sweep near the ground. Less commonly the nests are placed in clearings beyond the spread of the lower branches, but rarely are they more than eight feet from a pine. Thus, the female usually builds in a location which she can approach without leaving the shelter of pine branches. Occasionally

Table 7

Proportions of Materials Found in 20 Nests of Kirtland's Warbler
(After Southern)

Material	Percentage of nests N = 20	Percentage of nest weight
Coarse grasses and sedges	100	60–97
Jack-pine needles	100	trace–9
Fine grasses and sedges	88	trace–30
Mosses (fruiting stalks)	88	trace–9
Deer hair	84	trace–3
Broad leaves (fragments)	80	trace–4
Coarse twigs	72	trace–6
Rootlets	40	trace–2
Fine twigs	36	1–10
Lichens	36	trace–2
Unidentified black vegetable fibers	32	1–6
Red-pine needles	20	trace–2
Miscellaneous plant materials	20	trace–7
Feathers	12	trace
Wood chips	12	2–9

the nest is placed under a clump of oak sprouts, but always with pines nearby. Among 159 nests where the distance from the nearest tree trunk was recorded, the distances were as follows:

Percentage of Nests

30 centimeters or less...........................38
More than 30 centimeters but less than one meter....41
More than one meter but less than 2½ meters........17
More than 2½ meters........................... 4

Among naturally growing jack pines, I believe the number of nests within 30 centimeters of the trunk is even larger than this table shows; many of these nests were found in plantations where there was no ground cover at the base of trees, and the nearest concealment for the nest was on the ridges between rows about two meters apart —that is, between 30 centimeters and one meter from the trunks.

Nest Cover

Nests are usually concealed under vegetation less than one foot high. Since most of the nests are built before there has been much new growth, the cover consists mostly of dry grass or woody plants available from the previous year. The overwhelmingly preferred nest cover is supplied by tussocks of bluestem grass, whose curling dead leaves arch over to form canopies for nests, and blueberry, an abundant plant in the jack-pine plains. Among 170 nests where the covering vegetation was described, the following plants were recorded, alone or in combination with one another:

	Percentage of Nests
Grass and sedge, especially *Andropogon scoparius*, or *A. gerardii*, but also *Carex* and *Danthonia*	77
Blueberry, *Vaccinium angustifolium*	61
Sweet fern, *Comptonia peregrina*	6
Pine needles, usually *Pinus resinosa*	5
Bearberry, *Arctostaphylos uva-ursi*	5
Oak leaves, *Quercus* spp.	4
Bracken, *Pteridium aquilinum*	3
Wintergreen, *Gaultheria procumbens*	2
Pine twigs, usually *Pinus banksiana*	2
Cherry, usually *Prunus pumila*	2
Sheep laurel, *Kalmia angustifolia*	2
Goldenrod, *Solidago* spp.	1

Time of Start of Nest Building

We have very little information on the building of the very earliest nests. The earliest building we have observed was on May 20, in 1933, a nest judged in its second day of construction. Most of our information about the earliest dates of building are based on inferences from nests found later. From these it appears that the first nests may be started as early as May 16 or as late as June 2. These calculated dates are uncertain, because cold weather before the start of the egg laying slows all nesting activities.

Early arrival on the nesting grounds does not necessarily bring early nests. Both are determined by the weather, but by two sets of weather conditions not closely related to each other. Early migration takes place with favorable winds over a long distance southeast of the nesting ground in the first half of May, and early nesting is made possible by mild weather locally in the second half of May.

Renesting after Loss of Nest

After a nest has been destroyed or deserted, the female Kirtland's Warbler usually starts building another within one or two days, and lays the first egg of a new set five or six days after the loss of the previous nest. There is some uncertainty about the interval, because the time of the loss of the former nest is never known exactly; but in eight instances where it could be estimated fairly accurately, I judged the probable time in half the nests to be five days, and in half to be six days.

In building a new nest, the female moves a considerable distance, but does not leave the territory of the male. In 16 instances the new locations were from 10 to 250 meters away (average, 100 meters).

Two nests with eggs in a season are the greatest number observed for a female Kirtland's Warbler. However, I believe there are three attempts more often than we realize, and that the third has escaped attention because we have not been present long enough during the season to observe it. Once we suspected three attempts but did not see eggs in one of the nests. In the Ovenbird, Hann (1937:172, 210) knew only one female to lay three clutches of eggs, although several built four nests. In the Prairie Warbler, a much more successful and widespread species than the Kirtland's, Nolan (1955:57) reported that "five nesting attempts are not at all unusual" on his study area in southern Indiana.

Renesting after Fledging of Young

In our years of study, we have found renestings after fledging of young only twice, both in 1954. This rare event may occur more often than our records show, because not much of our field work has been done late in the nesting season. However, it is not a common occurrence, for diligent field work in several mid-summers has failed to disclose other such renestings.

In both these instances the males fed the first set of fledglings while the female was incubating the second set of eggs. The new nests were 10 and 70 meters away from the old. I did not see the incubating females feed young, although one was carrying food five days before she was discovered to be incubating a new set of three eggs; so she was probably already in the nest-building stage. One of the renesting females was found incubating a set of four eggs on June 30, the other on July 3. The exact dates of fledging at the earlier nests were not known, but were believed to be about June 22 and 25. One of the new nests was deserted after cowbird interference; the other was still under incubation when last seen.

I am at a loss to find anything unusual about the 1954 season to account for these renestings, except that the first nests of the year had completed sets of eggs about June 1—that is, three days earlier than in the average year, but not a remarkably early date. If we can generalize from these two cases against our background of knowledge of the species, we might suspect that renestings are possible whenever fledglings are produced by June 25.

Summary

The female travels extensively over the ground of the territory, as though searching, before she begins nest building. In renesting after the loss of a nest she may delay only one day in this activity, but at the start of the season she may spend several days in searching.

The female does all the nest building. She usually builds the nest in four days, and unless delayed by cold weather, lays her first egg on the fifth day. However, most of the construction takes place in the first two days.

The nest is built mostly of dead leaves of sedges and grass, and lined with fine vegetable fibers and sometimes deer hair. The nest is placed on the ground, frequently embedded in it, and is usually concealed under low vegetation (particularly bluestem grass and blueberry). The nest is usually placed near the base of a small jack pine.

The first nests of the year are usually built in the last days of May, but in some years may be delayed by cold weather until early June. After the loss of a nest, unless the season is too far advanced, the female builds another at an average distance of 100 meters, but still within the territory of the same mate. The interval between the loss of a nest and the laying of the first egg in the new nest is about five or six days.

8

Eggs

Description

The typical egg of the Kirtland's Warbler is ovoid and light in color, with small dark spots becoming more dense at the larger end. Wood (1904:8) described the first egg found, as "delicate pinkish-white (becoming white when blown and dried) thinly sprinkled with several shades of brown spots forming a sort of wreath at the larger end." However, the eggs are quite variable in color and pattern, and vary even within the same clutch. This variability is well shown by analysis of Van Tyne's field notes.

Van Tyne noted the pattern of spots on 109 eggs. In 47 per cent the spots were concentrated more heavily near one end, to form a "wreath," "circle," or "ring"; in 45 per cent the denser area was so broad that it covered one end of the egg, forming a "cap" or "nearly a cap"; and in 8 per cent the spots were distributed fairly evenly over the whole egg. Outside this area of concentrated spotting, some eggs were speckled lightly and some were almost immaculate. Usually the marks were more prominent at the large end, but occasionally so at the small end. A few eggs were so nearly elliptical that neither end seemed larger than the other.

The spots were described as "red-brown," "coffee-brown," "dark-brown," "medium-brown," "light-brown," "black," "purplish," and "lavender"—sometimes with noticeably different colors on the same egg. Van Tyne described the ground color of 23 eggs as follows: "brown," 11; "white," 5; "pink," 3; "buff," 3; "flesh-colored," 1. In one instance, with the Ridgway color standard at hand, Van Tyne described an egg's ground color as "Pale Cinnamon Pink," and the markings as "about Walnut Brown."

The shells are delicate, and any marking of eggs should be by brush, not pen or pencil, to avoid damage.

Measurements and Weights

The measurements of 154 eggs were as follows:

	Length (mm.)	*Breadth* (mm.)
Range	16.4–20.2	11.9–15.2
Median	18.1	14.0
Mean	18.1	13.9
Mode	17.8	13.9
Standard deviation	.81	.60

The weights of 106 eggs ranged from .90 to 2.39 grams. However, many of these eggs were of undetermined age, and some of the lighter ones may have been addled. The following statistical analysis of weights is based on a sample of 50 eggs, all of which were weighed within two days after clutch completion or were known to have hatched subsequently.

	grams
Range	1.47–2.21
Median	1.77
Mean	1.79
Standard deviation	.17

The variation from the smallest to the largest egg within a set, for 12 sets, ranged from .04 to .27 grams, both extremes in five-egg sets, with an average variation of .17 grams within a set.

The average egg weighs about 13 per cent of the breeding-season weight of the female Kirtland's Warbler. This proportion is slightly greater than the 10 to 12 per cent range in a group of 46 passerine species weighing less than 35 grams, as given by Huxley (1927).

The weights of 13 complete five-egg sets, including those of unknown condition, ranged from 5.89 to 9.79 grams. The weights of five five-egg sets of which every egg hatched ranged from 8.03 to 9.23 grams, and averaged 8.52 grams. Thus the weight of the usual set of eggs is a little more than 60 per cent of the weight of the adult female, as compared with about 50 per cent in other small songbirds (Nice, 1937:118).

I have weight information on only two complete four-egg sets, both renestings. One of these weighed 7.85 grams (1.96 grams per egg) as compared with 8.27 grams (1.65 grams per egg) for the five-egg set it replaced. Thus the second set, with one egg less, weighed only one-fourth of an egg less. Further, the lightest egg in the second set weighed more than the heaviest in the previous set; and each egg in the second set weighed less than its predecessor in the set (respectively, 2.05, 2.00, 1.93, and 1.87 grams). We cannot generalize from one example, but there is an interesting parallel here with Nice's finding on the Song Sparrow (1937:114, 118). She noted that "the eggs of four-egg sets are larger on the average than those of five-egg sets"—13 per cent larger in the Song Sparrow, as compared with 19 per cent in this example.

The other four-egg set also had eggs larger than those of the nest it replaced, which was also a four-egg set, although one of the eggs vanished before the weighing. The four eggs in the replacement set averaged 1.86 grams each, as compared with 1.81 grams for each of the three eggs weighed in the previous set.

I have also an instance in which three eggs were weighed in the order laid after the first egg was taken by a cowbird. Possibly this was a renesting, since the eggs were laid June 21–23. These eggs too were very large and declined in size as laid (2.21, 2.08, and 1.98 grams). On the other hand, I have a partial set laid on the same dates, June 21–23, and they were neither large nor laid entirely in decreasing size (1.55, 1.51, and 1.68 grams). Thus it may not be an invariable rule that eggs of second sets are larger or are laid in decreasing size in the Kirtland's Warbler.

Nevertheless, examination of the entire group of 106 egg weights shows a curious trimodal distribution, with modes in the 1.61–1.65 grams range, 1.71–1.74 grams range, and 1.86–1.90 grams range. It is possible these modes reveal two distributions, one for first sets and one for replacement sets, with a central mode where they overlap, but this series is not large enough to prove it.

It would be interesting to know the minimum and maximum size of eggs that produce living young. Because of uncertainties about which eggs have hatched, my sample is too small to represent the full range adequately, but I am certain that viable young have been produced from eggs as small as 1.47 grams and as large as 2.00 grams. I have one instance in which a cowbird destroyed all five eggs in a nest, the heaviest of which weighed 1.34 grams; one of the young in an egg pecked open was still breathing when examined, and seemed about ready to hatch. So it is possible that smaller eggs can produce young.

I have no direct information on loss of weight by Kirtland's Warbler eggs during incubation, but evidence from other species suggests it may be a little more than 10 per cent. Schrantz (1943:376) found that eggs in three clutches of the Yellow Warbler lost about 10 per cent in weight "from the time of the last-laid egg until hatching," periods of 9 to 12 days. Barth (1953:156) reported that the eggs of two small birds, House Martin and Willow Warbler, lost slightly more than one per cent per day during incubation.

The Kirtland's Warbler has the largest eggs of any species in the genus *Dendroica,* as shown by the compilation from Bent (1953) in Table 8.

Table 8

Comparative Size of Eggs in Genus Dendroica
(After Bent)

Species	N	Average length (mm.)	Average breadth (mm.)	Reference in Bent (page)
Yellow Warbler	50	16.6	12.6	168
Magnolia Warbler	50	16.3	12.3	200
Cape May Warbler	50	16.8	12.5	217
Black-throated Blue Warbler	50	16.9	12.8	229
Myrtle Warbler	50	17.5	13.3	244
Audubon's Warbler	50	17.6	13.5	264
Black-throated Gray Warbler	50	16.5	12.5	278
Townsend's Warbler	40	17.4	12.9	285
Black-throated Green Warbler	50	17.0	12.7	296
Golden-cheeked Warbler	50	17.7	13.1	319
Hermit Warbler	50	17.0	13.1	324
Cerulean Warbler	50	17.0	13.0	331
Blackburnian Warbler	50	17.2	12.8	341
Yellow-throated Warbler	50	17.1	13.0	354
Grace's Warbler	38	16.9	12.7	365
Chestnut-sided Warbler	50	16.7	12.4	371
Bay-breasted Warbler	50	17.7	12.9	383
Blackpoll Warbler	50	17.9	13.4	396
Pine Warbler	50	18.1	13.5	410
Kirtland's Warbler	154	18.1	13.9	This study
Prairie Warbler	50	15.9	12.3	432
Palm Warbler	40	17.4	12.9	453

Number of Eggs

Usually the Kirtland's Warbler lays five eggs in the first set and four eggs in a later nest of the same season. Occasionally a nest has six eggs or three eggs. It is always possible that cowbirds have removed eggs from sets examined, but I feel reasonably sure that some sets are complete with only three eggs. To calculate the proportion of sets of various sizes, I have considered only those not containing cowbird eggs and judged complete if observed for at least two days without a gain in number. These 67 nests held 310 eggs, 4.63 eggs per nest, distributed as follows:

Eggs per nest	Nests N = 67	Percentage of nests
3	7	10
4	13	19
5	45	67
6	2	3

Further evidence confirms the approximate correctness of the 3 per cent ratio of six-egg nests. In over 200 nests, including parasitized nests and nests seen only after the eggs had hatched, four were known to have received at least six warbler eggs each. Curiously, three of them were found in one year, 1951. One of these had also a cowbird egg and one had six young when found. It is probable that six warbler eggs were laid also in a few more nests that had lost eggs to cowbirds or through hatching failures before they were found.

In a world where variations so often occur in a "normal distribution," it is interesting that many birds with a usual clutch of five eggs have far more four-egg than six-egg clutches. The Ovenbird (Hann, 1937:172), Greenfinch (Monk, 1954:5), and European Robin (Lack, 1943:84) are other examples of such a distribution. However, as will be described later, a large number of four-egg sets are repeat nestings after the loss of earlier five-egg sets. When such repeat nestings are excluded by considering only those 38 unparasitized sets completed by June 14, we have a less skewed distribution:

Eggs per nest	Nests
6	2
5	31
4	3
3	2

We cannot be sure that there has not been cowbird interference and other damage to some of these eggs after they were laid.

The largest number of eggs found in a Kirtland's Warbler nest was seven. There were four such nests: two with five warbler eggs and two cowbird eggs, one with six warbler eggs and one cowbird egg, and one with four warbler eggs and three cowbird eggs.

Hann (1947:173) once found eight eggs, four of the host bird and four of the cowbird, in the nest of an Ovenbird.

Since repeat sets are usually smaller, the number of eggs per set will be affected by the number of renestings in the sample. It is difficult to be sure that nests are the first attempts of the year. To segregate first attempts from later ones, I have considered a group of nests where the set-completion dates could be estimated closely, from the hatching of young if not from direct observation. I have grouped these nests in four 10-day intervals, as follows:

	May 26–June 4	June 5–June 14	June 15–June 24	June 25–July 4
Nests, including those parasitized	36	38	9	9
Nests not parasitized	18	20	3	7
KW eggs in nests not parasitized	88	97	12	28
KW eggs per nest not parasitized	4.88	4.85	4.00	4.00

I believe that most of the sets completed by June 14 are first attempts of the year and that nearly all the sets completed after June 14 are later attempts. When we compare these two halves of the season for nests without cowbird eggs, we have an average of 4.87 eggs per set completed by June 14 and 4.00 eggs per set completed on June 15 or later. Thus there are about 18 per cent fewer eggs in renestings.

Early sets, however, are not always large, nor are late sets always small. I have records of three sets completed by June 1 with only three eggs, and one set, almost surely a renesting, completed on June 30 with five eggs.

In eight instances where the renestings were not parasitized, the number of eggs laid in the first and second clutches were as follows:

Nest	First Clutch (eggs)	Second Clutch (eggs)
47–6	4	4
48–17	5	4
54–1	5	4
54–2	5	3
54–12	5	4
48–4	? parasitized	4
55–12	? unknown	4
56–10	? parasitized	4
Average	4.8	3.9

The Kirtland's Warbler is similar in this respect to the Ovenbird, which nearly always has five eggs in the first clutch and three to five eggs in subsequent clutches (Hann, 1937:172). Stewart (1953:108) found a similar pattern in the Yellowthroat.

Egg-laying Dates

Kirtland's Warbler egg sets have been completed as early as May 26 and as late as July 7, but I have only five records of sets completed in July. Fully 75 per cent of all sets found were completed in the 15-day period from May 30 to June 13.

Egg-completion dates for the earliest nests of a year usually occur in a cluster; that is, the earliest nests of any one year all seem to have been started within a two- or three-day period, probably as a result of a period of favorable weather. By taking the average date of the nests in each cluster and combining these averages for a number of years, it is possible to calculate a "typical" egg-set-completion date for the first nesting attempts of the year:

Year	Average date of first cluster of nests
1944	May 28
1945	June 5
1946	June 6
1948	June 6
1951	June 4
1952	June 8
1953	June 4
1954	June 2
1955	May 31
1956	June 11
1957	June 1

Average date for 11 years: June 4

Hour of Egg Laying

The Kirtland's Warbler lays her eggs in the early morning, one on each successive day until the set is complete. At the time she lays an egg, she sits on the nest half an hour or more (observed instances, 28, 33, 36, 61, and 89 minutes; average, 49 minutes). One female, frightened from the nest when about to lay an egg, returned; frightened off again in six minutes, she had laid an egg in that short period.

These egg-laying periods usually begin soon after sunrise, which occurs at about 5 a.m. in the nesting season. In five cases where the female was not disturbed, these periods ended at 5:35, 5:53, 6:07, 6:18, and 6:42 a.m.

On the nest the female sits quietly but alertly most of the time, but occasionally she rises, fluffs her feathers, and looks into the nest under her body. Once a female was seen to hold herself half standing for a few moments while her body throbbed at a rate of perhaps twice a second.

On one June 12, at 6:20 a.m., Van Tyne watched a female warbler dozing on a horizontal twig. Between intervals of preening she fluffed out her feathers and appeared to nap. At first she had her tail to the wind, but when the wind ruffled her plumage she turned around to face it. Her neck was pulled in and her head was straight forward, with eyes closed. Her whole body pulsed to a rather slow rhythm (less than twice per second). She perched there for 20 minutes, and then resumed feeding and disappeared. Two days later her nest was found complete with four eggs. Perhaps she was in the egg-laying stage at the time of this observation and was deterred from going to her nest by the presence of the observer.

Summary

Kirtland's Warbler eggs are light in color and usually have brownish spots that become more dense at the larger end; they show considerable variation in this respect. The median length is 18.1 mm.; the median breadth, 14.0 mm.; and the median weight, 1.72 grams. The egg is slightly larger in proportion to the size of the adult bird than is the egg of most small birds.

The Kirtland's Warbler usually lays five eggs in the first set of the year and four eggs in replacement sets. Three-egg and six-egg sets also occur.

The earliest date known for the completion of a set of eggs is May 26, and the latest date, July 7, but in a typical year the extreme dates are about June 4 and June 30. Three-fourths of the sets found were completed by June 14.

Eggs are laid, one each day, on successive mornings until the set is complete. They are deposited in the two-hour period between sunrise and 7 a.m.

9

Incubation

Start of Incubation

Incubation is performed entirely by the female. Usually she begins incubating with the laying of the penultimate egg—that is, on the third egg of a four-egg set or the fourth egg of a five-egg set—but there is some variation. Once I found a female incubating at 1 p.m. on the day the third egg in a set of five was laid, and I have several records in which the females were not on the nest when it was visited after the laying of the third egg in a set of four. However, these findings are not conclusive, for the females sometimes start incubation later in the day. For example, in one case the eggs were cold at 7:30 a.m., although an egg had been laid that morning, but at 12:30 p.m. the female was incubating. Moreover, a female momentarily off the nest, or one that slips off unobtrusively before the observer sees her, is not likely to be recorded as incubating.

In some species birds have been known to sit on the nest without supplying sufficient heat for incubating the eggs. The only proof that incubation is in progress is the temperature of the eggs, and that we have never taken. It is therefore debatable exactly when true incubation begins in the Kirtland's Warbler. However, the eggs under a sitting female have always been warm to the touch when we have examined them, in contrast to the usual chill of unattended eggs in this climate. It is my impression that the female of this species sits steadily on the eggs once she starts; nearly, if not fully, as regularly as she does after incubation has been in progress for several days, although the evidence that would be provided by prolonged observations on incubation before the set of eggs was complete is lacking. Since the hatching of a set of eggs occurs over a number of hours, but usually less than 24, and the first egg laid is the first to hatch (evidence from one instance), it appears that incubation of some eggs in the clutch starts earlier than that of others.

In several other species of wood warblers that have been studied extensively, the last egg laid is the last to be hatched; for example,

Ovenbird (Hann, 1937:174), Yellow Warbler (Schrantz, 1943:376), and Prairie Warbler (Nolan, unpublished).

Few warblers have been studied closely enough to reveal the exact time of the start of incubation, but the usual pattern seems to be similar to that of the Kirtland's Warbler. It appears to be identical in three other ground-nesting species, namely, Ovenbird (Hann, 1937:173), Northern Waterthrush (Eaton, 1957:18), and Louisiana Waterthrush (Eaton, 1958:224). It is true also of the Prothonotary Warbler (Walkinshaw, 1941:9) and the Black-throated Green Warbler (Pitelka, 1940:6). The same pattern is implied by Bent (1953:200, 396, 536) for the Magnolia Warbler, Blackpoll Warbler, and MacGillivray's Warbler. Sturm (1945:195) reported one instance in which an American Redstart began partial incubation on the second egg and increased her attention to full incubation by the time the fourth (last) egg was laid; and the Yellow Warbler also seems to begin incubation at least two days before the last egg is laid (Schrantz, 1943:376). Probably many American Fringillids also begin incubating before the last egg is laid; for example, the Song Sparrow (Nice, 1937:122), Chipping Sparrow (Walkinshaw, 1944a:198), and American Goldfinch (Walkinshaw, 1938b).

Length of Incubation

The incubation period is the time required for the fresh egg to progress to hatching through the regular application of heat by the parent bird. Because of the difficulty of knowing when the adults in some species are supplying heat sufficiently and regularly enough for incubation, Nice (1954:173), Kendeigh (1951:38), and others have pointed out that a generally satisfactory measure is "the time from the laying of the last egg to the hatching of the last young . . . where all eggs hatch."

Because of the hatching failure of some eggs and other nest accidents, it is not easy to get a significant sample of records that meet this criterion. I have such data on only three eggs, yielding incubation periods of 13 days, 13¼ days, and 14½ days, to the nearest quarter day. And I do not believe these periods are typical, as I shall show.

To measure for eggs other than the last, simply from the date the last egg was laid, leads to absurdities in some species; for example, an eight-day incubation period in the Yellow Warbler (Schrantz, 1943:377).

By assuming, correctly, I believe, that the female Kirtland's Warbler normally begins incubating on the day before the last egg is laid, we may estimate the probable incubation periods on a much larger number of eggs. That is, we can assume that the last egg hatched was the last egg laid (even though not all were hatched), and that the incubation of the rest of the hatched eggs was begun one day earlier. I can apply this assumption to 23 eggs in 7 nests for which we knew both the day the last egg was laid and the day each young bird hatched. The results of applying this assumption follow.

Incubation Periods of 23 Eggs from 7 Nests

13 days for 6 eggs
14 days for 11 eggs
15 days for 3 eggs
16 days for 3 eggs

I have also records of 16 eggs in 8 nests in which the sets were complete when found, and in which incubation had therefore been under way for an unknown period before observation began. If we assume again that the last egg hatched was the last egg laid, and that incubation began one day earlier on the others, we have minimum incubation periods as follows:

13+ days for 2 eggs
14+ days for 7 eggs
15+ days for 7 eggs

Thus for 39 eggs the actual incubation periods appear to range from 13 to 16 days, with 14 days the usual period, and 15 days more common than 13 days.

Since less than a full day usually separates the hatching of all eggs in a clutch, and since this method assumes that incubation began a full day earlier on eggs other than the last, the incubation periods shown are probably about half a day longer than would be found by restricting our attention to the last egg laid in each clutch.

Corroboration for these incubation periods comes also from the hatching of cowbird eggs in the same nests. Cowbird eggs, as shown by this and other studies in this climate, most often hatch in 12 days, and in nests of Kirtland's Warblers, cowbird eggs usually hatch two or three days ahead of the warbler eggs.

In 8 nests, one or more warbler eggs were believed to require at least 15 days' incubation. Most of these were large clutches; one had seven eggs, including two cowbird eggs; two had six eggs, including two cowbird eggs each; three had five eggs, with two, one, and no cowbird eggs each; and two had four eggs, with one and no cowbird eggs each. This group, though small, suggests that larger clutches get less heat and require more time for incubation.

Thus, the Kirtland's Warbler has an incubation period longer than those reported for other North American wood warblers. The incubation periods for these warblers range from 11 to 13 days, with 12 the usual number, as shown in Table 9. These examples were chosen because based on extensive studies.

Table 9

Typical Incubation Periods of Various Wood Warblers *

Species	Incubation period (days)	Authority
Prothonotary Warbler	12	Walkinshaw, 1938a
Yellow Warbler	11	Schrantz, 1943
Black-throated Green Warbler	12	Pitelka, 1940
Kirtland's Warbler	14	This study
Prairie Warbler	11½–12	Nolan (unpublished)
Ovenbird	12	Hann, 1937
Northern Waterthrush	12	Eaton, 1957
Louisiana Waterthrush	12	Eaton, 1958
Yellowthroat	12	Hofslund, 1953
American Redstart	11	Sturm, 1945

* Species selected for comparison because they have been studied extensively.

Bent (1953) gives 12 days as the incubation period for a number of other species of warblers also, but most of these data are based on very few examples and on unexplained methods, and therefore need confirmation.

Prolonged Incubation

In one instance in which the eggs did not hatch, the warbler was still incubating 20 days after the last egg was laid, but she had deserted four days later; the last (fifth) egg was laid on June 14, 1947, the female was on the nest July 4, and the nest was deserted when visited on July 8. In another instance a set of five eggs was complete when found June 24, 1951; the female was on the nest 16 days later, on July 10, but the nest was deserted on the twentieth day of observation, July 14. The eggs in the second nest were examined by Dale Zimmerman; he found no development.

It is of interest that both these unproductive nests were unusual in other respects. The first belonged to one of two females nesting on the territory of one male. The second nest belonged to an isolated pair of warblers.

In the few species of passerine birds for which this matter has been investigated, most tend to incubate about twice the normal period before deserting the nest (Van Tyne and Berger, 1959:296). So the Kirtland's Warbler may incubate a little less persistently than most closely related birds, although the question must be examined more thoroughly before it can be answered with certainty.

Causes of Egg Failure

A great many eggs do not hatch; these amount to about 15 per cent of eggs laid in nests without cowbird eggs and 25 per cent in nests with cowbird eggs. What causes these eggs not to develop, we do not know. Those examined have been found in all stages of development.

The lower rate of success of eggs in the presence of cowbird eggs (which are larger in diameter), particularly with multiple cowbird eggs, suggests that insufficient heat may be a cause. When the entire clutch fails, prolonged chilling is a possible explanation. Before incubation begins, eggs can probably take rather severe chilling without damage. One morning early I examined a partial set of two warbler eggs and one cowbird egg. The female had not been on the nest the night before, the eggs were icy cold to the touch, and a heavy frost lay on the ground. The temperature of the eggs must have been close to freezing, but all hatched.

Some eggs may be damaged by minute punctures, as from the claws of the incubating warbler or of the laying cowbird, or from the bill of a cowbird on an egg-removal visit. Some eggs may be infertile because of malfunctioning of the male or female.

Incubation Routine

During incubation the females in my sample spent about 84 per cent of their daylight hours on the nest. Since at this season the time between sunrise and sunset is about 15 hours, and the females are believed to spend the entire night on the nest, they evidently spent about 21.6 hours out of each 24 hours (that is, 90 per cent of the time) incubating the eggs.

Hann (1937:216) found a daytime rate on the nest above 80 per cent in the Ovenbird, another ground-nesting warbler, and Sturm (1945:196) a similar rate for the Redstart. Nice (1943:221), summarizing the incubation routines of ten passerine species, found that they ranged from 60 to 84 per cent. Lawrence (1953b:138), summarizing six studies of wood warblers, found that attentiveness ranged from 67 to 83 per cent.

The high rate of attentiveness of the Kirtland's Warbler may be encouraged by the males' feeding the females on the nest. The male Pied Flycatcher also feeds the female on the nest; and in one instance in which a male was removed experimentally, the attentiveness of the female declined from 79 to 58 per cent (von Haartman, 1958).

Although the attentive and inattentive periods are irregular, they give remarkably similar totals for different females and for different days. The attentiveness does not vary significantly from the second to the thirteenth day of incubation.

This sample is too small to permit any generalizations about the relationship of attentiveness and temperature. In fact, it would be remarkable to find clear relationships without more refined measurements of temperature *at the nest* than I have used. The difference between ambient air temperature (a thermometer hanging in the shade) and the temperature experienced by a bird on the nest in the sun may be great. However, in view of Nice's observation (1947:175) that "the average length of periods on and off the nest increases with increasing temperature," it is of interest that the longest period on the nest (112 minutes) occurred in mid-morning, with the sun bearing directly on the nest and the female panting; and the longest period off the nest (48 minutes) occurred in late afternoon, with the air temperature 88° F.

I have summarized information on six incubating females in Table 10. All these observations, except the first, were taken from a blind which had been placed at least one day before any of these data were gathered. Notes on the length of periods on and off the nest are included only when a set of observations contained at least three measured periods, with the female leaving and returning without human interference.

Table 10

Incubation Routine of Kirtland's Warbler at Different Stages of Incubation

	Day of Incubation					
	2	2–3	8	8–11	11–12	13
Nest	57–2	47–12	44–1	44–3	46–2	56–3
Date	June 1	June 23–24	June 5	June 6–9	June 16–17	June 21
Total observation time (minutes)	322	229	640	503	196	884
Incubation time (minutes)	259	201	534	408	172	694
Percentage of time on nest	80	88	83	81	88	80
Shortest period on nest (minutes)	20	21	48	10	...	20
Longest period on nest (minutes)	56	41	112	105	...	110
Average period on nest (minutes)	39	44	71	49	...	55
Shortest period off nest (minutes)	5	5	4	5	...	5
Longest period off nest (minutes)	13	12	23	33	...	48
Average period off nest (minutes)	9	9	13	15	...	16
Observer	Walkinshaw	Van Tyne	Van Tyne & Mayfield	Van Tyne & Hiett	Van Tyne	Mayfield
Time of day and weather	2:58–8:20 p.m.	5:06–7:15 a.m. (June 23)	4:43 a.m.–3:23 p.m.	6:05–9:08 a.m. (June 6)	8:30–10:50 a.m. (June 16)	5 a.m. (sunrise)–7:44 p.m.
	Warm, sunny	Temp. 42°–50°, clear	Temp. upper 70's, nest in sun at midday	...	1:14–2:10 p.m. (June 17)	Temp. 56°–88°; clear
	....	4:15–5:55 a.m. (June 24)	....	12:32–2:02 p.m. (June 7)	....	....
	....	Temp. 47°–55°		12:00–2:45 p.m. (June 8)	....	....
	....			1:25–2:30 p.m. (June 9)	....	....
Feeding	Male fed female 2 times on nest	Male fed female 2 times on nest	Male did not feed female	Male fed female 3 times on nest, 3 times near nest	Male fed female 2 times on nest, 3 times near nest	Male fed female 6 times on nest, 3 times near nest

Behavior of the Incubating Female

The female usually sits on the nest with an appearance of alertness. She is responsive to sounds, particularly rustlings in the ground cover, and sometimes partially emerges from the nest to investigate. She shows awareness of the approach of the male by movements of her head.

At times she sits quietly, and even dozes for ten minutes or so; at other times she moves restlessly—rising, facing in a new direction, tugging at loose grass in the rim of the nest, and probing under her body, presumably turning the eggs. During the observation period of 10 hours, 40 minutes at nest 44–1 the female performed movements interpreted as egg turning 28 times.

When the female leaves to feed, she sometimes gathers food within six feet of the nest. But often she moves rapidly away from the nest and is lost from sight in the foliage until her return.

At nest 46–2, on the 11th and 12th day of incubation, the female tried four times to "feed" the eggs.

Behavior of Male during Incubation

The male usually utters his first song of the morning at a considerable distance from the nest, which suggests that his night roost may not be near the nest.

The male often carries food to the incubating female on the nest. If she is not present, he may put his head into the nest for a moment before flying away with the food. Males vary greatly in attentiveness. For example, at nest 44–1 the male did not bring food to the female in more than 10 hours; while at nest 44–3, in the same stage of incubation, the male brought food to the female on the nest three times in a two-hour period, and three other times approached with food which the female left the nest to receive. However, most Kirtland's Warbler males feed their incubating mates several times each day. This practice is often helpful to the observer in finding nests. It has been seen on every day of incubation. In 46 hours of observation, males were observed carrying food to incubating females on or near the nest 24 times.

Sometimes the male approaches the nest carrying food, but does not take it to the female. She then leaves the nest, goes to the male, quivering like a young bird "begging," and takes the food. Thereupon they fly together out of sight into a thicket, twittering.

Although I believe the male Kirtland's Warbler never incubates the eggs appreciably and have never seen one sitting on a nest, in rare instances the male has been observed to settle on the eggs momentarily. Middleton noted this behavior once in 1951. Ryves (1943) has noted that males of several species occasionally sit on the nest, although they do not do so regularly. Bent (1953) says males of a number of species of wood warblers incubate: Black-and-White Warbler (7), Nashville Warbler (109), Parula Warbler (141), Black-throated Green Warbler (293), Blackburnian Warbler (341), Pine Warbler (410), and Hooded Warbler (617). (References are to page numbers.) However, one of Bent's contributors (617) supplied a word of caution by admitting that early in his field work he had recorded male Hooded Warblers incubating, but later came to doubt his own records when he learned how closely some females can resemble males.

Summary

Incubation normally begins on the day before the laying of the last egg.

The incubation period may range from 13 to 16 days, with 14 days the most frequent period.

If no egg in a set hatches, the Kirtland's Warbler probably incubates from 20 to 24 days before deserting.

Some causes of failure to hatch may be lack of heat, tiny punctures, and faulty eggs (including infertility).

The females incubate fairly constantly throughout the period at a rate of more than 80 per cent of daylight hours and about 90 per cent of the 24-hour day. The average period on the nest is nearly an hour, and the average period off the nest is a little less than 15 minutes.

The male usually carries food to the incubating female several times a day—an average of once every two hours in my sample.

Nestling Period

Hatching

Kirtland's Warbler eggs have hatched as early as June 9 (1944) and as late as July 19 (1930), but more than three-fourths of the available hatching records fall within the 15-day period from June 12 to June 26. Young birds have been seen hatching at various daylight hours, and the finding of newly hatched young on early morning visits to the nest indicates that some may hatch during the night.

A young bird has been seen emerging from the shell 15 minutes after the egg was pipped, and one has been seen still imprisoned four hours after the egg was first pipped. An entire clutch usually hatches within 24 hours, but occasionally requires a little more than a day. However, it appears that hatching never requires as much as two full days. I have two cases in which it exceeded 21 hours, but was less than 48. With cowbirds hatching as many as three days ahead of the first warbler, the period from the hatching of the first to the last egg in a parasitized nest may be nearly five days.

When the young bird emerges, the eggshell often splits along the equator into two nearly equal halves. One of these halves may continue to hold the caudal portion of the young for several minutes. Sometimes a warbler egg may become captive in half the shell of a cowbird's egg, but I have never known this circumstance to interfere with hatching.

Removal of Eggshells and Other Objects

The adults promptly remove from the nest inanimate objects other than eggs, carrying them away in their bills. In one observed instance the female removed two halves of an eggshell in less than a minute, flying 30 feet away and out of sight each time. We have not seen a Kirtland's Warbler eat an eggshell, but the bird may regard it as edible; Van Tyne once saw a female make ten unsuccessful attempts to feed a portion of eggshell to a five-day-old cowbird; the female secured the shell elsewhere and brought it to the nest in three separate trips, repeatedly offering it to the young bird. Finally she took it away.

Damaged eggs are removed, as are twigs and pine needles that fall into the nest. Van Tyne had an experience which suggests that a warbler may drag young birds out of the nest in an effort to carry away bands attached to the legs of the young. At 8:30 a.m. on June 14, 1944 he banded three five-day-old warblers. While he was occupied near the nest, the female approached, lighted for a moment on his back, and then flew down to the cigar box holding his supply of bands. She hopped into the box, inspected the bands, picked up a string of aluminum bands, dropped them, and moved over to a side compartment holding colored bands. Here she pecked at them, picked up a string of yellow bands, and flew off to a perch eight meters away. She dropped the bands on a branch and flew back to the cigar box. At this point Van Tyne closed the box and retrieved his string of bands.

At 2:30 p.m. Van Tyne returned to the nest and found it empty. Then he saw one of the young about 30 centimeters away and subsequently found the other two young birds at distances up to four meters. They appeared unhurt, although cold and weak. He returned them to the nest, and in 10 minutes the female returned and began feeding the young.

On June 16 the three young were in place at 7 a.m. but missing at 10 a.m. The female approached, lighted on Van Tyne, hopped between his feet, and pecked at his rubber boots. He was unable to find the young, but both adults seemed agitated, as though young birds were nearby. At seven days, a very early age for fledging, they might have left the nest voluntarily—or with help.

Dead nestlings as well are removed from the nest. At 8:40 a.m. on July 12, 1955 I visited a nest and found the two-day-old warbler dead, trampled under the four-day-old cowbird in the nest. Virginia Mayfield was concealed in a blind, preparing to photograph the adult warblers. When I left the nest, both adults came to it, and there was much twittering and moving by both birds at the nest. Then the male fluttered away, as though carrying a load with difficulty. The female, still showing agitation, flew up to a twig two feet above the nest and then back down to it. Mrs. Mayfield quickly came out of the blind and found the dead bird gone.

Brooding Routine

During the first three days after the nestlings hatch, the female Kirtland's Warbler spends about as much time brooding the young as she spent incubating the eggs—about 84 per cent of the daylight hours and all of the night. However, when the nestlings are about four or five days old (from time of hatching), her attentiveness begins to slacken; and by the seventh or eighth day she broods little if at all during the daytime, although she still covers the young at night. On the night before the young left one nest, at age about 10 days, Walkinshaw found the female gone from the nest at 9 p.m., and believed she did not brood the young at all that night. This brooding rate is higher than that reported by Nice (1943:228) for the Song Sparrow, Ovenbird, and Black-throated Green Warbler.

There is a difference among females in the tapering off of attentiveness. One female with four-day-old young was not found brooding at any time, but she seemed exceptionally nervous and showed her awareness of the observer in the blind by constant "chipping." Other females have been found brooding young seven days old.

The male ordinarily does not brood the young but may rarely do so. Hann was able to photograph a male in this act in 1932, fully snuggled down on the young after feeding them.

Information on the brooding routines of six female warblers at different times in the nestling phase is summarized in Table 11. All notes were taken from a blind, which had been installed at least one day earlier. Except in the last column, where there were only two measured periods off the nest, and both were strikingly longer than any earlier periods off the nest, the shortest and longest periods on or off the nest are indicated only if the series included at least three such measured periods without human interference.

Feeding Routine

Both adults feed the nestlings, carrying food in their bills and placing it in the gaping mouths of the young. The male usually carries much more food than the female, but she is busier than he with other nest duties—brooding and defense of the young. In fact, I suspect that ants in the nest and the presence of birds or animals near the nest cause the female to carry less food than she otherwise would.

During the early days of nestling life, while the female is spending most of her time brooding, the male often brings food to her. She may eat it or feed it to the young; sometimes she eats a part and feeds the rest to the young. Often the brooding female leaves the nest to meet the approaching male, as during incubation; but now she may return to the young with all or part of the food. Occasion-

Table 11

Brooding Routine of Kirtland's Warbler

	Day of Hatching	Days after Hatching				
		1	2	3	4	5
Nest	44–2	46–2	44–3	36–1	36–1	44–3
Nest contents	2 corwbirds hatched same day	1 corwbird, 4 warbler eggs	1 corwbird 2 days old, 1 warbler hatched same day	2 warblers	2 warblers	1 corwbird 5 days old, 1 warbler 3 days old
Date	June 9	June 18	June 13	June 15	June 16	June 16
Total observation time (minutes)	240	152	275	630	195	100
Brooding time (minutes)	192	135	231	537	132	26
Percentage of time on nest	80	89	84	85	67	26
Shortest brooding period (minutes)	10	...	37	8	...	...
Longest brooding period (minutes)	33	...	73	79	...	...
Average brooding period (minutes)	19	...	51	35	...	...
Shortest period off nest (minutes)	1	...	6	1	12	25
Longest period off nest (minutes)	9	...	11	15	22	41
Average period off nest (minutes)	6	...	9	8	15	...
Time of day	9:45–11:45 a.m. 1:35–3:35 p.m.	5:55–7:25 a.m. 8:38–9:40 a.m.	8:15–8:50 a.m. 9:20–11:20 a.m. 12:45–2:45 p.m.	8:10–12:10 a.m. p.m. 1:45–5:45 p.m. 6:30–9:00 p.m.	8:55–9:55 a.m. 3:35–5:50 p.m.	2:40–4:20 p.m.
Observer	Van Tyne	Van Tyne	Van Tyne & Hiett	Van Tyne	Van Tyne	Van Tyne

ally the female meets the male at the entrance to the nest, but he, instead of giving the food to her, shoulders past to feed the young.

When the young are very small, the food particles fed them are small, usually hairless caterpillars. Later the mouthfuls are larger, and often they contain winged insects. The load of food brought in one trip is usually offered to the young in several pieces; large caterpillars are beaten and torn apart, and as much as three minutes may be required to feed one load. If, after such preparation, the food is still too large for the young to swallow, the adult eats it or carries it away. It challenges the imagination to understand how the adult can continue to capture live food, some of it winged, with a mouth already full—and, in the male, continue to sing all the while!

If the young do not gape at the approach of food, the adult arouses them with a low rasping note, "churk." The hungry young bird opens its mouth widely, presenting a food target of bright red ("Grenadine Red") outlined in yellow, vibrating rapidly. When the adult leaves, the young close their mouths instantly. An adult usually feeds only one young bird on one trip, but sometimes feeds two. How the adult selects a bird to feed is not clear. It is not necessarily the nearest one; the adult will sometimes reach over one or more and feed another on the far side of the nest. Perhaps the more hungry young gain the attention of the adult in some way, as by vibration of their gaping mouths.

The number of times per hour the adults carry food to the nest increases as the young become larger, but not in proportion to their size, for the adult compensates by carrying much larger loads of food to large young. In general the feeding trips in our sample ranged from two to eight per hour until almost the end of the nestling period. This rate is low compared with those of ten species whose rates were summarized by Nice (1943:235), but is comparable with the rate for the Ovenbird, the only wood warbler in her list; earlier (1932) she reported rather low rates for two Black-throated Green Warblers also. Sturm (1945:200) reported an average rate of about 12 trips per hour for the Redstart, a tree-nesting wood warbler. Lawrence (1953b:140) noted that in several species of wood warblers the rate of feeding was low but the amount of food carried each time was large. The number of trips probably reflects the size of the mouthful carried each time. (See Table 12 for feeding routine data.)

Table 12

Feeding Routine of Kirtland's Warbler

	Day of Hatching	Days after Hatching					
		2*	3	4	6	8	9
Nest	44-2	44-2	36-1	36-1	41-2	51-6	51-6
Nest contents (hatched)	2 cowbirds	*1 cowbird; day of hatching for 1 warbler	2 warblers	2 warblers	2 warblers	5 warblers	5 warblers
Date	June 9	June 13	June 15	June 16	June 18	June 22	June 23
Total observation time (minutes)	240	275	630	195	240	150	250
Total trips by female	5	2	11	3	8	3	42
Trips per hour by female	1.2	0.4	1.1	1	2	1.2	10.5
Total trips by male	21	15	12	5	21	17	30
Trips per hour by male	5.1	3.3	1.2	1.6	5.2	6.8	7.5
Total trips by both	26	17	23	8	29	20	72
Trips per hour by both	6.5	3.8	2.2	2.6	7.2	8.0	18
Fecal sacs removed (times)	2	4	6	3	9	4	11
Time of day	9:45-11:45 a.m. 1:35-3:35 p.m.	8:15-8:50 a.m. 9:20-11:20 a.m. 12:45-2:45 p.m.	8:10-12:10 a.m. p.m. 1:45-5:45 p.m. 6:30-9:00 p.m.	8:55-9:55 a.m. 3:35-5:50 p.m.	1:45-5:45 p.m.	8:35-9:25 a.m. 12-12:45 p.m. 1:07-2:03 p.m.	7:30-8:40 a.m. 10:38-1:35 p.m.
Observer	Van Tyne	Van Tyne & Hiett	Van Tyne	Van Tyne	Van Tyne	Van Tyne	Van Tyne

Nest Sanitation

It is usually just after being fed that the young void fecal sacs. At this moment the young bird turns away, lifts its posterior toward the adult, and produces the sac. The adult takes it immediately. For the first three days the adults eat the sacs, but on the fourth day they begin carrying some of them away. (With young cowbirds, which are much larger than young warblers, the adults may carry away droppings on the third day.) By the sixth day, the adults carry away all the sacs, flying 10 meters or more and out of sight.

Fecal sacs are not produced at each feeding. As shown in Table 12, excreta were removed 39 times in the course of 195 trips with food (20 per cent of the trips). This rate is comparable to the 25 per cent reported by Nice (1943:237) as the median of 35 studies of 28 species. In two instances of the 39 observed here, fecal sacs were removed by the female without feeding the young. This function is performed by whichever adult is present at the time. At no time have we seen the young defecate over the side of the nest.

Occasionally we have seen an adult peck at the bill of a young bird after it was fed. We have suspected that this was an invitation to defecate. Nice (1943:238) has suggested that other species sometimes peck the young, perhaps with this effect.

Care and Defense of Nestlings

Nest care and defense are almost exclusively the work of the female. When brooding, she rises from time to time to look into the nest beneath her and probe into it. Occasionally she removes and chews pine needles that have projected through the lining. Sometimes she shakes the lining vigorously, as though arranging it. Ants seem to be a special object of concern.

Ants of various kinds are numerous, especially in the hot part of the day. In an abandoned nest, a broken egg or a dead nestling is invariably covered with ants, usually small red ants, but sometimes large black ones. When a nestling is placed on the ground for banding or weighing, it is often attacked by ants. Accordingly, when an observer in a blind sees young birds tumble about violently in the nest and sees the adult female pick something off the nest or young, he assumes that the female is removing ants, even though the ants are too small to be discerned. We have never found external parasites on the young of Kirtland's Warblers.

In one particularly disturbed period, a brooding female arose and probed into the nest 15 times in a period of two hours. At nest 41–2 the female had quit brooding her six-day-old nestlings in the daytime, but between 1:45 and 4:45 p.m. she visited them 15 times without food in order to inspect them, and pecked at them daintily. Occasionally a male also has been seen pecking at young. The adults seem to eat whatever they take from the young or nest. However, we have never seen a warbler seek ants as food or carry them to the young. Ants collected by Van Tyne on June 27, 1935 from a nest north of Clear Lake in Montmorency County were identified by Frederick M. Gaige as *Crematogaster lineolatus* (Bent, 1953:427).

Even after the female has ceased to brood the nestlings in daytime, her attention continues unabated. At nest 41–2 the female with six-day-old young moved about near the nest as though patrolling. She perched for long periods just above the nest, dashing off to investigate every rustling in the leaves. Once she pursued a mouse-sized mammal from a distance of one to four meters from the nest. Later in the same afternoon she revealed by sharp "chips" that something was alarming her. Then a female cowbird came into view, walking directly toward the nest, craning her neck. When the cowbird reached a point one meter from the nest, the warbler darted down and put her to flight. Earlier in the day she stood her ground when a female cowbird approached within less than one meter; and two days later she routed and pursued a female cowbird that approached within 30 centimeters of the nest.

Once Van Tyne saw a female warbler chase a mouse-sized mammal that had approached within one meter of the nest, and once Virginia Mayfield saw a female warbler hover above and dart at a ground squirrel, *Citellus tridecemlineatus*, that approached within one meter of the nest. However, the female acts aggressively toward any small creature, even a songbird, if it comes too near the nest.

On such occasions the male usually neither shows excitement nor participates in the pursuit. But against certain types of encroachment he reacts vigorously, as though his concern is primarily for the *domain*, whereas the female's concern is for the *nest*. Once, when a male and female were feeding young almost ready to leave the nest, a strange female Kirtland's Warbler approached to a perch less than two meters from the nest. The resident female, carrying food, ignored her, but the resident male flew at her violently. She attempted to return and he attacked each time, in spite of the fact that she postured at first as though in invitation to copulation—crest up, head raised, body arched, with tail higher than the head. Later a strange male came to within two meters of the nest. Again the female ignored him, but after the visitor had been sitting quietly for some time, and then began gathering food, the resident male attacked and drove him away.

Prenatal Down

David K. Wetherbee examined two late-term embryos of Kirtland's Warbler in spirits in 1952 and analyzed the plumage as shown in Table 13.

Table 13

Analysis of Arrangement of Prenatal Down
in Kirtland's Warbler
(After Wetherbee)

Region	Younger embryo		Older embryo		Typical greatest length (mm.)
	Left	Right	Left	Right	
Coronal	8	9	8	7	7
Occipital	3	4	3	3	8
Mid-dorsal	2	2	3	3	8
Pelvic					
Upper		2		3	8
Lower		0		1	3
Rectrix * (outer)	1	1	1	1	1
Scapular	5	6	6	5	7
Femoral	5	4	6	5	7
Greater secondary covert †	4	5	5	5	5

* Inner 10 rectrices incipient.

† No middle secondary coverts. (They are present at least in *D. petechia* and *D. castanea.*)

Development of Nestlings

Young Kirtland's Warblers gain weight rapidly during their first five days of life, doubling their weight each two days. Then, in their remaining three or four days in the nest, their rate of gain decreases sharply. In these last days in the nest their energies go increasingly into maintaining their own warmth, developing plumage, and physical activity.

It may be significant that although the young have not then quite reached their final weight, their average increase in the last day in the nest is very small, and a few even lose weight at this time. Possibly hunger increases the restlessness of the young and hastens fledging.

The young in the weighed group may have left the nest a little earlier than they otherwise would because they were disturbed by daily removal from the nest.

The development of the young is described in detail in the following summary taken from field notes, especially those of Van Tyne, Walkinshaw, and Berger.

Day of Hatching

Young are weak, able to wriggle slightly, raise their heads, and open their mouths. When fed, they give faint calls. Eyes are closed, and the region of the eyes is blue through the skin. The skin elsewhere is flesh-colored and the inside of the mouth is similar. Down is fluffy, Hair Brown, and about 8 mm. long on the head, but a little shorter on the scapular, mid-dorsal, and femoral regions. Wing, 6.8 mm.; tarsus, 5.8 mm.; culmen, 3.7 mm. (Body measurements here and in next two paragraphs by Walkinshaw on five individuals.)

Newly hatched cowbirds are readily distinguished from warblers by their *white* down.

1 Day after Hatching

Down 8 mm. long, supraorbital, big; occipital, V-shaped; humeral, a short row; femoral, a short row; ulnal, a very short row; ventral, none. Body color, Pecan Brown (11″ i) to Terra Cotta (7″); lung area, more pink; legs, near Onion-skin Pink (11″ b). Bill, Clay Color (17″) to Mustard Yellow (19′ b) on edge of mouth. Mouth, largely yellowish, becoming pink in the throat. No egg tooth visible; tip of mandible dark. The young wriggle about and right themselves, using heels, wings, and head. They do not open their mouths when handled. Wing, 7.8 mm.; tarsus, 7.0 mm.; culmen, 4.0 mm. (Down and color descriptions by Van Tyne).

2 Days after Hatching

Young birds are stronger. They open their mouths for food when touched by hand, but usually do not make any sound. Yellow gape is very conspicuous. Primaries show through the skin. Other feather tracts are discernible. Wing, 9.2 mm.; tarsus, 8.6 mm.; culmen, 4.2 mm.

3 Days after Hatching

Feather tracts well defined. Eyes open. Wing, 11 mm.; tarsus, 10 mm.; culmen, 5 mm. (one individual measured). Quills visible.

4 Days after Hatching

Young birds wriggle and stretch. Some preening motions, especially under the wing.

5 Days after Hatching

Young lie quiet for periods and then wriggle and jostle one another. Wriggle on the scales when being weighed but make no attempt to move away. Eyes open. Basal one-third of mouth edge conspicuously yellow. Remiges much grown but not yet burst at tip ("covered with pin feathers"). Tail not visible.

6 Days after Hatching

Wing, 28.8 mm.; first primary, 14.0; tarsus, 18.4; culmen, 7.2 (average of five individuals in one nest measured by Walkinshaw; age estimated from their weights). Quills burst at tips. Young show fear and crouch in the nest; difficult to extract.

7 Days after Hatching

Young well-feathered and responsive to approach of adult with food. Come to attention when adult lights in front of nest. Young lying in full sun open their mouths and pant. The red of the mouths tends toward orange. Wing, 34.2; first primary, 18.6; tarsus, 19.0; culmen, 8.0; tail, 2.0 mm. (Measurements from same individuals as in preceding paragraph.)

8 Days after Hatching

Large, well-feathered, active. Larger young in same nest seem to be more active than the others, sometimes climbing on top of the others. Activity comes by spells, alternating with periods of dozing. Young strain wildly, calling "ti-ti-ti-ti-ti," at the approach of the adult. Mouths seem somewhat less prominently yellow-edged now, but presented to the adults energetically, not merely opened, but vibrated up and down like mechanical toys. The open mouths drop instantly when the adult departs. The young birds stretch their legs and wings, and preen their primaries, scapulars, and breasts. The young look and lean out of the nest, pecking at tiny objects, perhaps ants, on the edge of the nest and just outside it. They do not show any recognition of the alarm chip of the adult female.

9 Days after Hatching

Young birds sometimes get as much as 25 centimeters out of the nest in their preening, stretching, and pecking at nearby objects. Then they dash back in. They sometimes stand at the entrance of the nest, spreading and fluttering their wings. Their tails are mere stubs. Sometimes the smaller young open their mouths for food when another young towers over them. The mouths are Grenadine Red. The young crouch at a man's cough, even though pitched low.

Weights of Nestlings

No Kirtland's Warbler has been weighed before it has been fed after hatching. Huxley (1927) says the newly hatched, dry bird

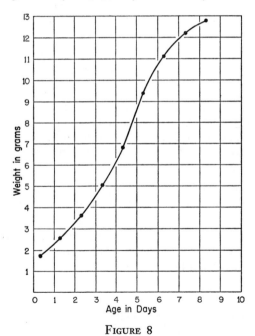

FIGURE 8

Weights of Kirtland's Warbler nestlings from hatching to fledging

usually weighs about two-thirds as much as a fresh egg. D. K. Wetherbee (Wilson Ornithological Society meeting, 1960) states that most songbirds at hatching weigh about 75 per cent as much as their eggs, and wood warblers nearer 70 per cent. Since the typical Kirtland's Warbler egg weighs 1.77 grams, we should therefore expect the newly hatched young to weigh about 1.3 grams, slightly less than 10 per cent of its adult weight.

After the first feedings the newly hatched young show an immediate gain, some of which consists of undigested food. But the gain in body weight is very rapid, and at the age of six days the

Table 14

Rate of Growth of Kirtland's Warbler

Day after Hatching	Birds (N)	Weight Gain from Previous Day Grams	Percentage
1	5	1.30 to 2.66 = 1.36	105 *
2	14	2.53 to 3.64 = 1.11	44
3	13	3.60 to 5.06 = 1.46	41
4	12	5.09 to 6.79 = 1.70	33
5	8	7.13 to 9.41 = 2.28	32
6	5	9.41 to 11.09 = 1.68	18
7	10	11.08 to 12.18 = 1.10	10
8	5	12.38 to 12.67 = 0.28	2

* The first day's gain as presented here is not strictly comparable, since the weight at hatching was estimated, the time from hatching to weighing on the following day was not known to the hour (but was more than 24 hours), and some of the gain consisted of undigested food. The average weight of these same five birds at 5 p.m., all having hatched since 6 a.m., was 1.66 grams.

average nestling weighs about 80 per cent as much as the average adult; when the nestling leaves the nest at about 9 days, it weighs 90 per cent as much as the average adult.

To examine the rate of growth more precisely, the weights of the same birds on eight successive days are given in Table 14.

The weights of nestlings in seven nests are shown in Table 15.

Fledging

Young Kirtland's Warblers usually leave the nest nine or ten days after hatching. I have records on 23 birds for which the day of hatching and the day of fledging were known definitely; 16 left at 9 days, 5 at 10 days, and 2 at 11 days. The average period in the nest was 9.4

Table 15

Weights of Nestling Kirtland's Warblers
(grams)

Nest	Day of Hatch- ing	Days after Hatching								
		1	2	3	4	5	6	7	8	9
38–3	1.7	2.7	3.8	....	....	.....	.....	.....	.....	.....
	1.8	2.7	3.7	....	....	.....	.....	.....	.....	.....
	1.6	2.7	3.6	....	....	.....	.....	.....	.....	.....
	1.5	2.6	3.5	....	....	.....	.....	.....	.....	.....
38–4	1.7	2.6	3.4	4.6	....	.....	.....	.....	.....	.....
48–17	...	2.46	3.60	5.43 †	6.61	9.00	.....	.....	.....	.....
	...	2.52	3.67	5.58	7.19	9.56	.....	.....	.....	.....
	...	2.54	3.86	5.29	7.20	9.70	.....	.....	.....	.....
51–2	...	2.88	4.42	6.13	7.96	10.05 ‡	12.06	12.85	12.76	Fledged
	...	2.26	3.40	4.94	6.97	8.54	10.56	11.73	11.77	"
	...	....	3.59	5.27	7.47	9.95	11.34	12.98	13.11	"
	...	....	3.72	5.37	7.27	9.68	11.29	12.88	13.47	"
	...	....	3.19	4.50	6.33	8.83	10.19	11.52	12.25	11.47
52–6	...	2.56	....	....	....	.....	.....	.....	.....	.....
53–10 *	...	2.14	3.48	4.84	5.68	.....	.....	.....	.....	.....
	...	2.35	3.70	4.87	6.62	.....	.....	.....	.....	.....
	...	2.38	3.61	4.15	5.49	.....	.....	.....	.....	.....
	...	2.54	3.20	4.60	6.65	.....	.....	.....	.....	.....
38–2 *	...	....	....	....	....	.....	10.8	12.9	Fledged	.....
	...	....	....	....	....	.....	10.8	11.9	"	.....
	...	....	....	....	....	.....	10.2	11.8	"	.....
	...	....	....	....	....	.....	11.3	11.9	"	.....
	...	....	....	....	....	.....	11.3	11.3	"	.....
Average	1.66	2.53	3.61	5.04	6.79	9.41	11.08	12.18	.....	.....

* Age estimated from initial weights; included for growth data.
† Fecal sac weighed .06 grams.
‡ Fecal sac weighed .29 grams.

days. In a few instances I suspected the young left the nest at 8 days, but was uncertain because I did not find the young.

Two other ground-nesting warblers studied, Northern Water-thrush and Louisiana Waterthrush (Eaton, 1957, 1958) also had nestling periods of 9 and 9 to 10 days; but two other ground-nesting warblers, the Ovenbird (Hann, 1937:186) and the Nashville Warbler (Lawrence, 1948:215) left the nest at 8 days—perhaps an indication that the hazards at their nests are greater. Various tree-nesting warblers have nestling periods of 8 to 10 days: Yellow Warbler, average 9½ (Schrantz, 1943:384); Black-throated Green Warbler, 8 to 10 (Pitelka, 1940:13); Chestnut-sided Warbler, 9 (Lawrence, 1948: 215), and Prairie Warbler, 9 (Nolan, unpublished). The cavity-nesting Prothonotary Warbler has a longer nestling period, averaging 10 to 11 days (Walkinshaw, 1941).

Perhaps birds disturbed by human observers leave the nest earlier than they otherwise would, particularly when the disturbance is gross, as in banding, weighing, and photography. Certainly birds ready to leave may be prompted to do so by even a minor disturbance, or, if removed from the nest, they may refuse to return. But I believe the effect of human observation and disturbance that does not include handling the nestlings is negligible; and that even this handling may advance fledging by only a day.

For example, young that leave the nest when disturbed in the afternoon probably would have left the next morning anyway. Conscious of the disturbance we create, we may easily overestimate it and at the same time underestimate the many irritations from other sources—biting ants, hot sun, and hunger, to name a few. While it is true that nestlings often leave when touched, it is also true that others, seemingly as well developed but presumably not quite ready to leave, settle docilely when replaced in the nest. Moreover, some of the individuals with the shortest nestling periods in my series were not visited between the day of hatching and the day of fledging.

Van Tyne (Bent, 1953:420) says, "The young normally remain in the nest 12 to 13 days"; but this account was written in 1946, before there was clear evidence on the matter, and may have been based on the report of Wood (1904:10), who had estimated, probably incorrectly, the ages of large young he found at the nest.

I believe the young most often leave the nest in the morning, though they sometimes leave in the afternoon. When they are ready to leave, a small disturbance will cause them to "explode" from the nest, while the same disturbance on the previous day would have caused them to huddle in the nest.

When the time comes to leave, one of the brood stands in the entrance of the nest, stretching its wings, as the young have been doing at times in the last day or two. Suddenly, with no warning from the young or adults, the bird takes flight from the nest. The first flight carries the bird to a point on the ground one to three meters away. The young bird pauses only an instant, and then flutters and scrambles onward, perhaps 10 meters, to a place of concealment under ground cover.

A few minutes later another young bird repeats the performance, traveling in a different direction. Usually within an hour or two the nest is empty, even though some of the young do not appear as well developed and vigorous as others. However, in a few cases I have known two young to leave, while the three remaining of the brood of five stayed on till the next day. Usually there is no backward glance at the nest, and the young never return to it after leaving. But once I saw a young bird fly out about one meter, pause, and then flutter back into the nest. It crouched in the familiar shelter two or three minutes and then departed, never to return again. Once, when the smallest and last of the brood left the nest, I captured it and placed it back in the nest; in two minutes it fluttered away again. Within the first day the young may move 20 to 40 meters away, and they are rarely found close to the nest after the first two or three hours.

I have not been able to detect any action by the adults tending to encourage the departure of the young. Often the adults are not present at the moment of departure, but when they are they show great agitation. Both adults "chip" excitedly, and I have seen a female hover over a fledgling as it moved away. However, as soon as the young bird finds concealment and ceases to move, the adults' attention subsides. The adults then immediately start feeding young birds out of the nest, and continue to carry food to any young still in the nest.

The earliest nests may fledge young by June 18; and the latest, about July 29. The earliest fledging actually recorded is June 21, and the latest record of young seen in a nest is July 23.

Summary

About three-fourths of all Kirtland's Warblers hatch in the period June 12 to 26. The hatching of a set of eggs spreads over a number of hours, but is usually completed in a day; cowbird eggs present in the nest usually hatch two or three days earlier.

Eggshells and other inanimate matter are carried away promptly in the bill of an adult.

The female does all the brooding of young, at first more than 80 per cent of the daylight hours, but tapering off after the young are three days old; after the sixth day the female does very little day-time brooding.

Both adults feed the young. They carry large amounts of food in their bills on each trip, and average 2 to 7 trips per hour until the last two or three days of the nestling period, when the rate is increased.

Fecal sacs are removed by both adults, this function being performed in about 20 per cent of the trips from the nest.

The female is the one primarily concerned with defense of the area immediately around the nest, but the male sometimes chases birds that enter the vicinity.

The late embryos and newly hatched birds have long, dark down, in contrast to the whitish down of young cowbirds.

The young birds weigh less than 1.5 grams when hatched, but at the end of six days weigh about 11 grams, or 80 per cent of the adult weight. Thereafter the increase is much slower.

Young Kirtland's Warblers usually leave the nest at nine days of age. Their first movement from the nest is by flight. Then by fluttering and scrambling they proceed to a place of concealment under dense ground cover.

II

Fledglings

First Week out of the Nest: Age 9–15 Days

When the young birds leave the nest they move rapidly to nearby patches of heavy ground cover and disappear under it. Although they move a little, they stay near, perhaps within 20 meters, for the first day or so. But the next day may find them much farther away, sometimes 100 to 200 meters. Then for about two weeks they circulate in an area not much larger than the original territory of the male, but not identical with it.

The adult male and female each care for a part of the brood, and henceforth the two segments of the family go their separate ways. Even within one of these subgroups, however, the young birds do not cluster. Although the subgroup stays together loosely, the individuals are usually not within three meters of one another. I have never seen an adult brooding a young bird out of the nest.

I have seen different families and different segments of the same family cross paths, but I have not seen an adult feeding any but the young birds of its own family segment, adopted the first day out of the nest. This specialized attention seems to be determined by the adults, for the hungry young will beg from any nearby bird, even another juvenile.

I suspect it is the adult that keeps the family segment in a limited area. The guidance of the adult is not immediately evident to the human observer. The young often seem to fly in random directions, and the adults often carry food to the young; so a person asks himself, "Which is following which?" But the young, when hungry, go toward the adult, and quite frequently, after being fed, they fly in the direction of the disappearing adult. Thus a shy adult always seems to be luring the young away from danger. I have seen a fledgling 13 days old fly 12 meters toward an adult to be fed. Thus, there appears to be a random, centrifugal tendency on the part of the fledglings, offset by the centripetal attraction of the adult as a source of food, and possibly companionship.

In addition to the cohesiveness within each family segment, there are indications of gregariousness among the adults after territorial defense subsides. It is common to find two or three family groups in a small area, and then to find no others for a long distance. Late in the summer an adult without family, or an independent young bird in first fall plumage, frequently utters the "zeet" location note, and usually another bird can be heard or seen nearby.

During the first few days out of the nest the fledglings are difficult to find. They spend most of their time on the ground under dense cover, sometimes sitting without movement for more than half an hour at a time. They seem rarely to go up into the trees except when frightened. They are usually silent but offer a faint chirp at the approach of an adult bird bearing food. The presence of young was often revealed to me by the agitation of the parent, and their exact location by the parent carrying food.

In the first day or two out of the nest the young birds can be caught by hand. If well concealed, they sit still until a person comes within arm's length. On the ground they can be stepped on accidentally. When flushed, they usually fly to a perch in a small tree five to fifteen meters away. Here they sit without movement, looking remarkably like unopened pine cones. This perch is usually in the densest portion of a small pine, one to two meters from the ground. If not well concealed, a fledgling may flush when a person is two meters away; but, if closely surrounded by foliage, it may continue to sit still even though a person brushes the tree in which it is perched. Although the young bird sits as though frozen, its eye regards the intruder steadily, with an appearance of alertness.

The young bird can fly when it leaves the nest, but weaker fledglings can maintain level flight for only one meter or so. Thus when they launch themselves from a perch, they slant downward to a landing, sometimes tumbling to the ground. Although they can alight on a twig, they teeter there precariously. At this period, virtually tailless, they fly in almost straight lines. This knowledge is helpful to a person attempting to follow them through thickets.

The young birds spend much of their time sitting quietly, preening, and dozing with eyes closed. I have seen a 12-day-old bird sit on a branch for 40 minutes without moving. Quiet periods alternate with restless periods, when the birds hop about on the ground or take short flights. Occasionally they work themselves up by stages to perches as high as four meters, but they rarely pause long in any place not offering concealment. From the first day out of the nest they peck at things about them. Sometimes they peck at objects, perhaps tiny insects, too small for the human watcher to see. They also peck at branches and leaves. These actions seem to be exploratory. They do not appear to search for food aggressively or to recognize it more than an inch or two away, and then, I suspect, only if it moves. They confine their attentions to objects they can reach by extending their bills. Already they wipe their bills on a branch after eating or preening, a common gesture of the adults.

The fledglings are alert to the approach of an adult bird carrying food. The begging chirp of a young bird often gives the first inkling of the approach of an adult. Often, if the adult has been out of sight for some time, it gives the "zeet" location note, perhaps to be answered by "chips" from hungry young in two or three directions. The adult that approaches a young bird and does not get a "chip" may pass on to another bird. A fledgling may be fed two or three times in as many minutes and then not again for half an hour. Young birds are often fed on the ground, in dense cover.

At this stage the best field mark to indicate the age of a fledgling is the length of the tail. At fledging (age 9–11 days) the juvenile appears tailless; after three days out of the nest (age about 12–13 days) the tail is about half an inch long; and at the end of the first week (age about 15 days), the tail is about one inch long. This field observation was confirmed by Berger's measurements of a captive bird; its tail was 17 mm. long at about 14 days of age and 24 mm. long a day later.

From the time the tail is first noticeable, the white spots on the outer rectrices flash prominently—much more so than in an adult— as the bird flies away. Although these spots also appear on the Vesper Sparrow and the Slate-colored Junco, two other species common in this region, they provide a helpful means of identifying and following the young of Kirtland's Warbler. Perhaps the white tail flashes also help the warblers find one another.

Some adults are bolder than others in feeding the young, but it is my impression that females usually are more difficult to observe than males. They make less noise and are more likely to approach the young by traveling through the densest thickets. One female that I watched at length never fed the young in an exposed position; if the young bird was in the open, she waited for it in a thicket until it went to meet her there.

It is my impression that a male traveling with a segment of the family rarely sings when he and the family are outside his territory, but often sings when back in the familiar area. Between feedings the parent may go a considerable distance away. I have heard a male singing fully 200 meters from the young he was feeding.

The agitation of the adults when a person is near a young bird gradually declines from its peak, which occurs at the moment the young leave the nest.

Second Week out of the Nest: Age 16–22 Days

In the second week out of the nest the young birds become more active and alert. Although they still doze at times, they give an appearance of greater alertness than characterizes them in the first few days of freedom. Now they move about more, flush at a greater distance, and fly farther. The young bird seems to gather some food for itself, but begs loudly, with a rapid series of "chips," when the adult is near. It is thus easier to find a family in the second week out of the nest than the first, even though the adult no longer shows agitation when a person is near the young. The begging of the young, which is inconspicuous in the first week, becomes the best guide to the family in the second week.

From a distance of less than two meters I watched a young bird about 21 days old for an uninterrupted hour and a half. Although at my approach this bird flushed from the ground at about two meters, and from a tree branch at about four meters, it seemed oblivious to me when, after approaching very slowly, I had sat quietly for a few minutes. For about an hour of this time the fledgling stayed on a patch of ground not more than half a meter square. At times it shifted position to bask in the warmth of the sun. At other times it nestled in the grass. But its eyes were alert and it turned its head quickly to observe the switching of a branch or the passing of a bee. It did not move in search of food, but sampled various things within reach, as though testing them for edibility. It tugged at a dried fern frond, pulled energetically at blades of grass, sliding them through its mandibles, chewed a pine blossom, and ate a small pine needle. It also ate objects too minute for me to identify. Once it caught a green larva nearly an inch long, moved the food through its bill until mashed from end to end, and then ate half of it, abandoning the other half to meet the adult approaching with food.

As the young become more active and noisy, the cohesiveness of the family segment is much more apparent. Each bird moves about with seeming independence, but the several members of the family being fed by one adult are usually found within a circle 30 meters in diameter. An hour later they may have moved 200 meters, but they are still together. I have seen a young bird of this age go 10 meters high in a tree to meet an adult with food. Usually a young bird makes a flight of 7 to 15 meters immediately after being fed. The young birds still spend much time on the ground, but they now spend much more time in the trees, usually in the middle branches; rarely, if at all, do they reach the high limbs of large trees, though they are quite capable of doing so. They seem to frequent large trees only if the lower limbs are near the ground.

The general appearance of the plumage does not change much in the first two weeks out of the nest, except for the rapidly growing tail. At the start of the second week (age about 16 days), the tail is about half its adult length, judged in the field to be one inch. (On Berger's captive it measured about 27 mm.) At the end of the second week, the tail is slightly shorter than an adult's. (On Berger's captive it measured 50 mm. at 23 days.) Now, like an adult, with the help of the tail the young bird is capable of sudden changes in direction of flight. The underparts of the young bird are still gray with dark spots, and the upper parts continue to match the mottled gray of a pine cone or branch.

In the field I have noticed tail bobbing first at the age of about 18 days; Berger noted it in a captive at about 17 days.

The male seems more closely attached to his territory than does the female. His wanderings with his family segment bring him back again and again to the original territory, while some females, I believe, never bring their young back to the vicinity of the nest. After the nest ceases to exist, the female may feel no further attraction to the territory.

Third Week out of the Nest: Age 23–29 Days

In the third week out of the nest the young birds gather much of their own food. Probably they could sustain themselves if necessary, but they still pursue the adults, begging energetically when the adult comes into sight. They crouch, quiver, and reach up, putting themselves in a lower position than the bird approached. The adult may feed the young four times in 15 minutes and then disappear for half an hour. The young also beg in the presence of strange adult birds, and once I saw a young bird of this age go toward a strange bird in its first fall plumage. The stranger repulsed it with a flick of the wing and flew away rapidly.

At age about 23 days, Berger found a captive bird had the ability to discriminate between ants and other insects, for it discarded the ants. At first the bird would pick up ants crawling on the floor and then reject them, but at age 23 days the bird no longer touched the ants. Several times the bird started after a moving object on a leaf and then stopped when close enough to see it was an ant.

The juveniles now fly with almost the speed and maneuverability of adults, sometimes going to perches high in the tallest trees. I saw one bird 29 days old take a high, arching flight 200 meters in length. Once a family group 27 days old, accompanied by an adult male, was 500 meters from the nest site, much farther away than any younger group seen. Yet, they were together in the same place on two consecutive days. The young stay within sight of one another even though the adult is not near.

Since the tails of the young now seem to be of full adult length (57 mm. on Berger's captive at about 28 days), the tail is no longer a clue to age in the field. But other plumage changes begin to appear, the most conspicuous of which are yellow feathers on the breast. I first noted yellow feathers on one bird at the age of 24 days, and on another at 28 days; Berger noted them on a captive bird at 26 days, when the first yellow feathers began to unsheathe at the tips. These feathers first appear in a spot on each side of the breast, near the bend of the wing. These spots enlarge noticeably day by day, and in about five days unite high across the chest, forming an inverted V down the sides to the abdomen.

Now, too, other signs of molt are visible. The young bird begins to look shaggy, especially on the crown. Bristly feathers of unequal length, some much lighter than others, give the crown a salt-and-pepper pattern. At age 23–25 days Berger noticed that the breast feathers seemed loose on his captive bird.

Fourth and Fifth Weeks out of the Nest: Age 30–43 Days

During the fourth and fifth weeks out of the nest the molt of the young birds is virtually completed, and feeding by the adults tapers off toward the vanishing point. The juveniles continue to pursue the adults and call, but often get no response. I once saw an adult female feed a 44-day-old warbler, but on the same day I followed the adult male of this pair for about an hour without seeing or hearing any of his three young, which a few days before would have been much in evidence. The time of season may have some bearing on how long fledglings are fed. I have not seen young warblers fed after August 12, although some were then still begging and did not yet have any yellow plumage.

The search for food by the young of this age still seems to be partly exploratory. I watched a 30-day-old bird pull pieces of rotten wood out of a stump, discarding it piece by piece. At this time, when one of the siblings happened to come within 15 centimeters, one or the other gaped and reached for food. Once this 30-day-old bird approached a strange adult. The adult sat quietly until the young bird was within wing's length, and then with an abrupt motion put it to flight.

Berger's captive bird at this age could eat cabbage butterflies, wings and all. In preparing to eat a large insect, the young bird first passed it back and forth between its mandibles, shaking it, and beating it on branch or floor like an adult, but doing so awkwardly. It tended to swallow large morsels—butterflies, mayflies, grasshoppers—head first.

Although the young birds fly widely, I have never seen them anywhere except in typical Kirtland's Warbler habitat, or on the edge of it.

The yellow of the underparts reaches the throat and midline of the abdomen last. By 38 to 42 days the underparts are completely yellow, with delicate black spotting across the breast and down the sides. The yellow of this first fall plumage has an orange tinge lacking in breeding birds. The upper parts, especially on the head, are brownish gray, where earlier there was no suggestion of brown. By the 44th day just a suggestion of shagginess remains; otherwise the bird is in its full first-fall plumage. A young bird 45 days old, found 55 meters from the nest on August 5, seemed to be independent of adult help and in almost full winter plumage. Yet, the final evidences of molt may linger, for an immature bird collected at Mt. Pleasant, South Carolina, on October 29, 1903, was recorded as having its "molt not yet complete" (Wayne, 1904).

Berger noted that at 27 days a captive bird looked bald because so many feathers on the anterior part of the head were sheathed. At 28 days, the manus had bare areas anterior to the major primary coverts, and the underprimary coverts were new, still mostly sheathed. At 31 days the feathers on the top of the head, chin, and throat were new, still sheathed; there were still bare spots on the manus anterior to the greater primary coverts; the feathers on the back still had sheaths at the base; and the greater secondary coverts were molting. At 35 days the feathers on the throat began to unsheathe, giving a yellow throat that joined the yellow pectoral tracts along the sides of the breast. The molt seemed essentially complete by 43 days. There was no sign of molt at any time in the secondaries, primaries, or greater primary coverts of fledglings.

Food

The food of both fledglings and adults seems to consist entirely of insects, both larvae and winged forms, until the blueberries ripen early in August. Then the birds feed themselves and their young large quantities of blueberries, selecting only the dark, ripe fruit. Fledglings even less than 24 days old (still without yellow on the under parts) hop about on the ground eating the berries. Once in mid-August I watched adults carry food to fledglings over a period of three days, and was not able to identify any food other than blueberries.

Weights of Fledglings

Fledglings weigh about 12 grams when they leave the nest. An immature wild female 45 days old weighed 13.6 grams. If the weight of the plumage after the postjuvenal molt is 10 per cent of the body weight, an appreciable part of the gain after fledging may consist of feathers; Pitelka (1958:38–49) found the plumage of Steller's Jays comprised about 10 per cent of the body weight after the fall molt. Berger's captive warbler seemed to reach maximum weight at about 20 days, that is, shortly before it began its postjuvenal molt. At this time it weighed 16.5 grams at the close of the day; that is, more than any wild Kirtland's Warbler we have weighed. This captive bird showed as much as 2 grams variation from early morning, when hungry, to evening, when well fed.

Fledglings of Other Species

Finding and following a young warbler is a challenge to the best field worker. Accordingly, it is not surprising that little is known about this stage of life in closely related species.

The Ovenbird (Hann, 1937:186–196) leaves the nest at 8 days and sometimes even earlier, but cannot yet fly. The parents divide the brood, as in the Kirtland's Warbler, and continue feeding them until they are about 28 days of age. Young Ovenbirds also show some gregariousness, as they move about with the young of other families. The Louisiana Waterthrush (Eaton, 1958:228) is independent in about a month from hatching, and the Black-throated Green Warbler (Pitelka, 1940:16) at about 28 days.

Nolan (unpublished) has found the Prairie Warbler to be partially dependent until about 45 days old, with some individuals still being fed when 50 days old. Walkinshaw (1952:108) found a Chipping Sparrow still receiving food from a parent when at least 51 days old.

Nice (1943:70) found that the age of independence for nearly all of twenty species of passerine birds was 26 to 32 days, with longer periods only for the dippers and shrikes. Thus the period of dependence in the Kirtland's Warbler (as long as 44 days) is longer than in most closely related species so far reported, but not uniquely so. I suspect the young are capable of caring for themselves earlier if necessary, and the young of later broods are not fed as long. Doubtless the rearing of second broods cuts short the feeding of young in some species.

Summary

When the young of the Kirtland's Warbler leave the nest, each parent takes a part of the brood and cares for it exclusively. In the first week out of the nest (age 9–15 days), the young are quiet and move little; they stay in concealment, often on the ground. In the field the length of the tail reveals the age of the bird fairly accurately.

In the second week out of the nest (age 16–22 days) the young become more active and noisy and gather a portion of their own food. Tail wagging is noticeable. The part of a family fed by one adult moves about together.

In the third week out of the nest (age 23–29 days) the young gather so much of their own food that they might be able to sustain themselves if necessary, but the adults still feed them. At this time they begin the postjuvenal molt, which first becomes identifiable in the field by the appearance of a yellow spot on each side of the breast.

During the fourth and fifth weeks out of the nest (age 30–43 days) the birds molt their body feathers but not their remiges or rectrices. The adults have been known to feed young as old as 44 days.

The food of fledglings seems to consist entirely of insects until the blueberries ripen in early August. Then young and adults eat heavily of the dark, soft fruit.

The fledglings weigh about 12 grams when they leave the nest. At the completion of the postjuvenal molt, a month later, they may weigh only 1½ to 2 grams more.

12

Song

General Description of Normal Song

The Kirtland's Warbler has a striking song, though like other members of its family it can scarcely be called an accomplished singer. The nesting grounds were discovered when the bird's distinctive voice caught the ear of fishermen on the Au Sable River, and even today the bird would rarely be found except through its song.

The song is not truly musical but, rather, loud, clear, emphatic, and frequently repeated. It invites such descriptive terms as "bright," "peppy," "bubbling," "arresting," and "sharply defined." It has none of the buzz and trill so common among wood warblers, but reminds the listener of the chattering quality of a House Wren's song, though it is briefer. Field students are reminded of the song of the Northern Waterthrush and some notes of the House Wren, but the resemblance usually is not close enough to cause one to mistake the Kirtland's Warbler for either. Human syllables serve better to recall a bird song once heard than to describe a song to someone who does not know it. A variety of syllables have been used to describe this song. But instead of repeating these syllables, and at the risk of compounding the confusion, I suggest that the staccato tones, emphatic nature, and duration of the typical song may be roughly conveyed through the title of an erstwhile popular song: "ch-ch-chattanooga-choo-choo"—uttered rapidly, with a stuttering start, a drop in pitch, and a double note at the close.

Axtell (1938:481–491) has given a good account of the song, explaining how variations among birds and differences in auditory perceptions among people cause widely differing impressions of this bird's song to reach print. However, from discussions with a number of people in the presence of the singing Kirtland's Warbler, I believe that only an unusual bird or an unusual ear would account for some of the suggested resemblances mentioned in the literature: oriole, presumably Baltimore Oriole (Wood *in* Chapman, 1907:207), Yellowthroat (Roberts, 1932:243), Yellow-throated Warbler (Hoxie,

1886:412), and Black-throated Green Warbler (Saunders, 1908:422).

The loudness of the song is exceptional among warblers. Under favorable conditions it can be heard at a distance of a quarter of a mile. However, in ordinary field work, with moderate wind and intervening trees, the song of birds over 200 meters away may be missed. In an attempt to measure the carrying power of the song, I once selected a male singing at the edge of a cleared strip where an electric line cut through the forest. Here I had a straight, unimpeded path to the singer. It was 6 a.m., and a gentle breeze, estimated at three to five miles per hour, was rustling the foliage gently, and blowing from the bird toward me. There was no other background noise. I was able to hear and count the warbler's songs at 400 meters, but not at 500 meters. In several instances I have stepped off distances of 400 to 450 meters to singing Kirtland's Warblers. Of course, the songs of some individuals are louder than those of others.

The statement by Axtell (1938:484), quoted in Bent (1953:424), that the bird can be heard "from a quarter to a half mile," and by Arnold (1905:2), that it can be heard half a mile away, while perhaps true under special atmospheric conditions, should not be used as a guide to censusing practice.

Technical Description of the Song

Donald J. Borror, with the aid of audiospectrographic analysis of tape recordings taken in 1956, has supplied information on the song of the Kirtland's Warbler which is not obtainable through the human ear alone. (For his method, see Borror and Reese, 1953:271–276.) In general, his analysis confirms Axtell's report, which was based on observations by ear and by photographic enlargement of a motion picture sound strip.

As illustrated in Figure 9, the "normal" or waterthrush type of song lasts between 1 and 1½ seconds. It consists of three parts: (1) an opening of three to six low-pitched notes, beginning weak and increasing in loudness, at a rate of 3–8 per second; (2) two or three loud, slurred, higher notes at a rate of 5–6 per second; and (3) an ending of one to three sharp notes, usually of lower pitch, at a rate of 6–8 per second.

For a warbler, the song is low-pitched. Since none of these notes are of pure or sustained tone, it is difficult to ascribe a musical pitch to them; but it can be seen that most of the song is delivered between C''' and C'''', that is, between three and four octaves above middle C.

C''' falls a little above 2 kilocycles per second; C'''', a little above 4 kilocycles per second. Although some notes touch 6 kilocycles per second, they are at this pitch too short a time to register that frequency on the human ear. In the audiospectrograms (Figure 9), songs 2773–1, 2764–1, 2769–1, and 2762–1 are of this type.

The "chatter" or wren type of song is more monotonous and shorter in duration, lasting about one second. It is heard by the human ear as about eight rapid notes, "chu-chu-chu," etc., sometimes rising a little in pitch and volume toward the end. In Figure 9, songs 2761–3 and 2775–5 are of this type.

Some whisper songs, prompted by playback of recorded song, were mostly of the "chatter" type. Songs 2790–405, 2790–739, and 2790–602 were whisper songs (Figure 9).

For comparison, we have audiospectrograms (Figure 9) of the songs of the two birds most often said to resemble the song of the Kirtland's Warbler. Songs of the Northern Waterthrush are 1414–3 and 1411–4. Songs of the House Wren are 2728–1 and 3435–2. It is apparent that both have longer songs than the Kirtland's Warbler; the song of the House Wren is more than twice as long. It is also apparent that the Kirtland's Warbler note is more nearly a pure tone, that is, less buzzy than either of the others.

Variations in Song by Same Individual

Until nearly the end of June, perhaps 80 per cent of the songs of the Kirtland's Warbler are of the "normal" kind just described. Sometimes, for no apparent reason, fragments of song are given.

The "chatter" song is a variant used regularly by a few males, and occasionally by many of them, throughout the nesting season. This song becomes common late in the season, and is often predominant by mid-July. It is a simplified version of the usual song, and of the same loudness and quality, without the distinctive beginning or end, thus, "chu-chu-chu-chu-chu-chu," uttered very rapidly.

The "whisper" song may be of the "normal" or "chatter" kind, but is delivered so softly that it might not be heard more than 30 steps away. I have heard it given when I had no reason to believe the male was disturbed in any way, but I believe it is most often given under conditions of stress or uncertainty, as when a male is at the extreme edge of his territory. I have heard it when two males were near each other but not in open conflict, and most frequently of all at a time when a male was being subjected to the playback of a re-

"NORMAL" SONGS OF KIRTLAND'S WARBLER

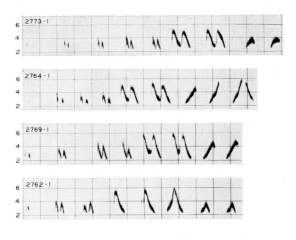

"CHATTER" SONGS OF KIRTLAND'S WARBLER

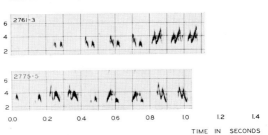

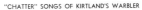

TIME IN SECONDS

FIGURE 9

Showing audiospectrographic analysis of normal, chatter, and whisper songs of the Kirtland's Warbler. Analysis of songs of Northern Water-thrush and House Wren shown for comparison. (Donald J. Borror)

WHISPER SONGS OF KIRTLAND'S WARBLER

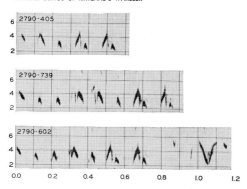

SONGS OF NORTHERN WATERTHRUSH

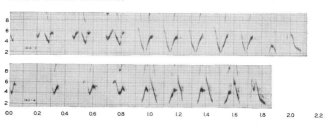

SONGS OF HOUSE WREN

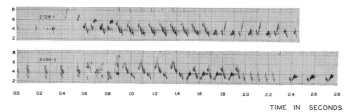

TIME IN SECONDS

FREQUENCY IN KILOCYCLES PER SECOND

corded song, and was searching in vain for the intruder. Young (1951:1–37) regards the whisper song in the Robin as "primarily a threat." Amadon (1944:6) thought that the whisper song in the Scrub Jay might at times indicate perplexity.

Variations among Individuals

The songs of nearly all males are superficially alike, so that, having heard one bird, one ordinarily has no difficulty in recognizing the song as that of the Kirtland's Warbler when one hears another. Nevertheless, there is a characteristic individuality to the song of each bird. When beginning field work in a colony of a dozen warblers, one has the casual impression that all the birds sing alike, but after a few days one finds it possible to identify every individual by song alone. The variations in beginning and ending are particularly noticeable. Detailed analysis shows that there are also small differences in the way the same bird gives successive songs in a series, but these differences do not obscure the individual pattern of the singer. I have heard one sing a series of accelerating notes on one pitch, much like the song of a Field Sparrow, but of harsher quality; and I have heard a House Wren in Ohio singing a partial song which I took at first to be that of a Kirtland's Warbler. These examples illustrate some of the uncertainties of bird identification by ear alone.

More extreme variants crop up occasionally. Individuals with unusual songs are often useful for study and may provide an audible landmark in an unfamiliar colony. I have heard a male repeat over and over again an unmusical rattle almost like that of a Brown-headed Cowbird.

Variations in Singing Rate during the Season

In early May the males are singing in migration as far south as South Carolina (Hoxie, 1886:412; Jenness, 1925:252), and they continue to sing with vigor through the various stages of nesting until early July. Then their singing becomes more sporadic, and by about July 10 some have ceased singing entirely, although a few sing occasionally until at least August 5. By August 10 all singing has stopped. The latest songs I have heard have been given by males feeding young, but I have also seen males feeding young in mid-August without singing. The birds stop singing at about the time of their postnuptial molt; however, I have seen males sing a few times after they had shed their tail feathers.

It is my impression that the males sing more when not in close company with the female—that is, if unmated, or if the mate is incubating eggs or brooding young—and less while the pair are in close companionship during pre-incubation. Some males are very quiet while accompanying the female on her travels in search of a nest site. In many other species, singing declines markedly, perhaps more so than in the Kirtland's Warbler, when the male acquires a mate.

The Kirtland's Warbler sings persistently—through the time of territory establishment, nest-site searching, nest building, egg laying, incubation, nestling care, and fledgling care—until the season of song passes. In the early part of the season nothing interferes with his singing for long except heavy downpours of rain and cold weather. The bird often sings early on a clear, still morning even

Table 16

Half-hour Song Counts in a Kirtland's Warbler Colony
(9:00–9:30 a.m.)

Date	Songs (N)	Birds (N)	Temperature F.	Weather Conditions
June 27	402	6	75°*	Light breeze
July 3	462	6	80°*	Light breeze
July 4	192	4	85°*	Moderate breeze
July 5	408	6	75°*	Clear, calm
July 6	122	3	85°*	Light breeze
July 7	466	6	80°*	Light breeze
July 8	461	4	76°	Partly clear, light breeze
July 9	83	4	78°	Clear, light breeze
July 10	21	3	70°	Clear, light breeze
July 11	7	1	68°	Clear, moderate breeze
July 12	10	2	70°	Clear, light breeze
July 13	94	2	72°	Clear, light breeze
July 15	104	4	72°	Cloudy, light breeze

* Estimated.

though frost is on the ground. One bird sang 165 times between 5:16 and 6:30 a.m. on June 5, with the temperature at 28° F. at the start and 33° F. at the end of the period. Sometimes in late May and early June extremely cold days occur, occasionally with snow flurries, and at these times all Kirtland's Warbler song is suspended. Later in the season song seems to decline, particularly on the hottest afternoons.

The erratic decline in singing frequency in early July is shown in Table 16. These song counts were taken near the center of a Kirtland's Warbler colony, within hearing distance of about six birds. Each of the counts was taken in a half-hour period, from 9:00 to 9:30 a.m.

Rate of Singing During the Day

Most Kirtland's Warblers sing at a rate of six to nine songs a minute. The rate is more likely to be rapid when the bird gives a short

Table 17

Songs of Kirtland's Warbler in the Prenesting Period *

Period ending:	Minutes				Total	Temp. F.
	15	30	45	60		
Hour	Songs (N)					
4 †	0	59	96	36	191	28°
5	51	61	66	69	247	29°
6	62	54	52	47	215	43°
7	34	47	28	25	134	52°
8	47	31	29	30	137	62°
9	35	54	11	0	100	68°
10	21	32	3	34	90	75°
11	28	18	0	0	46	81°
12	0	0	15	1	16	77°
1	2	7	10	0	19	73°
2	0	0	11	8	19	71°
3	7	0	0	0	7	65°
4	0	0	0	6	6	60°
5	2	0	0	0	2	..
Total					1,229	

* Observations June 8, 1945; male accompanied by mate, two days before start of nest building, six days before laying of first egg. Observer: J. Van Tyne, not concealed.

† First song, 4:18. Sunrise about 5:00.

song. For brief periods birds have been timed singing as fast as eleven times a minute, but usually the rate is fairly constant for a given individual. Songs are offered in courses, that is, periods of steady singing, for several minutes at a time. These courses of song often last 15 minutes or more in the morning, but in the afternoon they are likely to last only two or three minutes. There are momentary interruptions in this rhythm, and thus there is rarely a five-minute period with as many songs as would be expected from the rate per minute. In addition to these momentary pauses, there are longer

PLATE 1. *Young jack pine five years after forest fire. Note bare sand and fire-killed trees. Kirtland's Warblers first appeared in this area three years later. (Photograph by Harold Mayfield)*

PLATE 2. *The author among jack pines and ground cover typical of Kirtland's Warbler habitat. (Photograph by Edwin Way Teale)*

PLATE 3, A. *Kirtland's Warbler habitat viewed from a slight elevation. Openings among the pines are characteristic but here are more extensive than usual. (Photograph by Josselyn Van Tyne)*

PLATE 3, B. *The author among jack pines of the right size for Kirtland's Warblers, looking toward pines much too large for the nesting habitat of these birds. (Photograph by Edwin Way Teale)*

PLATE 4. *Male Kirtland's Warbler facing canopied nest. (Photograph by Harold Mayfield)*

PLATE 5, A. *Female Kirt-land's Warbler displaying extreme tameness near her nest. (Photograph by Lawrence H. Walkin-shaw)*

PLATE 5, B. *Kirtland's Warbler nest and eggs, the cover pulled back slightly to reveal the con-tents. The usual number of eggs would be five in-stead of three. (Photo-graph by Lawrence D. Hiett)*

PLATE 6, A. *Rare instance of male Kirtland's Warbler brooding young. The male may be distinguished by its white eye-ring.*

PLATE 6, B. *Female on same nest. (Photograph by Harry W. Hann)*

PLATE 7, A. *Adult Kirtland's Warbler feeding fledgling recently, and perhaps prematurely, out of the nest. (Photograph by Roger Tory Peterson)*

PLATE 7, B. *Adult male Kirtland's Warbler and Brown-headed Cowbird about seven days old. The young cowbird was taken from the nest for photography but did not remain in it when replaced. (Photograph by Harold Mayfield)*

PLATE 8. *Fledgling Kirtland's Warbler 12 days old. Note how its color pattern and value blend with pine bark. (Photograph by Harold Mayfield)*

silent periods. These silences may last a few minutes or, in the afternoon, an hour or more. In his all-day song count, Van Tyne found that the male he was observing gave partial songs in 12 per cent of its utterances, and that these were less frequent in the first three hours of the morning, when the bird was singing most vigorously.

There are probably great differences between individuals in song output, just as there are seasonal differences in the same bird. Van Tyne's count of the songs of a mated bird two days before the

Table 18

Songs of Kirtland's Warbler in the
Incubation Period *

Period ending:					Minutes								Temp.	
	05	10	15	20	25	30	35	40	45	50	55	60	F.	Remarks
Hour				Songs (N)								Total		
4	..	..	..	..	..	..	..	..	0	0	0	21	21	56°	First song, 4:57. Sunrise c. 5:00. Calm, clear overhead, but foggy; visibility, 200 yards.
5	13	13	18	9	0	6	26	0	0	0	0	2	87	58°	Calm, sunny, slight fog.
6	29	6	4	32	25	32	23	29	33	26	27	16	282	66°	Calm, sunny.
7	3	22	21	28	30	33	33	29	29	23	23	31	305	68°	Sunny, light breeze.
8	33	27	0	0	16	27	34	25	7	15	32	30	246	72°	Sunny, light intermittent breeze.
9	29	27	10	19	28	31	21	0	0	32	30	11	238	76°	Sunny, light intermittent breeze.
10	0	3	0	21	30	28	14	14	28	19	22	21	200	80°	Sunny, light breeze.
11	32	28	28	30	24	12	0	0	0	0	0	3	157	83°	Sunny, light breeze.
12	3	0	3	11	13	15	17	6	12	21	21	0	122	86°	Sunny, light breeze.
1	0	0	0	0	24	10	4	9	24	21	21	8	121	87°	Sunny.
2	3	1	1	19	23	3	0	0	0	0	0	22	72	86°	Partly cloudy.
3	0	5	6	18	24	7	6	8	18	32	10	34	168	88°	Partly cloudy.
4	21	25	19	14	9	2	0	0	0	0	0	0	90	88°	Partly cloudy.
5	0	13	2	0	0	0	0	0	0	0	0	0	15	82°	Clear.
6	0	0	0	0	0	0	5	0	0	0	0	5	10	78°	Clear.
7	0	5	0	4	0	0	7	9	11	23	15	4	78	76°	Clear. Last song, 7:56. Sunset c. 8:25.

Total	2,212

* Observations June 21, 1956, about the 13th day of incubation, one day before first warbler egg hatched. Observer: Harold Mayfield, concealed in a blind.

start of nest building was 1,229 songs in a day. As stated earlier, I believe male Kirtland's Warblers sing less at that time than when unmated or when dwelling with a female spending most of her time on the nest. My count of 2,212 songs by a male with a mate, near the end of the incubation period, is a very high figure for a mated bird. Yet other warblers may do as well. The Nices (1932) counted 1,680 songs from a Black-throated Green Warbler in seven hours on July 15.

The greatest numbers of songs reported have been those of unmated birds. Nice (1943:122) counted 2,305 songs from an unmated Song Sparrow on May 11, and commented that it was the largest number she could find in the literature up to that time. A British author reported 6,140 songs by an unmated European Blackbird on April 5, 1948 (Rollin, 1950:23–27); most mated European Blackbirds sing only a fraction as much.

The record for songs in a day is held by a Red-eyed Vireo, a male newly arrived on the nesting ground but not yet mated, which sang 22,197 times on May 27, 1952 (Lawrence, 1954:111).

Beginning and End of Daily Song

The Kirtland's Warbler starts singing in the morning later than most birds. It never sings in the pale light of early dawn, rarely sings before sunrise, and usually gives its first song a little after sunrise. Meanwhile most of the other birds in the neighborhood have already announced the morning. Once, on June 5, the Brown Thrasher was heard at 4:00; the Mourning Dove, Hermit Thrush, and Rufous-sided Towhee at 4:10; the Blue Jay, Common Crow, Black-capped Chickadee, Robin, Ovenbird, Vesper Sparrow, and Chipping Sparrow at 4:22; the sun rose about 5:00, and the first Kirtland's Warbler sang at 5:16. Another time, on June 26, the following birds sang before the first Kirtland's Warbler, in this order: Robin, Field Sparrow, Rufous-sided Towhee, Vesper Sparrow, Eastern Bluebird, Eastern Kingbird, Clay-colored Sparrow, Mourning Dove, Chipping Sparrow, and Brown Thrasher—and then the Kirtland's Warbler.

In uttering its first song of the day, the warbler may give two or three "warm-up" starts, "chuck-chuck," before bursting into full song.

The last song of the day is usually given half an hour or more before sunset. We have never heard a Kirtland's Warbler sing in the evening twilight, when many nearby birds are singing well, notably the Hermit Thrush.

Singing Behavior

The Kirtland's Warbler's song appears to come forth with an almost explosive force, seeming irresistible as a sneeze, even though the time is inappropriate. The birds sing in the presence of intruders. They sing up to the very entrance of the nest. They sing with bills loaded with food. They sing in the midst of short flights. However, we have never seen any special flight songs or flight display while the Warbler was singing; rather, it has been as though the impulse to sing came in mid-air, and burst forth before the bird could alight.

The birds sing in all parts of their territories. Often they sing as they move about, feeding—at all levels from the topmost branches down to the ground. Often while singing they perch on dead stubs that tower above the small pines of the nesting habitat. I suspect that unmated males sing more often from high perches than do males with mates. Birds may sing in certain places repeatedly, but not with sufficient frequency or predictability to permit one to label these song perches. For example, a photographer would not be able to focus on a certain twig with assurance that a bird would sing from it, as he might do with some other species.

Some people have thought that a disturbance—a gunshot, the slamming of a car door, or a person walking through the territory—causes a male to begin singing. However, as the all-day song records in this section show, the birds sing so frequently, with or without disturbance, that it would be easy to ascribe the cause mistakenly to some circumstance of the moment. For the same reason it is difficult to prove that birds are caused to sing by other songs nearby. There is seldom a prolonged period of silence in a Kirtland's Warbler colony on a June morning.

The songs are given by adult males. No one has heard song from a female or immature male Kirtland's Warbler, although Berger heard a few formless whisper notes from immature captive males at about 38 days of age.

Song and Silent Periods as They Affect Censusing

In making a count of singing males, it is important to know the probability that a male will be singing during the time a visitor is within earshot. On several occasions I have found that independent counts of the same area have agreed very well, differing by not more than one or two birds in a colony of twelve, and have been confirmed by intensive field work in the same area.

This is possible because the Kirtland's Warbler is so persistent a singer. To determine how persistent their singing is, I have attempted to gather precise information on known birds. In each case, notes were taken on a bird for several hours. All these observations were taken before 11 a.m. on days of moderate weather in June. Included are notes on eight males taken on twelve days at various stages of the nesting process. Since the results were similar at different dates, and at different nesting stages, all the records have been combined in the summary (Table 19).

Table 19

Song and Silent Periods of Kirtland's Warbler

Hour (a.m.)	Period (minutes)							
	5		10		15 *		20	
	N	Silent	N	Silent	N	Silent	N	Silent
5–6	34	6	15	1	10	0	7	0
7	102	13	50	3	37	0	24	0
8	108	22	54	6	40	2	27	1
9	91	10	45	3	34	0	22	0
10	80	14	39	4	30	2	18	0
11	65	6	31	2	24	0	13	0
Total	480	71	234	19	175	4	111	1
Periods with song (per cent)	85		92		98		99	

* Includes one extra set of observations collected on 15-minute basis.

For each five-minute unit of time, a bird was recorded as singing or silent. (A unit of five minutes was chosen as appropriate because it was assumed that a walker proceeding deliberately through a colony would remain within hearing distance of each bird for at least five minutes.) If a bird sang even once in a five-minute period, the period was recorded as a singing period. However, because of the bird's tendency to sing in courses of many songs each, it is unlikely to give only a song or two at a time.

In 480 five-minute periods, 85 per cent contained song. There appeared to be no significant difference between the earlier and later hours of the morning as preferred singing periods. Therefore, I have concluded that the probability of song from one bird is 85 per cent in any five-minute period after sunrise, and before 11 a.m., in moderate weather in June. Consequently, a colony of several birds is rarely silent during the usual hours of field work at this season.

I have also analyzed these data as though they had been collected for 10-minute, 15-minute, and 20-minute units of time, with the following conclusions for census takers: in a 10-minute period the probability that a given male will sing is 92 per cent; in a 15-minute period, 98 per cent; and in a 20-minute period, 99 per cent.

It should be understood that there were more silent periods of 10, 15, and 20 minutes than this analysis shows, because some of them fell in such a way as not to include wholly any of the arbitrary units selected; that is, 20 minutes of silence might overlap two 15-minute units, so that neither of these units was silent. Nevertheless, it is of interest that these 40 hours of observation yielded only one silence of 35 minutes for one bird and one silence of 25 minutes for another.

Other Vocalizations

Aside from the singing of the male, the Kirtland's Warbler is a quiet bird. A person may watch a female or nonsinging male for a considerable time and not hear a sound. However, prolonged acquaintance with the bird reveals a number of distinctive notes by which it communicates. Without attempting to report the full repertoire of sounds uttered by the Kirtland's Warbler, I shall describe those of particular interest which I have entered in my records.

Begging by fledglings. "Chi-chi-chi-chi-chi-chi," uttered as rapidly as a human being can say these syllables, is the begging note of fledglings. This is an important field aid to the observer hunting for family groups. It is distinct from the sustained, quavering note of a cowbird fledgling. The notes are probably rapid repetitions of the single "chip" with which the fledgling responds at a distance to the location note of the adult approaching with food.

Location note. "Zeet," high-pitched and sibilant, is the location note. It is much like the notes commonly heard from warblers of many other species when migrating overhead at night or foraging unseen in the treetops during the autumn migration. I believe it is given by a warbler seeking another it does not see—an adult bearing food to a hidden fledgling, a male or female rejoining its mate after an absence, and individuals wandering through the pines in late summer.

Alarm note. "Check," a dry chip much like the alarm notes of other warblers and sparrows, is the alarm note. It is given when an enemy is near the nest or a concealed fledgling. It is sometimes given at a rate of 25 to 35 per minute.

Arousal note. "Churk," a faint, hoarse chip, given by the adult when it approaches sleeping nestlings, is the arousal note. Although it is so low in volume that it would seldom be heard except by a person concealed very near in a blind, it brings the young to instant attention, with open mouths.

Pursuit note. "Tzit-tzit-tzit-tzitt-tzit," as rapidly as a person could utter these syllables, is the sound made during pursuit. It is sometimes given during the pursuit of one male by another in a territory dispute, as they twist and turn in rapid flight through the trees.

Screech of terror. "Bzzrr," is the note given under conditions of extreme alarm. I have heard this sound from females when pushed from the nest or when handled for banding. I have also heard a similar sound from young birds as they leave the nest in fright when touched.

Summary

Singing is performed exclusively by adult males in the breeding season.

The song of the Kirtland's Warbler is loud and clear, and lasts about one second. The quality and pattern suggest most closely the songs of the Northern Waterthrush and the House Wren, although shorter than both, and much shorter than the wren's song. Most of the notes fall between two and four kilocycles, a low pitch for a warbler.

No two individuals sing exactly alike, and a few have strange songs indeed, but fully 80 per cent of all songs in June are of the normal type. However, at times individuals sing "chatter" songs, for no apparent reason, and also "whisper" songs, particularly at territorial boundaries.

Males are singing in migration before they reach the nesting grounds, and they continue to sing until about the time of the postnuptial molt, in July or early August. Most singing takes place in the morning before 11 o'clock, but there is some singing at all hours until about half an hour before sunset. One warbler sang 2,212 times in a day.

The males sing in all locations within the territory, from the ground to high perches, but they do not return with any great regularity to special singing perches.

If the listener is within earshot of the bird for five minutes, the probability of hearing a male is 85 per cent, if the month is June, the hour before 11 o'clock in the morning, and incubation has started.

13

Weights And Plumages

Weights

The Kirtland's Warbler is the largest of the dendroicas. The weights of some adults in breeding season are shown in Table 20.

Table 20

Weights of Adult Kirtland's Warblers
in Breeding Season

| | Weight (grams) | |
	Males (N = 64)	Females (N = 13)
Minimum	12.3	12.4
Maximum	15.2	16.0
Mean	13.7	14.2
Median	13.65	14.2
S.D.	0.6	1.1

Two immature males in postjuvenal molt weighed 15.8 grams and 15.9 grams. An immature female in postjuvenal molt weighed 15.5 grams; a female 45 days old, molt completed, weighed 13.6 grams. These examples showing high weights for immature birds, although few in number, tend to confirm Berger's experience with a captive bird, which reached a weight of more than 16 grams at the start of the postjuvenal molt.

It is probable that Kirtland's Warblers reach peaks in weight at the time of the fall and spring migrations. No bird of this species has been weighed during fall migration, but an adult male on September 1 weighed 15.0 grams, the second largest weight recorded for a male on the nesting ground. Only two individuals have been weighed during spring migration, both near the end of their northward flights, and both among the heaviest on record. These were an adult female, killed by flying into the Perry Monument, Put-in-Bay, Ohio, on May 24, 1954, which weighed 15.6 grams (Milton Trautman, letter); and a male, judged by its plumage to be a first-year bird, netted and released at Point Pelee, Ontario, May 10, 1959, which weighed 15.6 grams (Woodford, 1959:234).

One of Berger's captive Kirtland's Warblers weighed 19.6 grams when it died on October 4, 1959.

To compare the seasonal fluctuations in weights of a closely related species, the Myrtle Warbler, Robert W. Storer and I examined records on specimens of this bird in the Museum of Zoology, University of Michigan. Here ten adult males on the nesting ground had a mean weight of 11.8 grams; thirteen in spring migration, 14.3 grams; and three in fall migration, 14.0 grams. Four adult females on the nesting ground had a mean weight of 12.2 grams; and seven in spring migration, 13.6 grams. Thus this small sample indicates a considerable increase in weight of the Myrtle Warbler during spring and fall migration, when the males may average about 20 per cent heavier than on the nesting grounds.

Large weight gains at migration time have been demonstrated in a number of other songbirds as well. The full extent of this gain in individual birds may not be fully revealed by averages, as Wolfson has pointed out (1954:413–434). Birds in long flight burn fat rapidly and at migration time have the capacity to rebuild it at a surprising rate. Wolfson found that some captive White-crowned Sparrows, with heavy fat deposits removed by starvation, could become fat again in as little time as three days. He found also that male White-throated Sparrows in captivity gained about one-third in weight from their winter minimum to their premigratory maximum. The possible extent of such changes is illustrated by an adult male Bay-breasted Warbler weighing 19.2 grams—perhaps 60 per cent more than its breeding-season weight!—when killed by striking a television tower in fall migration (Tordoff, 1956:14).

Consequently, we should expect that the weight of birds in migration will vary considerably. Some may be very fat; others may be temporarily in a fat-depleted state at an interim point in a series of long flights.

Postnuptial molt

At about the time the males stop singing, the adults begin their postnuptial molt. Van Tyne (in Bent, 1953:421) says the molt may begin as early as July 4 (based on specimens examined in the hand). As early as July 7, a bird silhouetted against the light, preening energetically, appeared to have fine feathers protruding on the back and hind neck. However, these changes are not apparent on most birds in the field until about July 20. At this time many adults become shaggy, especially on the rump, crown, and abdomen. The impression of shagginess comes from a fluffy looseness of the plumage (not lying smoothly), bare spots, gray areas in the yellow breast, and later, brownish feathers intermingled among the gray of the upper parts. Some adults collected by Max M. Peet in the middle of August seemed not to have begun to molt, but by this time most adults are so ragged and patchy that it is difficult to distinguish males from females. During the first week of August many adults are tailless, some are still so in the middle of the month, and some do not begin molting until mid-August. In the case of one male, which had lost its tail earlier when captured for banding, the new rectrices were a little less than half full length on August 5. Judging from the noticeable growth of this bird's tail from one day to the next, and from the rate young birds grow their first tail, I estimated that this stub-tailed appearance of the molting adult would last about ten days. A comment on a specimen taken August 11, 1941, "Tail all new. Wing half-molted," suggests that the remiges may be replaced after the rectrices. By the end of August some adults seem to have completed their molt, while some still show signs of molt, especially on the throat.

During the molting period an adult gives much attention to its plumage. It runs its bill along the base of the primaries, under the wing and tail coverts, and through the feathers of the rump and breast. It seems to eat the feather sheaths. Sometimes a loose feather clings to the bird's head when it withdraws its bill after probing into the plumage. The bird then scratches its head and neck with its claws, reaching up over its wing; at least, this was the sequence of movements in each instance observed.

Prenuptial molt

The prenuptial molt takes place, according to Maynard (1896), "late in February and the new plumage is assumed by March 10." However, Bonhote (1903) described a male taken March 25 "undergoing a thorough moult of the head and throat." Hence, it is probable that the prenuptial molt begins in February and continues into April. Only the body feathers are involved.

Berger's captives began molting about the head (auricular region, forehead, crown, and chin) in the last week in December, and continued molting well into March. Then in May the first-year birds began another molt, and a two-year-old female began losing wing and tail feathers, as in postnuptial molt. It seems likely that some circumstance of captivity had disarranged the normal molting schedule; accordingly, the schedule in wild birds cannot be inferred from these observations.

It has long been suspected that in the nesting season first-year males can be distinguished from older birds by evidences of their first winter plumage, remaining through an incomplete prenuptial molt—by their more mottled appearance above, paler yellow under parts, and particularly by fine spotting across the breast, which in some individuals forms a necklace. In fact, Baird, in describing the type specimen, judged it "not quite matured." Van Tyne (in Bent, 1953:421) commented that the Kirtland's Warbler requires two years to achieve fully adult plumage, noting that this assertion had been made for only one other member of the genus, the Golden-cheeked Warbler.

Harrison B. Tordoff examined 95 specimens of males in breeding season at the University of Michigan Museum of Zoology. Twenty-six appeared not fully mature. The evidences of immaturity consisted of fine black spots on the yellow under parts, paler yellow of breast and abdomen, more brownish and fewer blue-gray feathers on the upper parts, a mixture of new and old feathers, especially on the crown and nape (as though prenuptial molt was incomplete), and retrices noticeably browner and worn. These evidences existed in various degrees, but tended to occur together. It is doubtful whether some of these birds would have been judged immature if seen under normal circumstances in the field. In all instances immaturity was merely inferred, for no Kirtland's Warbler known to be a yearling has ever been collected.

The proportion of presumed yearlings in this sample is 27 per cent, whereas in a stationary population the number of yearlings predicted from the adult mortality rate is 40 per cent. However, the birds collected may not be a random sample. There remains the possibility that some first-year males are indistinguishable from older birds.

It may be difficult or impossible to establish the number of first-year males with field glasses. I have estimated that fewer than 10 per cent of singing males are marked plainly enough, or seen well enough in the course of ordinary field work, to be recorded as immature. In one season of active field work Van Tyne (July 6, 1951) wrote me, "Only one speckle-breasted male was found nesting this year." It is of interest that males on new areas usually appear in the field to be fully adult, although the faithfulness of old birds to their territories suggests that young birds may pioneer new and marginal areas.

Probably first-year males are in full breeding condition. Males with the marks of immaturity have always been found on territory, like other males, and we have never detected a floating population of subadults. We have one instance in which a yearling female was known to nest successfully.

Tordoff was not able to distinguish immature birds from other males and females taken in the fall, and was not able to distinguish first-year birds among breeding-season females.

It is of interest that Sturm (1945) and Hickey (1940), in studying the American Redstart, a species with a highly distinctive immature plumage, found fewer than 10 per cent of males on breeding terri-tory identifiable as first-year birds. The time required to achieve adult plumage seems not to have been studied carefully in many species of warblers. However, the assortment of plumages seen in spring migration among the males of several species—the Myrtle Warbler, for example—suggests that many male wood warblers bear signs of immaturity as they go to their nesting grounds.

Postjuvenal Molt

As noted under "Fledglings," the postjuvenal molt begins at the age of about 26 days and is essentially complete at about 43 days. It involves body feathers but not flight feathers.

Summary

The Kirtland's Warbler is the largest of the dendroicas. The average male and female in breeding season weigh about 14 grams, and in migration probably somewhat more.

The adults begin molting in July or early August, and then ac-quire new flight feathers and body feathers. This process may be completed by the end of August in some individuals.

The prenuptial molt, affecting body feathers only, probably be-gins in February and is still in progress in some birds in April.

Some breeding-season males, almost equaling the number of first-year birds as predicted from the adult mortality rate, show signs of immaturity, but these signs are not always plain enough to be detected in the field. We have not been able to distinguish immature birds from adult males and females in the fall, nor first-year from older females in the breeding season.

The postjuvenal molt, involving body feathers but not flight feathers, begins at about age 26 days and is essentially completed at about age 43 days.

14

The Cowbird

The Cowbird, a New Problem

The Kirtland's Warbler is one of our rarest songbirds. Why? The explanation may be complex and not yet fully understood, but the Brown-headed Cowbird is a major factor. The cowbird builds no nest of its own but removes eggs from other birds' nests and imposes the care of its eggs and young upon these birds, including the Kirtland's Warbler. Therefore, the lives of these two species are so intertwined that a study of the Kirtland's Warbler becomes also in part a study of the cowbird.

Everyone who has seen a few Kirtland's Warblers' nests has expressed alarm over the depredations of the cowbird. Extensive study has not allayed that alarm. From the evidence now available, it seems that this rare warbler is particularly vulnerable; or, seen from the viewpoint of the cowbird, it is the perfect host.

Sentimentalists, of course, are prone to deplore the work of cowbirds whenever they see it. But studies of other species of birds have shown that the cowbird is not for them a serious enemy. With some species, only a few nests are molested; some birds eject the foreign egg or build a new floor over it; some abandon the parasitized nest and start again; some are successful in rearing their own young in spite of cowbirds in the nest; some produce broods, perhaps second or third broods, late in the summer after the cowbird has stopped laying. Some birds, like the Red-eyed Vireo, include in their range areas where the cowbird is scarce, and so partially escape cowbird pressure. In such instances the cowbird is likely to be one of the lesser hazards of nesting, easily overestimated because, of all enemies, it alone leaves a calling card.

The Kirtland's Warbler, however, has not developed any effective defense against the cowbird. The cowbird uses a great many nests of the Kirtland's Warbler, and takes a toll at each point in the nesting process where the production can be measured—in eggs to be incubated, eggs hatched, and nestlings fledged.

If we could assume that these two species had lived together as at present for thousands of years, we might look to the future with optimism, in spite of the evidence in this study. But I believe such optimism is not justified. On the contrary, I believe that the Kirtland's Warbler, always a marginal species, has felt the pressure of the cowbird only within the last eighty years. Here are the circumstances that led me to that conclusion.

In his classic study of the cowbirds, Friedmann (1929:150) stated his belief that the Brown-headed Cowbird originated in the open grasslands west of the Mississippi, which are still the center of abundance of the species. He believed it was "not present" in the virgin forest of the Eastern States.

The Brown-headed Cowbird seems to have been originally a bird of the short-grass plains, where it followed the bison, and earned the name "buffalo bird." It came into the forested part of the continent only when the farmer, with fields and livestock, duplicated the conditions of the Western plains. This circumstance has not been evident because in most areas the settlers came well ahead of the ornithologists. In most areas, as in the nesting range of the Kirtland's Warbler, the cowbird was already well established when the first ornithologists reported on the local birds. However, we have information about the advance of the cowbird in some portions of the North Central forests.

In the first check-list of the birds of Ohio, in 1838, Kirtland (1838:180) wrote, "The cow-bunting is admitted into our catalogue on rather doubtful authority." His statement would seem to indicate that this diligent field student had never seen the bird. Yet, in 1840 the rural population of Ohio had already reached nearly 1½ million people, distributed at average rates of more than six persons to the square mile in nearly all counties (Brown, 1940:6–7). At this same time the rural population in the southern two tiers of counties in Michigan was also more than six persons to the square mile (Bidwell and Falconer, 1925:151). The first check-list of birds for Michigan, based almost entirely on information from the southernmost part of the state, listed the cowbird without comment (Sager, 1839:414). But Charles Fothergill, whose careful notes on birds seen in southern Ontario from 1817 to 1840 are in the Royal Ontario Museum at Toronto, did not record the cowbird in 24 years of field work there. So it would appear that the cowbird began to move into the settled lands of Ohio and Michigan from the southwest just prior to 1840.

Although the cowbird was presumably absent before the settler arrived, there were originally about 1,500 square miles of treeless lands in Ohio, mostly in the northwest part (Utter, 1942:122). This was the tip of the "prairie peninsula," which reached up into southwestern Michigan as well. However, these were moist prairie lands, grown high in summer with towering grasses, and they may have been unsuitable for the cowbird, even though occasional bands of buffalo found their way into them, as into the Eastern forests.

Fifteen years after Kirtland admitted the cowbird, doubtfully, to the list of Ohio birds, Read said that in 1853 "it had recently greatly increased in numbers" (Wheaton, 1882:353). In his private notes in 1864, Kirtland wrote after the listing of the cowbird, "Abundant, formerly rare" (Christy, 1936:88). Thus in 26 years or less the status of the cowbird changed from rare to abundant in Ohio.

As late as 1903 Kumlien and Hollister wrote that, in Wisconsin, "The Cowbird is, without question, increasing steadily in numbers" (Friedmann, 1929:150).

In Michigan, too, it seems probable that the cowbird advanced with the farmer. By 1850 the tide of settlement had not moved appreciably north of the first four tiers of counties. The real rush to the pinelands did not begin until about 1870. The lumberman and farmer arrived together. In fact, on these poor soils the agriculture was often marginal, and the farmer could exist only as long as he had a ready outlet for his products in lumber camps near at hand. Thus, in the 1870's the northward tide of settlement linked the pinelands of Michigan with the short-grass plains of the Southwest, and the habitat of the cowbird became continuous up to the nesting ground of the Kirtland's Warbler.

If the cowbird arrived in this region in the 1870's, it may have built up to abundance in about twenty years, if the experience in Ohio forty years earlier may be taken as a guide. If so, the cowbird may have become numerous by about 1895, and, indeed, Wood and Frothingham (1905:49) found the cowbird common in the Au Sable valley in 1903.

While it is true that the Kirtland's Warbler nested in openings in the forest, which considered alone may have met the short-grass requirement of the cowbird, the habitat of the warbler consisted of temporary fire scars. These were mere islands in the forest, separated by several hundred miles of dense woods from the home of the cowbird in the central grasslands. These islands were a small part of the total pineland area. It is doubtful whether in total area they comprised a sufficient region to maintain a population of cowbirds apart from the main body of the species.

The comparative immunity from the cowbird of nests in the forest is illustrated by the Red-eyed Vireo, *Vireo olivaceus*. In western Pennsylvania, which is largely agricultural, Norris (1947:90) found this species one of the most heavily parasitized of the birds he studied. Similarly, in northern Lower Michigan, a region largely forested, but dotted with clearings, Southern (1958:194) found a remarkably high proportion, 72 per cent, parasitized in 104 nests of the Red-eyed Vireo. Yet, in a forested area of Central Ontario near North Bay, at a latitude only a little greater than Southern's location, Lawrence (1953a:71) found no parasitism in 44 nests of the Red-eyed Vireo, although there were a few cowbirds in the area.

The first nests of the Kirtland's Warbler, found in 1903 and 1904, did not contain cowbirds, but within the next twenty years the finder of the first nest, Norman A. Wood (1926:12), concluded that the cowbird was the worst living enemy of the Kirtland's Warbler. Barrows (1921:116–117) and Leopold (1924:57–58) expressed similar opinions in the same decade.

Sometimes human sympathy for the Kirtland's Warbler has made it difficult to gather accurate information on the subject. Even though the nesting areas are in remote places, visitors come to them to look and photograph. Some of them cannot refrain from helping the warblers by removing cowbird eggs or young. Such interference, known or suspected, has caused the disqualification of several records from this study.

Frequency of Cowbird Parasitism

The most obvious manifestation of cowbird pressure on the Kirtland's Warbler is the large number of nests parasitized. Of 137 complete sets of Kirtland's Warbler eggs, 75 sets (55 per cent) contained one or more cowbird eggs. (I have judged a set complete if it was seen on more than one day without a gain in eggs.) The total number of sets for analysis, with 67 not parasitized, comes to 142, because five sets were known to be complete before being parasitized, thus appearing in both groups.

About half of all parasitized nests contained one cowbird egg; nearly half contained two cowbird eggs; and a few contained three or four. The number of warbler eggs in parasitized nests ranged from zero to six, although no nest held more than seven eggs in total. Hence the number of eggs removed by cowbirds is variable; in some cases none are removed and in other cases several are taken. Details on the contents of parasitized nests are given in Table 21.

Table 21

Nests of Kirtland's Warbler Parasitized by the Cowbird
(Arranged according to Contents)

KW eggs per nest	C eggs per nest				Nests		Eggs		
	1	*2*	*3*	*4*			KW		C per
		Nests (N)			Total	Per cent	(N)	C(N)	nest
0	0	1	2	0	3	4	0	8	2.6
1	1	4	1	0	6	8	6	12	2.0
2	11	7	2	1	21	28	42	35	1.7
3	14	10	3	0	27	36	81	43	1.6
4	8	6	1	0	15	20	60	23	1.5
5	1	1	0	0	2	3	10	3	1.5
6	1	0	0	0	1	1	6	1	1.0
Total nests	36	29	9	1	75				
Percentage	48	39	12	1		100			
Total KW eggs	108	77	18	2			205		
Total C eggs	36	58	27	4				125	1.67
KW eggs per nest	3.0	2.6	2	2			2.73		

NOTE. In this table and subsequent tables C = cowbird; KW = Kirtland's Warbler.

All the nests analyzed held complete sets of eggs—judged complete because seen on at least two days without increase. There was also one record of a nest with four cowbird eggs and one warbler egg, but it was excluded from the analysis because it was seen only once, and therefore did not meet the criterion of a complete set.

So far as comparable information is available on other birds, I can find no other examples of such heavy pressure on a species. Where a study shows heavy rates of parasitism, there are always mitigating circumstances not present with the Kirtland's Warbler. For example, Hicks (1934:385–386), reporting on the cowbird in Ohio, had samples of more than 100 nests each for seven species, and found the highest rate of parasitism, 42 per cent of 146 nests, in the Yellow Warbler. But this species, like the Red-eyed Vireo in Southern's study, for which the rate was 72 per cent, and the Ovenbird in Hann's smaller sample, for which the rate was 52 per cent (1937:202), nests also in other areas where the cowbird is rare or missing. Unlike the Kirtland's Warbler, therefore, these other species do not feel the pressure on their entire populations. High rates of parasitism have also been reported for the Song Sparrow—44 per cent of 223 nests by Nice (1937:159) and 34 per cent of 398 nests by Hicks—and for the Rufous-collared Sparrow, parasitized by the Shiny Cowbird—61 per cent of 93 nests by Sick and Ottow (1958). But unlike the Kirtland's Warbler, both sparrows regularly produce several broods each year, and thus may reasonably expect to produce several young per pair of hosts in spite of cowbird interference.

Cowbird Parasitism by Dates

To determine whether cowbirds made more use of nests early in the season, an analysis was made of 102 nests for which the date of completion of each set of eggs was known, or for which it could be estimated fairly accurately from the hatching date. (See Table 22.) Egg sets were completed as early as May 26 and as late as July 4, a span of 40 days. When this time is divided into four 10-day periods, it is clear that more than four-fifths of the nests were completed in the first two periods; that is, before June 15. (Four-fifths may be higher than the true proportion, because more field work has been done in the early part of the nesting season. However, the

Table 22

Cowbird Parasitism of Kirtland's Warbler Nests by Dates for the Season *

| Clutch complete | Nests | | Kirtland's | Eggs | Total |
	Total	Parasitized		Cowbird	
May 26	2	0	10	0	10
27	0	0	0	0	0
28	2	2	5	5	10
29	1	1	3	1	4
30	4	4	13	5	18
31	6	2	24	5	29
June 1	8	3	34	3	37
2	7	3	30	3	33
3	5	3	23	5	28
4	2	1	8	2	10
May 26–June 4	37	19	150	29	179

Table 22 (Continued)

Clutch complete	Nests		Kirtland's	Eggs Cowbird	Total
	Total	Parasitized			
June 5	5	4	12	7	19
6	5	1	22	2	24
7	7	4	30	5	35
8	4	1	19	1	20
9	7	5	23	10	33
10	2	1	6	1	7
11	6	4	17	6	23
12	2	2	7	3	10
13	5	3	19	3	22
14	4	2	14	3	17
June 5–14	47	27	169	41	210
June 15	1	1	0	3	3
16	1	0	4	0	4
17	5	5	11	7	18
18	1	1	1	2	3
19	1	1	2	2	4
20	1	0	4	0	4
21	0	0	0	0	0
22	0	0	0	0	0
23	4	3	11	6	17
24	0	0	0	0	0
June 15–24	14	11	33	20	53
June 25	2	2	5	5	10
26	0	0	0	0	0
27	0	0	0	0	0
28	1	0	4	0	4
29	1	0	4	0	4
30	1	0	5	0	5
July 1	2	0	8	0	8
2	1	0	3	0	3
3	0	0	0	0	0
4	1	0	4	0	4
June 25–July 4	9	2	33	5	38
Season totals	107	59	385	95	480

* Includes only nests for which date of clutch completion was known.

majority of Kirtland's Warbler nests are certainly started by mid-June.)

Comparison of the four 10-day periods shows no significant variation until near the end of the nesting season, and here the evidence is too scant to be conclusive. (See Table 23.) I have no record of a

Table 23

Cowbird Parasitism of Kirtland's Warbler Nests:
Summary by 10-day Intervals *

| | Interval | | | | |
Nests	May 26–June 4	June 5–14	June 15–24	June 25–July 4	Total
Nests not parasitized	18	20	3	7	48
KW eggs	88	97	12	28	225
KW eggs per nest	4.88	4.85	4.0	4.0	
Nests parasitized	19	27	11	2	59
Total KW eggs	62	72	21	5	160
KW eggs per nest	3.26	2.66	1.91	2.5	
C eggs	29	41	20	5	95
C eggs per nest	1.53	1.52	1.82	2.5	
Percentage of all nests	51	57			58 †
All nests	37	47	14	9	107 †
Total KW and C eggs	179	210	53	38	480
KW and C eggs per nest	4.84	4.47	3.79	4.22	

* Includes only nests for which date of clutch completion was known.

† Since the purpose of this table is to show the time of Kirtland's Warbler and cowbird egg laying, five nests parasitized after the sets were complete are included. These nests are listed twice, first when completed unparasitized, then when parasitized. Thus the number of different nests was 102.

cowbird egg laid in a Kirtland's Warbler nest after June 25, but have only seven nests for which the sets were completed later than this date.

Other evidence suggests that the nesting season for the cowbird completely brackets that of the warbler. In southern Michigan, Berger (1951:33) found cowbird eggs laid from April 21 to July 26. In western Pennsylvania, Norris (1947:87) found that the peak of the cowbird's egg laying occurred about the end of May. Allowing a week or two of difference in nesting season as a result of climate, we judge that the cowbird probably begins laying about May 1 and continues beyond the middle of July in the Kirtland's Warbler region. Thus the cowbird begins laying before the warbler, reaches its peak of egg laying at about the same time as the warbler, and quits laying as the nesting season of the warbler draws to a close.

Thus, since none of the warblers nest outside of the cowbird season, there would appear to be little opportunity for the warbler to develop a more advantageous nesting time through selection.

Variation in Parasitism by Years

Field workers believe that the number of cowbirds in Kirtland's Warbler areas varies from year to year, although no exact counts have been made. Indeed, we should expect the population of any species to fluctuate to some extent, and that the cowbird pressure on Kirtland's Warblers would therefore be higher in some years than in others. Actually, the proportion of parasitized nests on the study areas varied from a statistically significant low point in 1951 (9 out of 33) to a significant high point in 1956 (15 out of 17). However, in general the samples are too small for us to be certain the population of cowbirds varied from year to year in this region. Information on

Table 24

Cowbird Parasitism of Nests of Kirtland's Warbler: Variation
by Years 1944–1957

Year	Total Nests N	Parasitized Nests N	Per cent
1944	6	5	83
1945	8	5	63
1946	13	7	54
1947	13	9	69
1948	19	5	26 *
1949	6	3	50
1950	6	3	50
1951	33	9	27 *
1952	23	8	35
1953	15	6	40
1954	17	3	18 *
1955	15	10	67
1956	17	15	88 *
1957	15	11	73

* Variations not explainable by chance alone (significant at 5 per cent level of confidence).

consecutive years with the greatest number of nests is given in Table 24.

Choice of Nests by Cowbirds

Diligent field work on the parasitic Cuckoo, *Cuculus canorus*, in England led Chance (1940) to believe one strain ("gens") of Cuckoos confined its attentions to one host species, unless no nests of that species were available, and laid a distinctive type of egg resembling the host's. However, some of his findings were inferred rather than observed directly; for example, the individual birds were not usually marked so that they could be identified with certainty.

Do certain cowbirds specialize in Kirtland's Warblers' nests? Having laid in a nest, does a cowbird tend to return to it, or to avoid it, when laying again? We cannot yet answer the first question, but perhaps we can throw some light on the second.

Most attempts to trace the activities of particular cowbirds have been based on the appearance of the eggs. The assumption that similar eggs were laid by the same cowbird and dissimilar eggs by different cowbirds is speculative, and I have not attempted to use it here. Certainly, this assumption would not be true of Kirtland's Warbler eggs, for those in the same nest often look so different from one another that one might think they were laid by different females.

A way of examining the work of cowbirds at large is to compare the distribution of eggs with that expected by chance. For this purpose we use the elements of a Poisson series, which express the probabilities of successive events when the average expectation is known, as in the following formula:

$$e^{-c}\left(1 + c + \frac{c^2}{2!} + \frac{c^3}{3!} + \frac{c^4}{4!} + \cdots\right)$$

where c is the average expectation and e is the base of natural logarithms.

In this instance 137 nests received 125 cowbird eggs. Therefore, the average expectation, c, would be $\frac{125}{137} = .91$ eggs per nest. However, the observed distribution was as follows: 0 cowbird eggs, 62 nests; 1 cowbird egg, 36 nests; 2 cowbird eggs, 29 nests; 3 cowbird eggs, 9 nests; 4 cowbird eggs, 1 nest. Expressing the distribution in percentages of 137 nests, and comparing the chance distribution with the observed distribution, we have the results shown in Table 25.

This comparison indicates that cowbird eggs are deposited almost as would be expected by chance; that is, there is no pronounced tendency to seek out or to avoid certain nests. However, the number of nests with no cowbird eggs is a little greater than expected by pure chance, and we have an explanation for it in the variation of parasitism by years on the study areas. The rate in some years was so low that we may reasonably conclude that there were no cowbirds in the vicinity of some nests, and that accordingly a few nests were not exposed to this hazard.

Now let us turn our attention to those nests we know were exposed to cowbird attention, since they received at least one cowbird

Table 25

Distribution of Cowbird Eggs among All Kirtland's Warbler Nests
$N = 137$

| | | | Percentage of All Nests | |
			Expected by chance	*Found*
C eggs per nest				
0	$e^{-.91}$	=	40	45
1	$.91e^{-.91}$	=	37	26
2	$\dfrac{(.91)^2 e^{-.91}}{2!}$	=	17	21
3	$\dfrac{(.91)^3 e^{-.91}}{3!}$	=	5	7
4	$\dfrac{(.91)^4 e^{-.91}}{4!}$	=	1	1

egg, and analyze the distribution of all cowbird eggs *after the first one*. Since there were 125 cowbird eggs laid in 75 nests, 50 eggs may be regarded as extra eggs after each parasitized nest received one.

The average expectation is $c = \dfrac{50}{75} = .67$ extra eggs per nest.

Here we compare the observed distribution of eggs with the distribution expected if 50 subsequent eggs were laid at random among 75 nests known to be accessible to cowbirds. Now, the observed distribution of extra eggs after the first in each nest is as follows: 0 extra eggs, 36 nests; 1 extra egg, 29 nests; 2 extra eggs, 9 nests; 3 extra eggs, one nest. Expressing this distribution as percentages of 75 parasitized nests, we have the results shown in Table 26.

Here the observed results are very close to those predicted by a chance distribution of all eggs after the first one in each nest. That is, what happens in nature is almost exactly what would be expected if, having used a nest, cowbirds distributed subsequent eggs with the impartiality of a roulette wheel.

Preston (1948:115–116) analyzed five studies of cowbird egg layings and similarly came to the conclusion that something other than chance influences the placing of the first egg in each nest, but that subsequent eggs are laid at random. He suggests that the first egg is placed "deliberately" (to describe the non-chance factor). I suggest

Table 26

Distribution of Cowbird Eggs among Parasitized Kirtland's Warbler Nests: Percentages Expected by Chance and Actually Found (N = 75 Nests)

		Percentage of Parasitized Nests	
C eggs per nest		Chance	Found
1	$e^{-.67}$	51	48
2	$.67e^{-.67}$	34	39
3	$\dfrac{(.67)^2 e^{-.67}}{2!}$	12	12
4	$\dfrac{(.67)^3 e^{-.67}}{3!}$	2	1

rather that, in addition to choice by the cowbird, it must frequently happen that no cowbirds are present at suitable nests as they are starting, and that these nests, not exposed to the hazard, are in effect not in the sample. Thus we might expect more nests to escape cowbird attention than would be predicted alone from the number of eggs to be laid.

Nice (1949:233) concluded from the scant information available that cowbirds lay eggs in "clutches," with perhaps five to eight days between series. This habit might also help explain how some nests escape parasitism.

Cowbird Eggs Laid before Start of Incubation

The timing of cowbird eggs is of interest. Little is known about the subject. The timing may give a clue to what brings the cowbird to ovulation, and it later has a bearing on the survival of warbler nestlings.

The cowbird usually places its eggs in Kirtland's Warblers' nests after the nest is complete, but before incubation has begun. In most cases this means that the cowbird is laying on the same days as the warbler. But sometimes the cowbird lays before the first warbler egg is laid. The opportunity for doing so is greatest when the nesting pace of the warbler is slowed by cold weather. Occasionally a nest is found with a cowbird egg embedded in the lining, presumably laid in the nest before it was complete and later nearly covered as the female proceeded with her building.

Most of our evidence on the day of laying of cowbird eggs is circumstantial; that is, when the nest is found, the cowbird eggs are already present or the young are already hatched, and we infer from their size or from the absence of warbler young that the cowbirds were hatched before the warblers. I have records of more than 50 nests where it was clear that the cowbird eggs were present before the warbler began incubation, but records of only a few for which the exact time of arrival of each cowbird egg was known.

I have records of six parasitized nests with 11 cowbird eggs in which the day of laying was noted for each egg until the set was complete. The timing of these 11 cowbird eggs may be shown by the following series, each number giving the day of arrival of a cowbird egg before the last warbler egg was laid—that is, the last warbler egg was laid on day zero: -7, -5, -4, -3, -3, -2, -2, -1, -1, -1, -0. The first five eggs in this list were laid before the first warbler egg in the nest, although in two of them (-3, -3) the first warbler egg was laid later on the same morning.

Cowbird Eggs Laid after the Start of Incubation

Sometimes the cowbird deposits eggs after incubation has begun. For several reasons these instances are of special interest. It seems probable that the cowbird encounters the incubating warbler at such times and that conflict may occur, although we have not witnessed it. Hann (1937:202) saw a cowbird force an Ovenbird off the nest. Leathers (1956:68) tells of an incubating Robin severely attacking a cowbird that slipped onto the nest in her absence; but the Robin, unlike the two warblers, is larger than the cowbird. Moreover, the cowbird often does severe damage to full clutches of eggs, as will be described later. So cowbird activity is more likely to lead to desertion of the nest when it occurs after rather than before the start of incubation. However, young cowbirds arriving after the warblers in the same nest do not seem to cause any appreciable damage to the warblers.

I have evidence of 15 cowbird eggs laid in 13 nests of Kirtland's Warblers after incubation began. All these nests were found after incubation began; the day each egg was deposited was therefore inferred from its hatching date or the relative sizes of the young when found. These laying dates, expressed in days after the last warbler egg was laid (one day after incubation began), were as follows: 3, 4, 4, 5, 5, 6, 6, 6, 6, 7, 8, 8, 10, 11, 18. The last egg in this list was laid in an empty nest three days after the nest had been abandoned and the remaining eggs had been taken by man. At the time of the abandonment of this nest, a four-day-old cowbird and a warbler egg had vanished.

There is also one published report of a cowbird egg laid in a Kirtland's Warbler nest after the young had hatched. It is not included in the list in the previous paragraph, but the event was so unusual that the circumstances are repeated here. On June 20, 1923, Leopold (1924:53) found a nest with ". . . two fledglings, one very small with eyes closed, the other much larger and with eyes opened. The latter we later ascertained to be a cowbird. After marking the tree, we retired in order not to disturb the family. . . ." The next day he returned to take photographs. "It was necessary to remove two small jack-pines and sundry other small foliage in order to permit the sunlight to enter the nest. We found beside the two nestlings one large speckled egg, probably a cowbird egg."

This is a rare event, but it has been reported also for other host species, namely, Indigo Bunting (Friedmann, 1929:186); Chipping Sparrow and Field Sparrow (Berger, 1951:30–31); Field Sparrow (Walkinshaw, 1949:84); and Red-eyed Vireo (Mumford, 1959: 367).

It would be interesting to know how many cowbird eggs are deposited after the warblers have started incubation. This question may be approached from three directions:

(1) Among the records of complete sets of eggs, we have 75 parasitized sets containing 125 cowbird eggs. Of these, 11 eggs in 9 nests were known to have been laid after incubation had started. However, this proportion (9 per cent of cowbird eggs laid) is certainly low, since some nests were not found until incubation was in

progress, and not all were followed to termination; that is, some of the eggs present when the nest was found may actually have been deposited late, and some others may have been laid after observation ceased.

(2) We can also calculate the proportion of late cowbird eggs by considering the number observed on arrival during incubation in relation to the time these nests were under observation. We have 878 nest-days of observation during incubation (480 in nests without cowbird eggs and 398 in parasitized nests). Eight cowbird eggs were laid during this period of observation, or one late cowbird egg for each 110 nest-days (exclusive of the egg laid late in an empty, abandoned nest).

To go from this figure to the proportion of cowbird eggs arriving late, we must first calculate how many nests would be equivalent to 110 nest-days if each nest ran a normal course to hatching, destruction, or abandonment. Since the loss rate of nests during incubation is .04 per day, the survival rate for 13 days is $(.96)^{13} = .59$. (I have used an average incubation period of 13 days, since half the nests contain cowbird eggs that hatch in 12 days and half contain only warbler eggs that hatch in about 14 days.) Applying these average expectations to a group of 100 nests, we find that 59 will hatch after an average of 13 days each and a total life of 767 nest-days with eggs; 41 will be destroyed or abandoned after an average of 6.37 days each (details of calculation not given here) and a total life of 261 days. Thus, 100 typical nests will exist 1,028 days with eggs, or 10.3 days per nest.

Accordingly, 110 nest-days with eggs, the period expected to produce one late cowbird egg, are equivalent to the exposure of $\frac{110}{10.3} = 10.7$ nests from the start of incubation to hatching, desertion, or abandonment. As shown earlier, 55 per cent of all nests are parasitized, with 1.67 cowbird eggs each; hence $10.7 \times .55 \times 1.67 = 9.83$ cowbird eggs expected in a sample of this size. Thus the amount of exposure expected to produce one late cowbird egg might be expected to produce a total of 9.83 cowbird eggs. Therefore, about 10 per cent of cowbird eggs probably arrive late; that is, after incubation has started.

(3) We may approach this question by considering the number of cowbirds known to have hatched after the warblers in the same nests. There were 8 such cowbirds in 7 nests. But I have records of

49 other nests with 77 cowbirds in which the cowbirds were probably hatched before the warblers. Forty of these were observed to be with warbler eggs when the cowbirds hatched, and nine contained only cowbirds when found. Thus, about 10 per cent of young cowbirds (8 out of 85) observed in the nest were believed to have been later than the warblers in hatching.

Thus three approaches to this question give approximations ranging from 9 to 10 per cent, with the first figure known to be too low. Accordingly, the number of cowbird eggs deposited after incubation has begun in Kirtland's Warbler nests is evidently about 10 per cent of all cowbird eggs laid in the nests.

Cowbird Procedure in Egg Laying

The female cowbird probably finds many nests by watching the female warblers carrying building material. To do so would not be difficult, for the warblers go about their work seemingly oblivious to cowbirds, as long as they stay at a distance. A cowbird nearby could scarcely fail to notice a female warbler as she makes 200 trips to the nest in three or four days, with tell-tale grass in her bill.

Van Tyne placed a mounted female cowbird near three nests at different stages—during incubation, one day after young birds had hatched, and two days after young birds had hatched. All three female warblers ignored the mounted bird, but one male warbler showed mild agitation. Frequently there are cowbirds of both sexes to be seen flying overhead or perched in look-out positions. The warblers give no sign of alarm. However, as will be described later, a cowbird advancing on the ground toward a nest will be opposed. Therefore, it would seem to be the manner rather than the appearance of the cowbird that brings a defense reaction.

Hann (1937:207) has suggested that the cowbird is brought to ovulation by the sight of another bird building its nest. If this is so, it would account for the excellent timing of most cowbird eggs.

However, the cowbird must be exposed to nest building almost continuously in late May and June. There were about 140 pairs of nesting birds of various species per 100 acres (40 hectares) in one part of the jack-pine plains. Many of these birds are possible hosts, and some will build two or three nests within the period (Van Tyne et al., 1942, 1943, 1944). So there should be new nests available within a moderate area on nearly any day.

It is probable that some nests are found by the cowbird long after they are built, particularly those nests receiving cowbird eggs a week or more after nest building has ceased. The cowbird's interest in nests with eggs, without the stimulus of building, has been demonstrated by Johnston (1957:278), who used a transported nest of a Rufous-sided Towhee, containing three eggs of the House Sparrow, to attract cowbirds into a trap.

To lay an egg in the Kirtland's Warbler nest, the cowbird visits it in the dim light about half an hour before sunrise. Usually incubation has not started, the female warbler is absent, and the nest is not defended. Yet the hesitant, alert manner of the cowbird as she approaches the nest suggests that egg laying may not always be free of hazard. She enters the nest roughly and hastily, lays her egg, and departs in less than half a minute. I once found a cowbird egg just outside the lip of the nest. I do not believe it was rejected by the warblers; instead, I suspect that the cowbird, as a result of haste or harassment, failed to get the egg in the nest cavity. In contrast to the haste of the cowbird, the warbler spends half an hour or more on the nest when laying.

I have no record of the laying of more than one cowbird egg in a nest in one day.

Egg Removal by the Cowbird

Evidence of egg removal by the cowbird is largely circumstantial. Such removal has never been observed at the nest of the Kirtland's Warbler, and has been witnessed only a few times at nests of other birds. In general I have assumed that the cowbird is responsible whenever some eggs, but not all, have vanished from a nest in which a cowbird egg has recently been laid, or which soon receives one. But, unless a nest is constantly under observation, the exact sequence of events is often puzzling. Host eggs may be taken so soon after they are laid that we do not see them, even when we make several visits to the nest each day. Or the cowbird may lay an egg and not take any.

Commonly the cowbird appears to return to the nest before 9 a.m. on the same day after laying its egg at dawn. If there are host eggs present, she removes one or more. Other eggs may be damaged at the same time. Sometimes this act takes place on the day before, or, less often, on the day after the cowbird has deposited an egg. I have not enough cases to calculate the proportion of each practice. The cowbird does not remove eggs in the predawn visit when she lays her own egg.

Since no one has seen a cowbird remove a Kirtland's Warbler egg, I assume the method is the same as with other host species reported by other observers, particularly Hann (1941:214, 219), who observed and photographed the act during his study of the Ovenbird, another ground-nesting warbler. Hann says the cowbird approaches the nest nervously, jabs into the nest with her beak several times, and flies away with an egg. By piercing the shell with open beak, she is able to grasp the egg and carry it. The cowbird then flies away a short distance and usually eats the contents of the egg. Sometimes she leaves the shell after eating the albumen and yolk, but not always. Occasionally this act takes place in the afternoon.

Other published examples, along with his own, are summarized by Norris (1944).

The cowbird rarely molests a nest after the young are hatched in it. However, DuBois (1956:286) has reported such a case. He saw a cowbird fly to the ground nest of a Song Sparrow and carry off a young bird. Now and then a nestling Kirtland's Warbler disappears, and it is possible the cowbird is responsible. I have one instance of a female cowbird's approaching three times within less than one meter of a nest containing two young warblers, estimated to be seven days old on the day of the first two visits and nine days old at the time of the third visit. These visits occurred at 9:40 a.m., 11:15 a.m., and 4:56 p.m. The cowbird was repelled each time by the vigorous defense of the adult female warbler.

The cowbird does not simply lay an egg and take one. It may lay several eggs and take none, or lay one egg and take several. But if there is only one egg in the nest, the cowbird does not take it. On the other hand, at a full nest the cowbird causes havoc. Although my cases are too few to prove the generalization, these circumstances suggest that the cowbird's drive may be not merely to remove an egg but rather to reduce a crowded condition in the nest.

I have no instance in which a warbler's egg was taken when it was the only egg in the nest; but only a few nests were found so early and observed so closely that a first egg might not have been laid and taken within a few hours without being seen. The host species also might not be aware of such a loss if the missing egg was replaced by a cowbird egg before the warbler arrived the next morning to lay a second egg. However, the cowbird has no reluctance to remove the last warbler egg if there are cowbird eggs in the nest.

The suggestion that cowbirds may attempt to reduce the eggs in crowded sets to a small number is supported by events when cowbirds enter nests already containing four or five eggs. The analysis shown in Table 27 is illustrative.

In this small group of nests, 24 warbler eggs out of 32 were destroyed as 8 cowbird eggs were being deposited. There was one other nest, 56–2, containing 2 warbler and 2 cowbird eggs when found, in which one cowbird egg revealed at hatching that it had been laid late. Since this clutch was completed about June 9, the

Table 27

Cowbird Damage to Full Kirtland's Warbler Nests (7 Nests)

Nest	Before cowbird visit		After cowbird visit		Interval
	KW eggs	C eggs	KW eggs	C eggs	(days)
46–5	5	0	3	1	1
48–7	5	0	0 *	1	1
49–3	5	0	1	1	1
53–6	3	1	0	2	7
53–7	5	0	3	1	2
54–17	4	0	1	1	2
57–3	5	0	0 †	2	7
Total........32		1	8	9	

* One remaining warbler egg was jabbed open in several places and lost, though almost ready to hatch.

† The nest was abandoned and may have been robbed by a predator, though this appears unlikely.

probable number of warbler eggs lost was three, but not necessarily with the laying of the late cowbird egg.

On the other hand, there were three nests in which hatching results showed that cowbird eggs must have been laid after the warbler sets were complete, and where perhaps no eggs were taken. The contents of these nests when found were as follows:

Nest	Contents
46–8	4 warbler eggs, 1 cowbird egg
46–12	5 warbler eggs, 1 cowbird egg
52–4	5 warbler eggs, 1 cowbird egg

In addition, there was one nest, 46–4, in which a parasitized set (4 warbler eggs, 1 cowbird egg) received another cowbird egg without loss. These examples show that the cowbird may sometimes add its egg to a full set and not remove any eggs. However, it appears that most parasitized nests found with a total of five or more eggs received their cowbird eggs while there were few warbler eggs present.

There is a possibility that in full nests some of the damage may come from accidental trampling as the cowbird walks roughly into the nest to lay. The warblers quickly remove leaking eggs.

Since it is difficult to watch the appearance and disappearance of eggs at any large number of nests sufficiently closely to infer the

Table 28

A Comparison of Parasitized and Unparasitized Nests of the Kirtland's Warbler

| KW eggs per nest | Nests | | | | | Parasitized Nests | | |
| | Not Parasitized | | Parasitized | | | KW and C | N | Total |
	N	Eggs	N	KW eggs	C eggs	eggs per nest		KW and C eggs
0	..	...	3	0	8	0	..	...
1	..	...	6	6	12	1	..	...
2	..	...	21	42	35	2	7	14
3	7	21	27	81	43	3	17	51
4	13	52	15	60	23	4	22	88
5	45	225	2	10	3	5	20	100
6	2	12	1	6	1	6	11	66
						7	3	21
Total	67	310	75	205	125		75	340
Per nest		4.63		2.73	1.67			4.53

Loss in Kirtland's Warbler Eggs

$4.63 - 2.73 = 1.90$ KW eggs per parasitized nest

$\dfrac{1.90}{1.67} = 1.14$ KW eggs per C egg in parasitized nests

$\dfrac{1.90}{4.63} = 41$ per cent of KW eggs laid in parasitized nests

Thus, if 55 per cent of KW nests are parasitized, $.55 \times .41$ or 23 per cent of all KW eggs laid are removed by cowbirds.

losses to cowbirds, I have deduced the losses by comparing the number of warbler eggs in parasitized and unparasitized nests. (See Table 28.)

Brackbill (1958:86), confronted by puzzling shortages in three parasitized nests of the Wood Thrush, *Hylocichla mustelina*, believed the presence of cowbird eggs might inhibit further egg laying by the host. In the Kirtland's Warbler, I attribute similar shortages to egg removal by the cowbird before or between visits of the observer. But in either case the loss to the host is the same.

Cowbird Discrimination between Its Own and Warbler Eggs

Another remarkable aspect of cowbird behavior is its ability to discriminate between its own and Kirtland's Warbler eggs. Though I have no clear evidence of the disappearance of a cowbird egg under circumstances implicating a cowbird, others have reported such instances with other species, and it may occur occasionally in Kirtland's Warbler nests. I have 13 examples where this ability was put to a test; that is, where a cowbird removed an egg from a nest containing both kinds. In these 13 instances the cowbirds were confronted with choices among a total of 23 warbler eggs and 19 cowbird eggs. The cowbirds did not make one mistake. By chance alone the cowbirds would have taken almost as many cowbird eggs as warbler eggs, and the odds against 13 consecutive right choices by chance would be about 3,000 to 1.

Among 75 nests with cowbird eggs, I have only two instances of the disappearance of a cowbird egg without destruction of the entire nest contents, and here there was no reason to suspect a cowbird. One egg was incubated for five days and one for eight days when lost.

Since the question is somewhat controversial and the events are inferred rather than observed directly, I have given in Table 29 the detailed circumstances in which I concluded the cowbird removed only host eggs when its own eggs were present in the nest.

Hann found that Ovenbird eggs present the cowbird with more difficult decisions. The egg of the Ovenbird is much nearer the size of the cowbird's egg, and the cowbird sometimes removed its own eggs from the Ovenbird's nest. The eggs of all three birds are whitish and lightly speckled. The mean dimensions of cowbird eggs (this study, Table 30) are 20.9 by 16.5 mm.; of Ovenbird eggs (Hann, 1937:172), 20.3 by 15.6 mm.; of Kirtland's Warbler eggs (this study), 18.1 by 13.9 mm.

Behavior of the Cowbird in Visits to the Nest

Since there are few eyewitness accounts of cowbirds at the nest—in egg laying or egg removal—the events at two nests watched by Van Tyne and the author are presented in detail.

Table 29

Observations of Laying and Removal of Eggs in Seven
Kirtland's Warbler Nests

Observations	Interpretation
Nest 45–1	
June 4. 1 cowbird egg.	Nest finished but egg laying by warbler delayed by cold weather.
June 5. 1 cowbird egg.	
June 6. 1 cowbird egg.	
June 7. Not visited.	
June 8. 6:40 p.m. 1 cowbird egg, 1 warbler egg.	
June 9. Not visited.	
June 10. 5:40 p.m. 2 cowbird eggs, 1 warbler egg.	
June 11. Not visited.	
June 12. 2 cowbird eggs, 2 warbler eggs.	Warbler presumed to have laid 4 or 5 eggs, beginning June 8, of which 2 or 3 were removed by cowbirds. In each instance the cowbird would have had a choice of cowbird and warbler eggs in the nest.
Nest 45–2	
June 12. 1 cowbird egg, removed by man.	
June 13. Still building.	
June 14. 1 warbler egg laid between 7:50 and 8:18 a.m.	Warbler laid its first egg.
June 15. 2 p.m. 1 warbler egg.	Another warbler egg laid, but one has been removed.
June 16. Early morning. 1 warbler egg, 1 cowbird egg.	At this time of morning the cowbird had laid, but the warbler probably had not.
June 17. Early morning. 2 warbler eggs, 1 cowbird egg.	The new warbler egg probably was laid the previous day.
June 18–23. Not visited.	
June 24. 2 warbler eggs, 2 cowbird eggs.	1 or 2 more warbler eggs were to be expected, but, if laid, were probably removed by cowbirds.
Nest 47–12	
June 20. Cowbird laid egg at 4:33 a.m. Warbler laid egg at 5:35 a.m. Warbler egg gone at 9:25 a.m.	With a choice of warbler egg or cowbird egg, the cowbird took a warbler egg.

Table 29 (Continued)

Observations	*Interpretation*

Nest 47–12 (Continued)

June 21. Second cowbird egg laid at 4:32 a.m. Second warbler egg laid about 5:53. Cowbird approached nest at 6:33 but did not enter; possibly frightened away by blind.

Nest not molested further.

Nest 48–5

June 20. 8 a.m. Nest not lined.

June 21. 7 a.m. 1 cowbird egg, 1 warbler egg (marked for identification) in nest, now completely lined.

June 22. 7:45 a.m. 2 cowbird eggs, a new warbler egg, first having disappeared.

With a choice of warbler egg and cowbird egg, 1 of each if 1 was removed on June 21, the cowbird took a warbler egg.

June 23. 8:45 a.m. 3 cowbird eggs, a new warbler egg, the second having disappeared.

With a choice of 2 cowbird eggs and 1 warbler egg (if the second was removed on June 22), the cowbird took the warbler egg.

June 24. Another warbler egg was laid, and no more eggs were lost.

Nest 52–9

June 20. Afternoon. 2 warbler eggs, 1 cowbird egg.

June 21. 9:30 a.m. 1 warbler egg, 1 cowbird egg.

Since the warbler is still laying, 2 eggs have been removed, with a choice between 1 cowbird egg and 1, 2, or 3 warbler eggs, depending on the time of removal.

June 22. 9:05 a.m. 2 warbler eggs, 1 cowbird egg.

June 23. 9:17 a.m. 1 warbler egg, 1 cowbird egg.

With 1 cowbird egg and 2 warbler eggs in the nest, the cowbird took 1 warbler egg.

Nest 54–5

June 16. 8:45. 3 cowbird eggs (1 removed by man), 1 warbler egg. At 1 p.m. the warbler egg had vanished.

With a choice of 2 cowbird eggs and 1 warbler egg, the cowbird removed the warbler egg.

June 17 and later. No further losses.

Table 29 (Continued)

Observations	Interpretation
Nest 57–6	
June 5. 1 warbler egg.	
June 6. 1 warbler egg.	1 warbler egg removed.
June 7. 2 warbler eggs, 1 cowbird egg.	
June 8. 1 warbler egg, 2 cowbird eggs.	1 or 2 more warbler eggs have been removed, with 1 or 2 cowbird eggs in the nest each time.
June 9. 3 cowbird eggs.	The last warbler egg was taken, with 2 or 3 cowbird eggs present at the time.

Table 30

Dimensions and Weights of Cowbird Eggs *

	Length (mm.) N = 24	Breadth (mm.) N = 24	Weight (grams) N = 20
Range	20.0–23.6	16–17.2	2.45–3.40
Median	20.65	16.4	3.10
Mode	20.6	16.2	....
Mean	20.9	16.5	3.06
S.D.	.859	.357	.253

* Excluding obviously defective eggs.

Nest 47–12. On June 17, 1947, I watched a female warbler putting the finishing touches on her nest. In the afternoon Van Tyne and I placed a blind at the nest, and the next morning Van Tyne entered the blind more than an hour before sunrise. Frost covered the ground, and sunrise came about 5 o'clock. He waited more than two hours without seeing a warbler or a cowbird, although the male Kirtland's Warbler sang a few times nearby.

On June 19 it was a frosty morning again (−3° C.), and Van Tyne was in the blind as before. At 6:45, nearly two hours after sunrise, six or seven cowbirds lighted on the ground about 8 meters away. There was some gurgling and posturing in the group, and a female detached herself and moved toward the nest. She did not come to it directly, but made several short flights to the side and out of the field of vision. Then she lighted less than one meter from the nest and walked toward it in a zigzag course as though unsure of its exact location. She appeared nervous. After looking first at the wrong side of the clump of grass under which the nest was placed, she turned toward the nest and thrust her head through the grass overarching it, not using the proper entrance. She peered in an instant, and then withdrew and flew hastily in the direction in which the flock had just flown. Van Tyne left the blind at 7:10 a.m. without having seen any other birds. (The behavior of this female was that of a cowbird entering a nest to remove eggs, but there were no eggs present.)

Early on June 20 Van Tyne inserted a decoy warbler egg from a deserted nest. At 4:23 a.m. he heard the cluck of a cowbird and a rustle of wings nearby, but the bird flew away. At 4:33 a female cowbird dropped down one meter from the nest and walked up to it without the hesitation of the previous day. She climbed awkwardly over the edge, peered in twice, and entered. She seemed to rotate her body until only her bill could be seen in the faint predawn light. She remained 20 seconds, then emerged and flew away quickly. She had laid an egg.

Twenty minutes later Van Tyne took his decoy egg out of the nest. By this time the cowbird egg was cold. The air temperature was $-3°$ C. At 5:02, 28 minutes after the cowbird's visit, the female warbler settled on the nest. Occasionally she arose and peered into the nest under her. At 5:35 a.m., 33 minutes after entering, she left the nest and moved in a leisurely way up into the trees, feeding as she went. A warbler egg was now in the nest. Van Tyne left at 5:45 a.m. Returning at 9:25, he discovered that the warbler egg laid at 5:30 was gone.

On June 21 he was concealed at the nest again. At 4:32 a.m. a female cowbird came to the nest, walking the last two meters. She approached the nest directly, looked in, hesitated, then entered. Her posture was not visible. In 25 seconds she shouldered out through the grass arching over the nest, not using the entrance, and flew away. Another cowbird egg had been added. Sixteen minutes later a cowbird, sex unknown, passed near, by short flights, but did not approach the nest.

At 5:17 a.m. the female warbler flew to a twig by the nest and entered without hesitation. As before, she sat quietly, except to rise and look into the nest under her two or three times. At 5:53 a.m., 36 minutes after she entered, the female warbler departed, leaving an egg. As she sat on the nest, the male warbler sang nearby, once within three meters of the nest. No warbler egg was removed on this day, but at 6:33 a.m. a female cowbird approached by short flights within 1½ meters of the nest, showing great nervousness, but after a few moments flew away, possibly disturbed by the blind, which was placed less than two meters away. (Is the drive to remove eggs less compelling than the drive to lay, or does the cowbird feel more vulnerable in broad daylight?)

On June 22 the male and female warbler approached the nest together at 5:06 a.m., he within 1½ meters. The female remained 34 minutes. During this time the male sang frequently and fed the female twice on the nest. At 6:03 and 6:08 the male brought food to the nest, but the female was not there. On this day a human visitor removed the two cowbird eggs, leaving the two warbler eggs in the nest.

On June 23 a female cowbird arrived at 4:35. She looked into the nest and flew away as though frightened. In two minutes she returned, this time walking over the top of the nest to the front, and then, after a pause, she entered. In 15 seconds she laid an egg. The light was too dim to be sure, but she seemed to hold herself half standing, with her tail still protruding from the doorway.

The male warbler, singing, brought a green caterpillar to the nest at 4:56, but the female warbler had not yet arrived. At 5:06 the female warbler arrived and snuggled promptly into the nest. At 5:57 she turned completely around in the nest, like an incubating bird. She became increasingly restless, and in 10 more minutes left to feed. Another egg was in the nest, her fourth, although one had been taken by a cowbird. Within 10 minutes she returned to the nest, and remained until 6:33. In 12 minutes she settled on the eggs again, and seemed to have begun incubation. (Did the presence of the incubating female prevent further damage by the cowbird?)

This nest was last visited on June 28. The egg count remained at 3 warbler eggs and 1 cowbird egg. (A final warbler egg may have been laid on June 24 and removed before we visited the nest, but it is not likely, since this was probably a second nesting attempt, and 4 eggs would have been the number expected.)

Nest 45–2. Van Tyne and I watched this pair of Kirtland's Warblers through the nest-building and egg-laying period. On June 8, 1945, the warblers were searching for a site; on June 10 the female began building; on June 12 the nest appeared complete to us, but the female was still bringing some fine grass for the lining.

However, before the warbler's first visit of the day, at 4:48 a.m., a male cowbird alighted on a dead stub nearby. Then a female cowbird, not seen until then, flew toward the nest from a perch below the male. She walked the last two meters, pausing to peer about with outstretched neck; she wandered among the blueberry bushes, as though in a hurry but unsure of the exact location of the nest. Nervously she retreated and flew away. Immediately she turned and walked near the nest again. Once more she flew away and returned. For a few seconds she was out of sight under the vegetation; possibly she was in the nest. Quickly she flew away. At 4:56 the male Kirtland's Warbler sang nearby, and the female warbler went to the nest for a moment. Soon after the female warbler left, a cowbird (presumably a female, although it was too dark to be sure) flew in, walked to the nest, and disappeared. In a few seconds the cowbird reappeared and hastily flew away. Thirty seconds later the female warbler approached the nest an instant and flew away. At 5:13 the female warbler visited the nest for three minutes. At 5:26 we examined the nest for the first time on this day and, to our surprise, found a cowbird egg in it, laid on one of the two occasions, about 4:50 and 4:59, when the cowbird vanished momentarily from our view. We removed the egg. At 6:30 a pair of cowbirds perched on a nearby stub and copulated on a dead branch 15 feet high.

The next day, on June 13, a female cowbird appeared at 7:10 a.m. and gave her rattling call. She walked 2 ½ meters to the nest and entered roughly through the grass arching over the nest at the rear. She paused in the nest, standing high and looking out the entrance. She gave her rattling call, stepped out, and flew away, calling. (There was no egg in the nest.) Twenty minutes later the female warbler appeared and began arranging the nest and adding fine grass. Within the next hour, as the female warbler carried material to the nest, a female cowbird and two males were seen and heard frequently, perched on high stubs within sight of the warbler. She paid no attention to them.

A little later, at 8:51, a female cowbird approached. She gave her rattling call and walked 1 ½ meters to the nest. As she did so, a male cowbird flew close, rattled, started to light on a small tree by the nest, and then moved over to another tree. The female started to enter the nest from the rear, but flew away, as though alarmed. Again at 10:03 a female cowbird walked to the nest and started to enter it from the rear. But she seemed nervous, and walked away.

Meanwhile a male cowbird remained on a high perch nearby, the other male having flown away. (Note that there were three visits from the cowbird at about 7, 9, and 10 o'clock, following a predawn visit the preceding day to lay an egg.)

On June 14, at 5:09 a.m., a female cowbird approached silently, flying from perch to perch. She paused at the nest, looking nervously in all directions. She started to enter, forcing an entrance through the grass over the rear of the nest, hesitated, and flew away, rattling. (If this was an egg-removal visit, it was at an early hour.) Forty minutes later the female warbler appeared, arranged the nest without adding more material, and settled in the nest to lay her first egg.

At 2 p.m. on the following day there was still one warbler egg; that is, one had been added and one removed by a cowbird earlier in the day. Now Van Tyne removed the cowbird egg laid on June 12. On June 16 another cowbird egg was added, but there was still one warbler egg; so one more had been added and another removed. On June 17 another warbler egg appeared. The nest was not visited then for a week, but on June 24 it held 2 warbler eggs and 2 cowbird eggs. Thus, 3 cowbird's eggs were laid and 2 or 3 warbler's eggs had been removed.

Cowbird Influence on Warbler Incubation and Hatching

Parasitized nests are not appreciably more likely than other nests to be destroyed or abandoned during incubation, as shown on page 193. Indeed, except for rare instances of abandonment as a result of removal of several eggs in a short time, we know of no reason why parasitized nests should fare differently from others during incubation. The warbler gives no sign that it regards the cowbird egg as a foreign object.

However, the presence of cowbird eggs tends to reduce the number of warbler eggs that hatch. Presumably this reduction is caused by the larger diameter of the cowbird eggs, which places them in better contact with the incubating female at the expense of the smaller warbler eggs adjacent to them. This reduction in heat to the warbler eggs may be even greater when the young cowbirds hatch and cover the warbler eggs with their bodies. Occasionally a warbler egg is found snugly enclosed in half a cowbird's eggshell after the cowbird has hatched. Whether this ever prevents the warbler from hatching is uncertain. This problem may be more important to the Kirtland's Warbler than to host species in milder climates, for the temperature on these nesting grounds often falls below 7° C. at night.

The view that larger eggs rob the warbler eggs of incubating heat is supported by the fact that the hatching rate in the presence of one cowbird egg seems to be greater than in the presence of two or more. However, the samples are rather small to provide reliable comparisons. In one overcrowded nest of the Ovenbird, containing four host and four cowbird eggs, Hann (1947:173) reported that only two cowbirds hatched, and then after an incubation period at least two days longer than normal.

It would be interesting to know also at what stage the development of the embryo usually stops, but I have not enough evidence to determine this point. The few overdue unhatched eggs I have examined ranged from almost complete development to none.

To isolate "hatching success" from earlier and later stages of nesting, the numbers of young birds hatched, as a percentage of eggs present at hatching time, are given. However, for warblers in the presence of cowbirds, this course has difficulties. Unless the nest is watched continuously, it is not always possible to be sure how many birds have been hatched in parasitized nests. The life of a newly hatched warbler, when unfed and trampled beneath one or more cowbirds, may be only a few hours. When a nestling dies, the parents promptly remove the body. The newly hatched warbler is feeble and weighs only about 1.3 grams, while the two-day-old cowbird in the same nest is vigorous and weighs about 10 grams. As a result, spaced visits to a parasitized nest at hatching time do not tell the full story. For example, on one morning the nest may contain two cowbirds, two days old, and two warbler eggs; the next morning it may contain two cowbirds and no warbler eggs. What has happened? I believe the most probable explanation is that two warblers have hatched and died. It is also possible that exceptionally fragile eggs have been broken by the young birds, but I have not seen this occur, and eggs often remain unbroken for many days under much larger young. Therefore I have assumed that warbler eggs, if they disappeared at hatching time, had hatched.

For comparative purposes hatching rates for both warblers in nests without cowbird eggs and for cowbird eggs are given in Table 31. The cowbird eggs that did not hatch were all present at least five days after the normal hatching date, except for one that vanished two days after the first cowbird hatched in the nest.

Table 31

Hatching of Kirtland's Warblers and Cowbirds

	Nests	Eggs present at hatching time	Number Young birds seen	Young believed hatched	Percentage of eggs hatched
KWs in nests with 2 or 3 C eggs	13	33	20	23	69
KWs in nests with 1 C egg	17	55	34	43	78
Total KWs in nests with C eggs	30	88	54	66	75
KWs in nests without C eggs	39	182	148	155	85
Cowbirds	35	57	50	50	88

Nestling Survival in the Presence of Cowbirds

I have no record of a nestling warbler more than four days old in a nest in which two or more cowbirds hatched ahead of the warblers. Consequently, fledging success of warblers in parasitized nests is reduced to a consideration merely of nests containing one cowbird and of nests in which the cowbirds were hatched late.

Nine nests, in which one cowbird, hatched ahead of the warblers, was present, were observed from eggs to fledging. Of 21 warblers hatched in these nests, 10 were fledged. Though regrettably small, this sample suggests that about 50 per cent of warblers hatched in the presence of one cowbird survive to fledging. Without cowbirds, and aside from nests destroyed or abandoned during the nestling period, this rate for Kirtland's Warblers is 92 per cent.

I have no record of the fledging of more than two warblers from a nest with one cowbird older than the warblers. However, I have one record of four warblers surviving five days in the presence of an older cowbird; the nest was then destroyed by a predator.

The first day is the crucial time for young warblers in a nest with a cowbird. Usually the cowbird is two days old when the warbler is hatched. At this time the cowbird usually weighs about 10 grams, but sometimes the cowbird is three days older than the warbler. In one such nest two cowbirds weighed respectively 12.70 and 12.47 grams, and in another, 13.00 grams, on the day when warblers were hatching; that is, virtually the weight of adult warblers. So it is not surprising that among 25 warblers hatched in the presence of one cowbird, only 14 lived to be two days old. But older nestlings are not always safe; they have been known to die as late as age seven and nine days in a nest with one cowbird.

The cause of death in these instances may be trampling as well as starvation. It is difficult for newly hatched young birds to lift their heads for food when pressed down under cowbirds six to eight times as large as themselves.

Berger, observing a three-day-old warbler in a nest with two cowbirds, noted that, though lively, it seemed not to have grown. The next day it was dead. On one occasion I found a cowbird ready to leave the nest; under it was a young warbler, breathing but unable to lift its head. As I examined the warbler, the cowbird left. The next day the nest was empty, and I suspected that the young warbler had died and had been removed.

However, I believe young warblers are not adversely affected by cowbirds hatched two or more days after the warblers. I have seen nests with three and four young warblers flourishing in the presence of a cowbird that hatched after the warblers. So the head start seems to be the key to nestling survival.

To calculate the total effect of cowbird nestlings on the survival of young warblers in the nests with them, let us assume 100 parasitized nests holding 273 warbler eggs at hatching time.

Let us look first at those nests with two or more cowbird eggs each. There will be 52 such nests (Table 21, the sum of the nests with 2, 3, or 4 cowbird eggs is 52 per cent of the parasitized sample), containing $\frac{97}{205} = 47+$ per cent of the warbler eggs, numbering 129; of these (Table 31), 69 per cent = 89 warbler eggs, will hatch, with 1.71 young warblers per nest in which two or more cowbird eggs were laid. But the deleterious effect of the cowbirds on warbler survival does not occur unless the cowbirds hatch, and hatch first; and we know that about 12 per cent of cowbird eggs fail to hatch, and another 10 per cent are laid after incubation has started. There was a total of 89 cowbird eggs in nests with two or more each, but 22 per cent = 20 cowbird eggs, must be excluded from our calculations for this subset of 52 nests. But these eggs will not all occur in different nests. They will have an average expectancy of $\frac{20}{52} = .38$, and will be distributed randomly (according to the Poisson series) as follows:

Multiple cowbird nests with no late or unhatched cowbird
   eggs, $e^{-.88} = .68$ of the set, or 35.

Multiple cowbird nests with one late or unhatched egg,
   $.38e^{-.88} = .26$ of the set, or 13.

   (Since three-fourths of the parasitized nests with more than
   one cowbird egg have 2 cowbird eggs each, we could assume
   that 10 of these eggs occurred in two-cowbird-egg nests and
   3 in three-cowbird-egg nests.)

Multiple cowbird nests with two or more late or unhatched
   cowbird eggs each = 5.

   (Four of these would probably occur in two-cowbird-egg
   nests and one in a three-cowbird-egg nest.)

So 18 nests containing 20 late or unhatched cowbird eggs are reclas-
sified as follows: 10 two-cowbird-egg nests and 1 three-cowbird-egg
nest become 11 one-cowbird-egg nests (to be treated later); 3 three-
cowbird-egg nests become two-cowbird-egg nests, to be added to
the 35 above in which all cowbird eggs hatched; and 4 two-cowbird-
egg nests may be treated as though they contained no cowbirds.

   Then, from 52 nests with two or three cowbird eggs each, we
have 38 nests with two cowbirds each hatching ahead of the warblers
in the same nests. With 1.71 young warblers hatched per nest, there
were 65 warbler nestlings in this set, *none* of which are fledged in the
presence of two or more cowbirds.

   Now, let us consider the nests in our hypothetical set with one
cowbird egg each. There were 48 such nests with 144 warbler eggs,
since the nests with multiple cowbird eggs held 129 of the 273 total
warbler eggs. Seventy-eight per cent hatch 114 young, 2.33 young
per nest. But in 11 (22 per cent) the cowbird nestlings will have no
effect because the eggs were late or unhatched. So we have 37 nests
with 2.33 young warblers each, or 86 young warblers. But 11
other nests which had two or more cowbird eggs each become in effect one-cowbird nests through late arrival or failure to hatch; these
nests have 1.71 young warblers each, or 19 young warblers. So 105
young warblers are subjected in the nest to the pressure of one cowbird larger than themselves. Of these, 50 per cent, or 53, are fledged
in the presence of one cowbird.

   Finally, we have some nests that received one or more cowbird
eggs, but that may be treated as though they contained no cowbird
young, since the cowbird eggs were late or did not hatch. Eleven of
these with one cowbird egg contained 2.33 young warblers each, or

26 young warblers. Four, with two cowbird eggs each, contained 1.71 young warblers each, or 7 young warblers. So 33 warbler young were not affected adversely by cowbirds. Of these, 30 were fledged.

Consequently, in this hypothetical sample of 100 parasitized nests not destroyed or deserted, of $89 + 112 = 201$ warblers hatched, $53 + 30 = 83$ (41 per cent) were fledged. Conversely, the mortality among nestlings in parasitized nests was 59 per cent of warblers hatched. But of 201 eggs hatched, 8 per cent would be lost from hatching to fledging as a result of other causes of in-nest mortality; so only 185 eggs should be considered in calculating losses attributed to cowbird nestlings alone. Hence, survival of nestlings in the face of cowbirds, neglecting other hazards of the nestling period, is $\frac{83}{185}$ or 45 per cent of nestlings hatched; and conversely, mortality of warbler nestlings attributed to cowbird nestlings alone is about 55 per cent in nests that are not destroyed or deserted.

Recapitulation of Warbler Losses Caused by the Cowbird

The pressure exerted by the cowbird at different stages in the nesting process is shown in Table 32.

Table 32

Warbler Losses Caused by the Cowbird in Parasitized Nests: Summary

	Losses as percentage of eggs laid	Remainder as percentage of eggs laid
41 per cent of warbler eggs removed by cowbird	41	59
10 per cent of warbler eggs present at hatching time fail to hatch as a result of cowbird eggs present (excess over hatching failures in nests not parasitized)	6	53
59 per cent of warblers hatched are not fledged as a result of cowbird nestlings present (excess over nestling loss in nests not parasitized)	31	22
Total	78	

Thus, as a direct result of the cowbird, 78 per cent of warbler eggs in parasitized nests fail to produce fledglings. Since 55 per cent of all

Kirtland's Warbler nests are parasitized, the cowbird causes the loss of about 43 per cent of all Kirtland's Warbler eggs between laying and fledging, in nests not destroyed or abandoned.

However, these figures are somewhat misleading, because they ignore the fact that many warbler eggs and young would have been lost anyway through other causes, particularly the destruction and desertion of nests. By suppressing one cause we inflate others, as by conquering diphtheria among children we increase the death rate from heart disease among older people. Therefore, we must not suppose that eliminating the cowbird would bring to fledging all the young whose loss is statistically attributable to cowbirds.

To show more accurately how much the warbler suffers from the cowbird—and how much better it succeeds without the cowbird—we compare the production of parasitized and unparasitized nests.

The average Kirtland's nest receives 4.63 warbler eggs. Without interference from cowbirds the probability that eggs will produce fledglings is .32, and the probable number of fledglings is 1.48 per nest. On the other hand, in parasitized nests the probability that eggs will produce fledglings is .07, and the probable number of fledglings is .32 per nest. Or, expressing these same relationships another way, eggs laid in nests without cowbird interference are more than four times as likely to produce fledglings as are eggs laid in parasitized nests.

Finally, we may consider how much the production of Kirtland's Warbler nests would be improved if there were no cowbird interference. For this question, we compare the present situation (55 per cent of nests parasitized) with the production of unparasitized nests. The probability that eggs will produce fledglings under present cowbird pressure (p. 201) is .19, as compared with .32 in nests not parasitized. Therefore, the probability would be increased about 60 per cent if there were no cowbird interference.

Incubation Period for Cowbird Eggs

The incubation period for cowbird eggs in Kirtland's Warbler nests is in no case known to the hour; that is, from the start of incubation to the hour of hatching. In view of uncertainties about the time incubation begins, exact measurement is possible only for those few cowbird eggs laid after incubation is in progress. Therefore, the incubation period is here expressed to the nearest day. In one case I have inferred a period of 12 days; in four other cases, a period of at least 12 days, and possibly 13. I believe 12 days to be the usual incubation period of cowbirds in Kirtland's Warblers' nests, with some eggs perhaps hatching in 11 days, and a smaller number in 13.

This period is consistent with the fact that cowbirds most often hatch two days ahead of Kirtland's Warblers, whose incubation period is about 14 days. Among 19 parasitized nests for which the time of hatching of cowbirds and warblers could be determined to the nearest day:

> 2 nests produced cowbirds 1 day ahead of the first warbler, but both produced other warblers a day later.
> 11 nests produced cowbirds 2 days ahead of the first warbler.
> 6 nests produced cowbirds 3 days ahead of the first warbler.

In the nest of the Ovenbird, whose incubation period averages 12.2 days, Hann (1937:204) reported the incubation period of the cowbird to average 11.6 days. Norris (1947:102) reported a similar incubation period for cowbirds, with a range of 11 to 13 days, in the nests of several host species. In the same climatic region as the Kirtland's Warbler, Southern (1958:199) found 12 days to be the usual incubation period of cowbird eggs in nests of the Red-eyed Vireo.

I believe that the hatching of cowbird eggs most commonly occurs in the morning. However, a number of newly hatched birds are found on early morning visits to the nest, and some of them may have hatched in the night. Some have been known to hatch in the afternoon. It would be misleading to calculate the proportions of each from my data, because the findings reflect in part the routines used in nest visits.

Development of Cowbird Nestlings

Our few data on the weights of cowbird nestlings are consistent with more extensive information gathered by others. The weights of three young cowbirds in the nests of Kirtland's Warblers were as follows: later in day of hatching, 3.09, 3.16, and 3.55 grams; one day after hatching, 4.42, 5.55, and 6.20 grams; three days after hatching, 12.47, 12.70, and 13.00 grams.

Others (Friedmann, 1929:266; Nice, 1937:223; Hann, 1937:228–229; Norris, 1947:95–100) have found that the weights of cowbirds in the nests of various species were as follows: newly hatched, about 2.5 grams; at 2 days of age, 8–10 grams; and at fledging (8 or 9 days), about 30–33 grams, or more than twice the weight of adult warblers.

In those few examples available in which cowbirds hatched after the warblers, the cowbirds did not seem to suffer. I have one instance in which a cowbird was hatched in a nest with four warblers about five days old; the cowbird weighed 3.55 grams when the warblers weighed from 8.80 to 10.40 grams each. But the cowbird flourished.

Fledging of Cowbirds

I have five instances of cowbirds' leaving the nest at 9 days of age; three instances, at 8 days; and one instance, at 10 days. Thus the nestling period of the cowbird is about the same as that of the Kirtland's Warbler, which is 8 to 11 days, and most often 9 days. So if the cowbirds hatch first, as they usually do, cowbirds in a nest with warblers leave about two days earlier than the warblers.

Cowbird Success from Laying to Fledging

We calculate the total success of cowbird eggs by combining what we know about their success at each stage. Since Kirtland's Warbler nests during incubation have a loss rate of .04 per day, and the losses of individual cowbird eggs, without the loss of nests, are negligible, the probability that cowbird eggs will survive twelve days to hatching is $.96^{12} = .61$. The probability that cowbird eggs present at hatching time will hatch is .88. The probability that nests with young birds will survive nine days to fledging, with a nest-loss rate of .03 per day, the loss of individual nestlings being negligible, is $.97^{9} = .76$. Combining these probabilities, we have $.61 \times .88 \times .76 = .41$, the probability that cowbird eggs laid in Kirtland's Warbler nests will produce fledglings.

Behavior of Cowbird Fledglings

Fledglings out of the nest are usually located by ear. When small, they stay in concealment and move about very little. The begging notes of the young cowbird are easily distinguishable from those of young warblers. The cowbird gives a sustained quavering or vibrating note, while the young warbler begs with a rapid series of chips.

As they get older, the cowbirds are wilder than the warblers. They flush at a greater distance and fly farther when flushed. Sometimes, for no apparent reason, cowbirds three or four weeks old fly up above the pines and travel 100 or 200 meters in high, rapid, curving flight before dropping back into the foliage. Sometimes the fledglings beg for food on high dead stubs—the kind of perch that would be used by adult cowbirds. At such times the adult warblers often approach with food, chipping, but seemingly reluctant to leave the concealment of the pines below. The cowbird, which seems to seek wide open spaces as it approaches independence, thus behaves quite differently from the warbler, which seems to prefer at nearly all times to dart through the branches.

As the cowbirds become better fliers, they become noisier and more insistent in their begging; they often follow adult warblers closely even when the adults are not carrying food. I have seen a cowbird still being fed on July 23, at the age of 29 days, and also a cowbird of unknown age being fed by a Kirtland's Warbler as late as August 15.

In one instance of behavior that I interpreted as the beginning of the gregarious tendencies manifested by adult cowbirds, I saw a banded cowbird 25 days old flying about with an unbanded cowbird several days older, without begging. On the same date, July 22, flocks of 10 to 20 adult cowbirds were still to be seen in the vicinity; but when I returned, on August 3, I saw no more adult cowbirds in the Kirtland's Warbler area, although young cowbirds were still present.

Summary

The Brown-headed Cowbird, a major depressing factor on the population of Kirtland's Warblers, was originally a bird of the short-grass prairies. It probably reached the range of the Kirtland's Warbler in the 1870's, and became numerous there in the 1890's.

About 55 per cent of Kirtland's Warbler nests are parasitized by the cowbird. One to four cowbird eggs are laid in each parasitized nest, and the distribution of all eggs after the first is random. Some nests escape parasitism presumably because there is no cowbird at hand when the nest is started. Cowbirds start laying earlier in the season than warblers and continue laying as long as the warblers. Ninety per cent of cowbird eggs are laid before the host begins incubating.

The female cowbird probably finds most nests by watching the warblers build them. Then she goes to the nest about half an hour before sunrise, and in a few seconds lays an egg. Later in the day, or sometimes on the preceding or following day, she returns to remove eggs. She shows ability to discriminate between her own and Kirtland's Warbler eggs, for she takes only warbler eggs, though never the sole egg in a nest. If the nest has several eggs she is likely to destroy more than one.

In parasitized nests, the average number of cowbird eggs was 1.67, with 1.89 fewer warbler eggs in these nests than in unmolested nests. Hence, 1.13 warbler eggs were removed for each cowbird egg laid. The loss of warbler eggs in parasitized nests was 41 per cent of the eggs laid; the loss in all nests, 55 per cent of them parasitized, was 23 per cent of warbler eggs laid—these losses from egg removal alone.

The cowbird takes a heavy toll at every step of the nesting process. The probability that eggs present at hatching time will hatch is 85 per cent among warbler eggs alone, but 75 per cent with cowbird eggs present; the rate is lower in nests with several cowbird eggs than in nests with only one. The presence of young cowbirds in the nest reduces by .55 the probability that warblers will be fledged. The presence of two or more cowbirds hatched ahead of the warblers is lethal to the warbler nestlings.

Comparing the present situation, with 55 per cent of the nests parasitized, with the success of eggs in nests not molested by cowbirds, we conclude that Kirtland's Warblers would produce 60 per cent more fledglings if there were no cowbird interference.

The fact that the cowbird, with an incubation period of about 12 days, usually hatches two days or more ahead of the Kirtland's Warblers, puts the warblers at a crucial disadvantage. When the cowbird eggs are laid and hatched after the warblers, the warblers do not suffer. Cowbird nestlings two or three days old weigh 8 to 13 grams each when the warblers, weighing about 1.3 grams, are hatched.

Cowbirds, like Kirtland's Warblers, commonly fledge at nine days, and sometimes a day earlier or later. The probability that cowbird eggs laid in Kirtland's Warbler nests will produce fledglings is .41.

Cowbird fledglings may be fed by adult Kirtland's Warblers until at least 29 days old, and as late in the season as August 15.

15

Reproduction and Mortality

Losses in the Nest

Losses in the nest may be classified as follows:
1. Removal of individual eggs by cowbird (treated in another section).
2. Nest destruction, usually by predators.
3. Nest desertion.
4. Failure of eggs to hatch.
5. Disappearance of individual eggs from a continuing nest.
6. Disappearance of individual nestlings from a continuing nest.

Predators

Two-thirds of all Kirtland's Warblers' nests lost are believed to be destroyed by predators. My records show 38 out of 57 nests lost in this way.

It may be significant that the predators which appear to be most important—Blue Jay, Common Crow, Red Squirrel, and Thirteen-lined Ground Squirrel—are a threat only to the nest contents, and not to the adults or flying young, both of which seem to have a remarkably high survival rate on the nesting ground.

Whenever the entire contents of a nest have disappeared, I have attributed the loss to a predator. However, no one has ever seen the destruction of a Kirtland's Warbler or its nest under natural conditions, and the circumstantial evidence has never been sufficient to identify the predator with certainty.

Occasionally a nest may be destroyed also by other agencies—for example, the hoof of a deer or a falling limb—but we have never witnessed the destruction of a nest from these causes. However, I have one record of the loss of all but one nestling in a clutch when a heavy rain occurred at hatching time.

Our only case of predation in which the agent was known occurred under other than natural circumstances. On May 21, 1933, Van Tyne, experimenting with a trammel net to capture birds for banding, found in the net a male Kirtland's Warbler killed by a male

Sharp-shinned Hawk, which also was entangled in the net. Yet in 1945 a pair of these hawks nested in a tree overlooking a colony of Kirtland's Warblers we were studying, and no losses of warbler adults or young were attributed to them.

In several instances, circumstantial evidence has seemed to implicate bird predators, as illustrated by the following observations.

Dale Zimmerman saw a male Marsh Hawk pursue a Kirtland's Warbler briefly on July 6, 1951. Zimmerman had been watching a male warbler which was carrying food to a young bird out of the nest. Suddenly his attention was drawn to an unusual sound from the warbler, a series of rapid, high-pitched, but not loud, notes. Then the warbler flew off over the tops of the low pines, and a Marsh Hawk appeared perhaps five meters behind the warbler. Zimmerman yelled and waved, and the hawk shot upward, circled once, and flew out of sight. The warbler dropped down into the trees.

On June 19, 1951, Douglas Middleton visited a nest which had held five young birds at least five days old. When he arrived at 10 a.m., the nestlings were strewn about within 50 centimeters of the nest. Two were dead and bore head wounds, as though pecked. Three were living, and these he warmed in his hands and replaced in the nest. Both parents were scolding nearby. On the following day the three young birds were dead in the nest. Two days later a Common Crow was seen near the nest.

Mary Jane Williams, returning on July 30, 1946 to a Kirtland's Warbler nest she had found a week before, found a Great Horned Owl in the vicinity. The nest, which had contained young birds, was empty, and an owl pellet lay seven centimeters from the nest. The pellet contained bones of four shrews, some bird bones, and the skull of a warbler, species unknown.

In more than a dozen instances in this study, eggs or young have vanished, perhaps as a result of predation, without the loss of the entire nest. Possibly such eggs were removed by cowbirds that did not return to lay, or were broken accidentally and removed by the warblers themselves; such nestlings may have died in the nest and may have been removed by the adults. But some instances were especially puzzling. For example, on three occasions an egg was moved three to six inches away from the nest. In another, a three-day-old nestling was found dead two feet from the nest. And in another instance a nestling vanished on the third day after hatching, a second nestling disappeared on the fourth day, and the last two nestlings with an unhatched cowbird egg were gone on the fifth day. Hann (1937:199) attributed a similar piecemeal destruction of an Ovenbird's nest to a Red Squirrel.

The behavior of adult warblers has given us few clues to the enemies of the Kirtland's Warbler. As noted elsewhere in this study, the nesting female acts aggressively toward any small bird or mammal that approaches the nest, "freezes" when a large bird or animal is at a distance, and flees, attacks, or gives distraction display when a large creature is very near the nest, or near fledglings still under parental care.

Frequently the contents of nests were removed without damage to the nest structure. Such removal has occurred even in nests with delicate tunnel entrances. Usually the contents were removed completely, but twice a pierced egg was left; once, shell fragments were left; and once a breast feather of an adult warbler remained. In those instances where the nest was not damaged, it seems probable that a bird was responsible for removing the contents, since even a small mammal would be likely to tear the nest lining with its claws. On the other hand, a number of destroyed nests were disarranged or pulled from their positions; since the details were not always recorded, the extent of the damage and the nature of the predator cannot be stated.

In general, I believe most predation on Kirtland's Warblers and their nests is done by birds. I suspect that Blue Jays and Crows, after the cowbird, are the most frequent invaders of nests. It is possible that the cowbird, in addition to its regular practice of removing eggs, may occasionally remove nestlings. It is also possible that House Wrens, which nest in some Kirtland's Warbler areas, may pierce eggs in the nest, as it has been reported to do with the eggs of other species.

The larger birds of prey are not common in Kirtland's Warbler areas. The hawk most often seen is the Marsh Hawk; next, the Sharp-shinned Hawk. The Cooper's Hawk and Great Horned Owl are rare in this habitat.

Reptiles are probably not an appreciable threat. The only reptile I have seen in the vicinity of Kirtland's Warbler nests is the Smooth Green Snake, *Opheodrys vernalis,* and the ones I have seen appeared too small to eat an egg or nestling. In the same general region there are garter snakes, *Thamnophis* (sp.) and Eastern Hognose Snakes, *Heterodon platyrhinos,* but I have never seen them in the situations where the Kirtland's Warblers nest.

The mammals that I suspect to be the most serious predators on the eggs and young of the Kirtland's Warbler are the Red Squirrel, *Tamiasiurus hudsonicus*, and the Thirteen-lined Ground Squirrel, *Citellus tridecemlineatus*. Both are found in nearly every Kirtland's Warbler area. Other mammal predators in the region, none of them numerous, include the Striped Skunk, *Mephitis mephitis;* Weasel, *Mustela* (sp.); and Red Fox, *Vulpes fulva*.

Invertebrate Enemies

Ants are numerous about the nests of Kirtland's Warblers and cause discomfort among nestlings, as noted in an earlier section, but probably are not a danger while adults are in attendance. The adults are diligent in removing ants from the nest and young. However, nestlings in a deserted nest are soon eaten by ants.

Ectoparasites are seldom seen on Kirtland's Warblers. Van Tyne found mallophaga only once. No other invertebrate parasites have been found on the bodies or nests of this species.

Causes of Nest Desertion

One-third of all losses of nests are caused by the female's deserting them; in my records, 19 of 57 nest losses are thus accounted for.

When a female warbler abandons a nest with eggs or young, I believe one of the following factors is likely to be the cause:

Disturbance by another creature. Some female warblers seem much more persistent than others. When building, some will drop nesting material at the approach of a man and not resume in his presence; others will ignore him if he remains at a distance. I doubt whether the female Kirtland's Warbler ever deserts a completed set of eggs merely as a result of a person's flushing her from the nest and making a brief examination of the contents; however, some females will desert if the disturbance is prolonged or if the nest surroundings are disarranged, as by a photographer. Coulson (1958:135), in a study of a large number of nests of the Meadow Pipit in England, found no relation between nest mortality and the number of visits by observers. Other disturbances which may cause desertion of the nest are readily conjectured. Thus a nest location might prove intolerable if too near a mammal runway, if a deer were to bed down by a nest for hours, or if a predator were to remain near the nest for a long time.

Flooding. I have records of four nests in which eggs were standing in water several hours after a rain, and these nests were not used further. In view of the porous, sandy soil of the habitat, flooding probably occurs only through a combination of extremely heavy rain and unfortunate nest location.

Death of the female warbler. Sometimes we do not find the female warbler again after the loss of a nest. The females are often difficult to find even when nesting again in the same territory; they are nearly impossible to find if they leave the territory. These circumstances, along with the facts that we have never lost a banded male during the nesting period, and that the annual survival rate of females is about the same as that of males, make us slow to assume the destruction of an adult female, although it undoubtedly occurs at times. The brooding or incubating female may be more vulnerable than the male, especially at night, but, on or off the nest, she is much less conspicuous than the male, and this quality may offset any disadvantage to her when on the nest.

Removal of eggs by cowbird. The Kirtland's Warbler does not often desert as a result of egg removal by cowbirds, but occasionally she does so. In one nest three of four eggs were removed as they were laid, and were replaced by only one cowbird egg, but the female warbler continued with the nest. On the other hand, one nest was deserted after a full clutch of five warbler eggs was replaced by two cowbird eggs. In another instance a nest under incubation was deserted when an unknown agent reduced the clutch from four to two eggs. Since these females were incubating, there may have been much disturbance and even conflict as the cowbird came to lay and came again to remove eggs.

The limit of one incubating warbler's tolerance for egg removal was put to a test by Van Tyne, who removed four cowbird eggs in three days from an incubated nest containing four cowbird eggs and two warbler eggs. The first day he removed one, the second day, another; the third morning, another; and the third afternoon, the last cowbird egg. The female warbler was on the nest at each of these four visits, but had deserted when the nest was seen on the day following that on which the third and fourth eggs were taken. I believe cowbird interference rarely causes desertion except when it takes place after incubation has begun, and in these cases it may involve struggle at the nest.

Long incubation. The female warbler deserts the nest if no egg hatches after an unduly long period of incubation. In one instance a female was still incubating on July 4, 20 days after the clutch was completed, but she had abandoned the nest when it was next visited, four days later. In another instance a female was incubating on July 10, 16 days after the nest was found, but had deserted four days later; how long she had been incubating was not known. Both of these cases occurred near the end of the nesting season, and the nests themselves may have been second or third attempts. Early nests might be incubated longer.

Losses during Building and Egg Laying

Nests may be lost by destruction or desertion before incubation begins—that is, during building and egg laying—but information on these early stages is scant.

I have fragmentary information on 16 nests where the females were seen building. Of these, four were deserted before any eggs were laid, two while still incomplete, and two that appeared complete. In the two complete nests, it is possible the first egg was laid and destroyed, causing the females to desert. It is of interest that one of the four empty nests was torn out, as though by the claws of an exploring mammal.

The numbers are too small to permit the calculation of loss rates for this step in the nesting process. The nest-building period continues for a minimum of four days, but it may be prolonged for two or three more days if daytime temperatures are near freezing, as happens occasionally in late May and the first week of June.

Among 25 nests observed for a total of 64 nest-days before completion of the clutches, I have no record of the loss of a nest by destruction or desertion during the egg-laying period. Although losses surely occur, it appears that the loss rate is at a minimum during this stage, when the female is visiting the nest only for a brief period each day, in contrast with the building period, when she makes over 200 visits in about four days, and in contrast with the incubation and nestling periods, when both adults are traveling to and from the nest many times a day.

Rates of Success during Incubation (as Customarily Presented)

To calculate the rate of successful nests, it would be advantageous to have a large series of nests, discovered before incubation began, and observed all the way to natural or accidental termination. However, most Kirtland's Warbler nests have been found sometime after incubation has begun; the same is true in most other studies of open-nesting birds.

Therefore, although the authors are often silent on this point, it would appear we are to assume that most nests reported with eggs were found sometime in the course of incubation. If so, the success rates calculated from these samples will be higher than the true rates. How much higher is uncertain. If we could assume that the days of discovery were distributed randomly throughout the incubation period, we could easily calculate the true success rate from the observed rate; but this is not possible, because the time of discovery of nests may vary widely according to the habits of the bird and the methods of the observer.

An offsetting uncertainty, this one tending to lower the observed success rate below its true value, is introduced by excluding nests with outcome unknown. This procedure favors the inclusion of nests of short life; that is, some nests lost might have been excluded if they had survived longer, say, until the observer had left the area. Presumably this uncertainty also exists in many other studies.

Later in this section I have treated the data in another way. However, in order to compare the Kirtland's Warbler with other species, my findings are first presented in the usual manner in Table 33. Here and elsewhere I have assumed that the nests found were typical of all nests of the species and that, except as noted, my own observations did not interfere with the nests.

Nice (1957:305–307), summarizing 35 major studies of open-nesting altricial birds, found that 60 per cent of the eggs hatched, with a range of 45.8 to 77.8 per cent.

Studies of three other species of wood warblers have shown proportions of eggs hatching as follows: Ovenbird, 63 per cent of 322 eggs (Hann, 1937:198); Yellow Warbler, 71 per cent of 168 eggs (Schrantz, 1943:385); and Prothonotary Warbler, a cavity-nesting bird, 41 per cent of 645 eggs (Walkinshaw, 1953:168).

Thus the Kirtland's Warbler, with a hatching rate of 52 per cent of eggs found, without cowbird interference, has a low production rate among songbirds, especially since, unlike many others, it usually produces only one brood per season. The activity of the cowbird depresses this rate even further; in fact, substantially below the 47 per cent shown in Table 33, because records based on eggs seen do not reflect adequately the eggs removed by cowbirds, most of which

Table 33

Nest Success during Incubation

	Without C eggs	Nests With C eggs	Total
Total number of nests	79 *	75	154
Nests excluded because outcome unknown	15	12	27
Nests excluded because later parasitized	5	0	5
Nests excluded because of human interference	0	9	9
Nests with outcome known	59	54	113
Nests deserted during incubation	8	8	16
Nests destroyed during incubation	11	8	19
Nests hatching no eggs	2	0	2
Nests in which eggs hatched	38	38	76
Percentage of nests with outcome known hatching eggs	64	70 ‡	67
KW eggs seen in nests with outcome known	273	154 §	427
KW young seen in nests with outcome known	142	58	200
Percentage of KW eggs seen that hatched	52 †	38 †	47
C eggs seen in nests with outcome known	0	78	78
C young seen in nests with outcome known	0	54	54
Percentage of C eggs seen that hatched	0	69	69

* Group of 67 nests on page 147, plus 6 nests from which cowbird eggs had been removed, plus 6 nests in which the set of eggs was not proved complete, although the outcome was known.

† The number of young hatched was undoubtedly higher than this figure, because some of these nests were not seen immediately after hatching.

‡ Larger proportion of parasitized nests hatch eggs because they usually have a shorter incubation period by two days than do nests with KW eggs only.

§ An undetermined number of KW eggs were removed by cowbirds before many of these nests were found.

were removed before the nests were found and which were therefore not seen.

Rates of Success during the Nestling Period (*as Customarily Presented*)

It is not easy to determine accurately how many young birds have left the nest safely. We seldom witness their leaving, and great effort is required to find them after they leave. Usually we infer that young Kirtland's Warblers have left if the nest becomes empty when the young are old enough to leave; that is, at about eight days of age.

Here (Table 34) I have assumed that young have fledged if they have been seen in the nest over a period of at least seven days. To enlarge the sample as much as possible, I have included several nests found when the young were hatched recently (judged not over two

Table 34

Nest Success during the Nestling Period

| | Nests | | |
	Without cowbirds	With cowbirds	Total
Total number of nests	35	27	62
Nests deserted	2	2	4
Nests destroyed	5	8	13
KW nestlings seen	136	43	179
KW young fledged	104	25	129
Percentage of KW nestlings seen that fledged	76	58 *	72 *
C nestlings seen	0	31	31
C young fledged	0	19	19
Percentage of C nestlings seen that fledged	0	61 †	61 †

* This small sample yields a fledging rate for warblers that is obviously too high, because many newly hatched warblers are killed by cowbirds and removed by parents without being seen by an observer.

† This small sample yields a fledging rate for cowbirds that is almost certainly too low.

days old). In view of the uncertainties, these figures should be considered approximate. Of 62 nests, 45 (73 per cent) fledged young.

In order to represent properly nest losses from desertion and destruction, only those are included which were lost at such a time that an observer would still have been present if the nest had survived its full period.

In Table 35 are shown further data on nest success, but from nests not seen early enough to be included in previous tables.

Rates of Success from Eggs to Fledging (as Customarily Presented)

To draw from the data shown in Tables 33 and 34 rates of nest and fledging success comparable to those of other studies, the rates of success during incubation and the nestling period, computed in two

Table 35

Birds Produced per Nest Fledging Young *

	N	Per nest fledging young
Nests without Cs	42	
KW young fledged	164	3.9
Nests with Cs	27	
C young fledged	39	1.4
KW young fledged	27	1.0 †

* Note that all nests in this group succeeded; that is, none that were deserted or destroyed are included.

† This yield is probably too high, since it contains an abnormally successful parasitized group.

earlier sections, are combined. The results are shown in Table 36.

The nest success rate yielded by this method for the Kirtland's Warbler, 49 per cent, is exactly that found by Nice (1957:305–307)

Table 36

Success from Eggs to Fledging *

Nest Success/Egg Success	Rate
To fledging, without Cs (During incubation, 64 per cent; during nestling period, 76 per cent)	.64 × .76 = 49 per cent of nests found with eggs
With half the nests parasitized (During incubation, 67 per cent; during nestling period, 73 per cent)	.67 × .73 = 49 per cent of nests found with eggs
KW egg success to fledging, without C's (During incubation, 52 per cent; during nestling period, 76 per cent)	.52 × .76 = 40 per cent of eggs seen
KW egg success to fledging, including parasitized nests (During incubation, 47 per cent; during nestling period, 72 per cent)	.47 × .72 = 34 per cent of eggs seen

* Note that these figures are certainly too high, because they are based on eggs seen, and do not take account of eggs removed by cowbirds before the nests were found.

for 7,788 open nests of several species of altricial birds. However, she found a fledging success of 46 per cent for 21,951 eggs in various studies of open-nesting altricial birds, with a range of 22.4 to 70.6. Hann (1937:198) gives 43.5 per cent fledging success for the Ovenbird, and Schrantz (1943:386), 54 per cent for the Yellow Warbler, in spite of cowbird interference with both species. The Prothonotary Warbler, nesting in cavities, fledged about 30 per cent of its young, according to Walkinshaw's studies (1953:168).

Comparatively, the Kirtland's Warbler is not a productive species. Even without cowbird interference, its fledging success for eggs, 40 per cent, is a little below that of most other comparable birds. Again, this low production rate per nest may be especially significant in the Kirtland's Warbler, which ordinarily rears only one brood each summer, while many other species rear two or more broods.

Success Calculated from Exposure

The hazards of existence for a nest will vary according to the length of time it is exposed. Therefore, we may study the mortality and survival of nests in terms of units of exposure. A convenient unit is the nest-day; that is, an amount of exposure equivalent to one nest for one day. For example, five nests, all of which were observed for five days, would represent a total of 25 nest-days exposure. However, a nest seen only once represents no exposure at all; it must have been seen on at least two different days to represent any elapsed time. If a nest was lost at some unknown time in an interval of more than a day, I have arbitrarily assumed it was lost at the midpoint of the interval.

By this means it is possible to utilize fragments of information, whether for long or short periods, even if no change occurred in the nest; also to extrapolate to the beginning of incubation and thus to estimate how many nests were lost from the very start, even though not all were seen at that time.

In the following calculations the rates of success at each stage of the nesting process are calculated in terms of probabilities, after Davis (1952:316–320). For ease in computation, half of all nests (instead of 55 per cent) are often assumed parasitized. This simplification is, I believe, permissible in view of the modest level of precision of the basic data. It should be noted also that the sample size varies at each step; that is, some nests were seen during incubation but not at hatching time, and similarly at other steps.

Success during Incubation (Calculated from Exposure)

Since the consequences are similar, whether nests are destroyed or deserted, these two events are considered together in calculating success during incubation, as shown in Table 37.

The results show that the presence of cowbird eggs does not increase the rate of nest loss.

The sample of nests without cowbird eggs is a little larger than would be expected, because cowbird eggs were removed from a few nests, which were then treated in the group without cowbird eggs. Also there was a tendency not to visit nests at a distance when they were known to be heavily parasitized. The rate of loss appears to be

Table 37

Success of Nests during Incubation

	Nests	Nest-days observed	Nests deserted	Nests destroyed	Nests lost	Nests lost per nest-day
Without C eggs	79	480	8	11	19	.040
With C eggs	75	398	8	8	16	.040
Total	154	878	16	19	35	.040

roughly constant throughout the incubation period, although my data do not prove it conclusively; that is, losses have been recorded early as well as late, but the losses occurring at known points were too few in number to allow exact comparison of one part of the period with another.

If the loss rate per nest-day is r, the survival rate is l-r, and the proportion of nests remaining after d days of exposure is $(l-r)^d$.

Thus among nests without cowbird eggs, incubated 14 days, with a loss rate of .04 per nest-day, the probability of a nest remaining to hatching time will be $(.96)^{14} = .56$. Disregarding the very few nests that are incubated for the required time but hatch nothing (they will be considered later in the calculation of hatching rate of eggs), the success of nests to hatching, without cowbird eggs present, is therefore about 56 per cent of the nests that start incubation—instead of the 64 per cent that results if the data are presented in the customary way.

Similarly, the probability of survival of a parasitized nest to hatching, with a 12-day incubation period, is $(.96)^{12} = .61$; that is, 61 per cent of the nests at the start of incubation, instead of the 70 per cent that results if the data are presented in the customary way.

For all nests, about half of which are parasitized, and which thus have an average incubation period of 13 days, the probability of survival of nests is $(.96)^{13} = .59$; that is, 59 per cent of the nests at the start of incubation, instead of the 67 per cent that results if the data are presented in the customary way.

In order to compute the probability of egg survival for the incubation period, we must consider also the loss of individual eggs from continuing nests. The exposure may be expressed in egg-days (eggs times days in periods of observation). I have records of six warbler eggs that vanished during incubation from nests, including parasitized nests, but under circumstances suggesting the work of some agency other than cowbirds. The total exposure of the eggs in my entire sample was 3,181 egg-days; the rate of loss from these unknown causes was therefore .002 per egg-day. The probability of egg survival for 14 days of incubation is thus $(.998)^{14} = .97$, or 97 per cent of eggs incubated, and a virtually identical rate for 12 or 13 days of incubation.

What happened to these eggs is uncertain. They may be broken by the female in the nest, perhaps because of weak shells. They may be

Table 38

Probability of Survival of Eggs during Incubation Period

Nest		Survival Rate (Percentage of eggs at start of incubation)
Without C eggs	.56 × .97 =	54
With C eggs	.61 × .97 =	59 *
All nests	.59 × .97 =	57

* Survival rate is higher because incubation period is shorter.

taken by cowbirds. There may be some unidentified predator that will take one egg and not return for more.

The probability of survival of eggs during the incubation period is therefore as shown in Table 38. These figures, it should be noted, indicate nothing about the number of eggs that hatch; they merely indicate the probability of survival to hatching time.

Hatching Success and Loss of Individual Nestlings

Before we can link survival during both incubation and the nestling period in order to calculate nest success, we must know the hatching success of eggs present at hatching time. But for reasons stated in the section on the cowbird, it is impossible to be sure of this figure unless every nest is under constant observation. For example, a nest containing five eggs on one afternoon may contain one egg and three young when visited the next morning. How many hatched?

The parent warblers promptly remove dead nestlings and damaged eggs. Both a young bird that pips its shell but does not emerge fairly soon and a nestling that does not show movement are in danger of removal. Accordingly, when eggs vanish at hatching time it is possible that they hatched young and that the young were removed by the parents. In the data given in Table 39 only those eggs still

Table 39

Hatching Success in 69 Nests

Nests N = 69	KW eggs at hatching time N	Young seen		KW eggs two days later N	Young presumed hatched	
		N	Per cent		N	Per cent
39 unparasitized	182	147	81	27	155	85
30 parasitized	88	54	61	23	66	75
Total	270	201		50	221	

present two days after the first warbler egg hatched were numbered among the unhatched eggs.

If nestling warblers (without cowbirds present) survive the first day or two of life, and if the nest is not deserted or destroyed, the nestlings are almost certain to live to fledging. I have recorded only one loss of such a nestling after the first day of life, and that happened on the second day. In view of the uncertainty about exactly how many warblers hatched, it is difficult to separate hatching mortality from individual nestling mortality in the first day or two of life. I have therefore treated these two components together in calculating the probability of survival for the hatching period. In the unparasitized nests tabulated in Table 39, from 182 eggs in nests without cowbird eggs, 142 nestlings were present two days after the first one in the nest hatched. Therefore, the probability of survival of the hatching period was 78 per cent in nests without cowbird eggs.

The survival of the first two days of life (142 out of 155 nestlings) is 92 per cent of the birds hatched, which may be taken also as the approximate probability of survival from hatching to fledging in unparasitized nests not destroyed or deserted.

In parasitized nests, the presence of cowbirds causes the death of Kirtland's Warblers from hatching right up to fledging time, so it is not easy to segregate the mortality of the hatching period from that of later nestling life. However, if we assume that the portion of it not attributable to cowbirds occurs at the same rate as in unparasitized nests (where it reduces the presumed probability of hatching from 85 per cent to a probability of survival for the hatching period of 78 per cent), we conclude that the presumed probability of hatching of 75 per cent in parasitized nests may be reduced to a probability of survival for the hatching period of about 69 per cent, without taking

Table 40

Hatching Success in Typical Population
(Hypothetical Sample)

Nests	KW eggs at hatching time N	Young presumed hatched N	Per cent
39 unparasitized	182	155	85
43 parasitized: weighted sample	126	94	75
Typical population	308	249	81

into account any deleterious effect of the young cowbirds on the newly hatched warblers. (This factor is taken into account in treatment of the nestling period.) And this percentage should be reduced further, owing to two extra days of exposure in the hatching period for warbler eggs, at the nestling period nest-loss rate, to 65 per cent probability of survival for the hatching period in parasitized nests. This figure is exclusive of any mortality of warbler nestlings attributable to cowbird nestlings in the same nest.

In computing the probability of survival for the hatching period in all nests, parasitized and unparasitized, it is not proper to combine directly the two samples in Table 39, since the sample of parasitized nests is smaller proportionately than in nature. If we assume that 55 per cent of all nests are parasitized, we may weight the parasitized group properly by enlarging it to 10 per cent more than the unparasitized group, that is, to 43 nests. If these, like the sample of 30 parasitized nests, hold 2.93 warbler eggs each, or 126 warbler eggs in all, 94 eggs, or 75 per cent, are presumed to have hatched. Combining the parasitized group with the unparasitized sample, we have the results shown in Table 40. Thus among warbler eggs present at hatching time in all nests, the probability of hatching is 81 per cent.

Similarly, we may treat this group to show survival of the hatching period in parasitized nests, excluding the effect of nestling cowbirds on nestling warblers, as shown in Table 41. Thus among war-

Table 41

Survival of Hatching Period in Typical Population
(Hypothetical Sample)

Nests	KW eggs at hatching time N	Young surviving hatching period	
		N	Per cent
39 unparasitized	182	142	78
43 parasitized: weighted sample	126	82	65
Typical population	308	224	73

bler eggs present at hatching time in all nests, the probability of surviving the hatching period is 73 per cent, exclusive of losses attributable to the effect of young cowbirds on newly hatched warblers.

Rates of Success during the Nestling Period (Calculated from Exposure)

Now we can consider the mortality and survival of nests during the nestling period in terms of nest-days of exposure, as we have done for the incubation period. The results are shown in Table 42.

When nests containing eggs are compared with nests containing young, we see that the number destroyed is about the same for a similar amount of exposure in both periods; but the number deserted is five times as high per nest-day with eggs as with young. There are two obvious reasons: (1) untenable nest sites are abandoned early, and (2) the female warbler is much more attached to young than to eggs.

In presenting this material, I have considered that a nest is in the nestling period when the first young bird hatches, since a new set of hazards comes into existence at this point, even though there are still eggs in the nest. Eggs that do not hatch usually disappear sometime during the nestling period—perhaps they are removed by the adults after being damaged by wear-and-tear from the young birds—but some eggs remain throughout the nestling period. Such eggs have been treated in the section on hatching success, and are not considered further here.

In this sample, nests containing cowbirds were destroyed at more than twice the rate of nests containing warblers alone. It is possible that cowbirds are more easily found by predators because they are larger and noisier than warblers. However, I am not sure that the

Table 42

Success of Nests during Nestling Period

	Nests	Nest-days observed	Nests deserted	Nests destroyed	Nests lost	Nests lost per nest-day
Without C young	86	424	2	6	8	.019
With C young	58	311	1	13	14	.045
Totals	144	735	3	19	22	.030

difference is significant. The number of nests lost is small, and the difference may be due to chance. In the computations that follow I have therefore used the rate based on the totals of the two groups.

With a loss per nest-day of 3 per cent, and with young birds leaving the nest typically at nine days, the probability of nest survival for this period is $(.97)^9 = .76$; that is, 76 per cent of *nests* with young survive nine days. This is virtually identical with the proportion of nests with young that fledge young (73 per cent), presented in the customary way. (See page 190.)

Since all the losses of individual young birds without total loss of the same nest are already included in the probability of survival for the hatching period, computed in the previous section, the probability of survival of nestlings is identical with the probability of survival of nests during the same period, that is, 76 per cent, excluding the mortality of nestlings during the hatching period—for nests without cowbirds.

To compute the survival of young warblers during the nestling period in nests with cowbirds, we combine our information about the probability of survival of nests with young (76 per cent) with other calculations showing that survival of the cowbird hazard is 45 per cent and survival of other nestling hazards is 92 per cent. Thus, the probability of survival to fledging of young warblers in parasitized nests is about $.76 \times .45 \times .92 = 31$ per cent of the warblers hatched. (This figure is not strictly comparable to the "58 per cent of warblers seen" in the data as customarily presented, because in parasitized nests a large number of warblers that are hatched are killed and removed before they are seen; also, the 31 per cent figure is based on a larger amount of data.)

To calculate the survival of young warblers during the nestling period in all nests, half of which are parasitized, we combine the parasitized and unparasitized samples weighted properly for the number of warbler eggs in each, as in the following paragraph.

In nests containing Kirtland's eggs alone, the probability that warbler eggs will survive incubation (.54) and the hatching period (.78) is $.54 \times .78 = .42$. These nests begin incubation with 4.63 eggs each and come through the hatching period with $4.63 \times .42 = 1.95$ nestlings each. Of these, 76 per cent, or 1.48 nestlings, are fledged per nest.

In nests with cowbird eggs, the probability that warbler eggs will survive incubation (.59) and hatch successfully (.65) is $.59 \times .65 = .38$. These nests begin incubation with 2.75 warbler eggs each and hatch $2.75 \times .38 = 1.05$ nestlings each. Of these, 31 per cent, or .32 warblers, are fledged per nest.

Therefore, equal numbers of parasitized and unparasitized nests will fledge young in the proportion of 1.80 fledged (the sum fledged from both classes of nests above) to 3.00 hatched (the sum hatched from both classes of nests above); that is, 60 per cent of the young that survive the hatching period will survive the nestling period to fledging.

Rates of Success from Laying to Fledging (Calculated from Exposure)

We may complete the account of nest success by combining the rates of survival for incubation and for the nestling period, as in the following paragraph.

In nests containing warbler eggs alone, .56 (probability of nest survival during incubation, p. 193) × .76 (probability of nest survival during nestling period, p. 198) = 43 per cent probability that nests starting incubation will survive until young are fledged.

In nests containing cowbird eggs, where the fledging of a cowbird constitutes "success" and where the period required is two days shorter than for a warbler, .61 (probability of nest survival during incubation, p. 193) × .76 (probability of nest survival during nestling period, p. 198) = 46 per cent probability that parasitized nests starting incubation will survive to the fledging of at least one cowbird.

In all nests, about half of them parasitized, .59 (probability of nest survival during incubation, p. 194) × .76 (probability of nest survival during nestling period, p. 198) = 45 per cent probability that nests starting incubation will survive until young are fledged. The total group shows a slightly higher probability of nest success than the group of warblers alone, because here a nest is called "successful" if it produces any fledgling, even a cowbird, which has two days less exposure from the start of incubation to fledging.

To calculate the probability of egg success, we proceed in a similar way: For nests without cowbirds, .54 (probability of egg survival during incubation, Table 38) × .78 (probability of survival for the hatching period, Table 41) × .76 (probability of survival for the nestling period, p. 198) = 32 per cent probability that warbler eggs at the start of incubation will be fledged. As shown in the preceding section, this indicates an average yield of 1.48 fledglings per nest starting incubation without cowbird interference.

For nests with cowbird eggs, .59 (the probability that eggs will not be removed by cowbirds, Table 32) × .59 (probability of warbler egg survival from the start of incubation until the first cowbird egg hatches, Table 38) × .65 (probability of warbler survival of hatching period exclusive of effect of young cowbirds present, Table 41) × .31 (survival of warbler nestlings in presence of young cowbirds, p. 199) = 7 per cent probability that warbler eggs laid in parasitized nests will produce fledglings. As shown in the preceding section, p. 199 this indicates an average yield of 0.32 warbler fledglings per parasitized nest starting incubation.

For all nests, about half of which are parasitized, .77 (probability that warbler eggs laid will not be taken by cowbirds, Table 28) × .57 (probability of egg survival during incubation, Table 38) × .73 (probability of survival for the hatching period, Table 41)

× .60 (probability of survival for the nestling period, p. 199) = 19 per cent probability that warbler eggs at the start of incubation will produce fledglings.

Since 4.63 warbler eggs were laid per nest, the yield in fledglings is about 0.9 young per nest starting incubation. This low yield may be more credible when I point out that on our study area in 1955 we doubted whether any of the 14 nests we found produced fledglings.

The egg success reported here, 19 per cent, is less than half the average figure, 46 per cent, given by Nice (1957:305–307) for a large number of open-nesting altricial birds.

For three reasons I believe this rate of laying-to-fledging success, 20 per cent, is more nearly accurate than the 34 per cent rate resulting from presenting my data in the customary way. These reasons are: (1) The rate is corrected for warbler eggs removed by cowbirds before the nests were found; (2) it is corrected for nests deserted and destroyed before they are found; and (3) it includes a much larger sample of nests and periods of exposure than it would be possible to include in the usual way.

Production per Pair

Up to this point we have considered the success of nests and eggs. But much more significant in our study of the survival of the species is the production of fledglings per pair of adults per year. We cannot go from one to the other without considering the replacement of nests that are destroyed or deserted. Attempts at second broods after young birds have fledged are so rare in the Kirtland's Warbler (two known instances) that this source of production is ignored here.

Desertion and destruction are a special class of loss because, unlike other kinds of losses, they are usually replaced by prompt renesting. The result, then, is *delay* rather than *loss*. It is misleading in terms of ultimate production to make no distinction between mere interruptions and true losses.

If every nest deserted or destroyed were replaced, the net loss in nests would be zero. However, the loss in eggs would be about 18 per cent because of smaller clutches in the renestings. But the nests lost after about June 25 are not replaced. Presumably by this time the female has progressed too far in her annual cycle to start a new nest, although she would have carried on with an existing nest for many more days.

Further, if each nesting attempt were broken up on the first day of building, it would be mathematically possible for a female to make ten or more starts before the drive to build left her. Actually, however, there may be physiological and psychological limitations that would stop her long before she reached a theoretical maximum. Most observed interruptions occur after incubation has started, and there is time for only three such attempts in a season. We have never been sure of more than two nesting attempts by a female, although I have no doubt that some females will make at least three attempts if the interruptions occur early enough in the cycle.

To calculate the production per pair of birds for the season, we may start by considering the number of nests built and carried to a successful conclusion. In a typical year the average date for the completion of the clutch of eggs for the first "cluster" of nests is June 4 (page 87). Since incubation usually begins on the day before the set of eggs is completed, the first day of incubation is completed on June 4, which may be considered day 1 in the first nesting attempt; June 25, after which no lost nests are replaced (page 80), is therefore day 22.

If we have a number of nests, a, at the start of incubation, with a loss rate per day during incubation, r_1, and a loss rate per day during the nestling period, r_2, the number of first-attempt nests still existing on day, d, during incubation will be $a(1 - r_1)^d$; but when d = 13, the average day of hatching for nests half of which are parasitized, the loss rate during the nestling period, r_2, now applies, and the first-attempt nests existing on any day after hatching, d = 14, 15, . . . 22, becomes a $(1 - r_1)^{13} (1 - r_2)^{d-13}$. If we assume a typical nestling period of 9 days, the day of fledging for the average nest is day 22, June 25, which from other considerations was believed to be the day after which no new nest building would be started. (This may suggest also why so few Kirtland's Warblers start new nests after their first set of young have fledged.) Therefore, as computed previously, if we start with 100 nests on day 0, then on day 22 there will be $100(.96)^{13} (.97)^9 = 100 \times .59 \times .76 = 45$ nests remaining.

Ignoring for the moment nests lost during the building and egg-laying phases, all 55 nests lost up to day 22 are replaced by second attempts. But the earliest of the second attempts begin incubation on d = 9, with the first installment consisting of nests lost on d = 1, the intervening 8 days having been spent in searching, building, and laying. Although the second attempts begin in daily installments from d = 9 to d = 22, and fledge young in the same way, they will ultimately succeed in the same ratio as the first attempts, that is 45 per cent of the second attempts starting incubation.

To deal with the third attempts, however, we must recognize that second attempts lost after $d = 22$ will not be replaced. The general statement for second attempts existing on day, d, is $(d - 8)ar_1$ $(1 - r_1)^{d-9}$. The number existing on any day multiplied by the daily loss rate, r_1, becomes the number lost on the next day and the number starting incubation in the next attempt 8 days later, provided we do not count losses beyond $d = 22$, after which no more nests are replaced. The number of second attempts lost up to and including $d = 22$ is $ar_1^2 [1 + 2(1 - r_1) + 3(1 - r_1)^2 + \cdots + 12(1 - r_1)^{12}]$ $= 10$, which is the total number of third attempts started.

The number of third attempts lost in time to permit a fourth attempt would be negligible.

Combining first, second, and third attempts, but still neglecting losses during building and egg laying, we have the results shown in Table 43.

Table 43

Success of Nests: First, Second, and Third Attempts
(Hypothetical Sample)

Attempt	Nests started	Nests lost	Nests succeeding
First	100	55	45
Second	55	30	25
Third	10	6	4
Total	165 *	91	74

* Considered to be upper limit; actual number, lower than this.

However, it is apparent that this calculation gives an unrealistically high ratio of nest successes for the population as a whole. It is a theoretical upper limit, and would be true only if all pairs started nests in the first "cluster" each year and if no losses occurred during the building and egg-laying periods. The first condition is unlikely and the second is untrue, for we know some nests are lost before incubation begins. But we do not know how many pairs start their nests with the vanguard each spring, and our information on losses during building and egg laying is too scant to guide our calculations accurately.

To illustrate that early losses may be appreciable, if we assume the loss rate during building and egg laying to be half the rate during incubation, .02 per day, the loss for seven days would be $.98^7 = .87$. That is, 13 per cent of the nests at the start of construction would be lost before incubation could begin. Of course, most of these nests would merely be delayed from 2 to 8 days (an average of about 5 days), and would be quickly replaced, but the time available for re-nesting is so limited that even a little delay in some instances would prevent another attempt. Therefore it would seem reasonable to adjust the number of nests in Table 43 downward, say 10 per cent, to 150 nests incubated, of which about 67 succeed per year for 100 pairs of Kirtland's Warblers.

If 150 nests produce an average of 0.9 fledglings each, the young fledged by 100 pairs of adults will number 135, an average of about 1.4 young per pair of Kirtland's Warblers.

If these 150 nests had held no cowbirds, the yield would have been about 1.48 fledglings per nest starting incubation, 222 fledglings in all, an average of 2.2 young per pair of Kirtland's Warblers. Thus, even without the effect of the cowbird, the Kirtland's Warbler has a low yield.

Lack (1954:83) has found production of fledglings per year per pair of adults ranging from 1.7 to 8 in several other passerine species. Hann (1937:198) found that the Ovenbird produced 2.9 fledglings per female but probably brought only 1.6 fledglings to the point of complete independence.

Survival of Adults

For a species to survive, the production of young must be sufficient at least to replace the loss of adults. It is therefore necessary to consider the survival of adults.

Over a period of years a number of Kirtland's Warblers were color-banded for identification. To study their survival rate, I analyzed the returns of banded adults on three areas, where sufficient field work was done in subsequent years to make it probable that a bird returning to the same area would be found. All these birds were banded at the nest in June, and were seen in later years, if at all, in the same month; the survival rate is therefore calculated from one June (nesting season) to the next. (See Table 44.)

Obviously, this method gives a minimum survival rate; the true figure will be higher than this one if any birds live undetected in later years.

I believe the true survival rate for adults from one nesting season to the next is about 60 per cent, as shown for the Old Mack Lake area. This area was small enough to allow virtually all of it to be searched each year, and it was at least three miles from any other nesting colony. The other two study areas were so large or so near other nesting areas not searched that warblers which moved even a short distance may have escaped detection.

When we calculate survival rates from numbers of birds seen in the wild, there is always a question about how many birds still living

Table 44

Survival of Adult Kirtland's Warblers: Males and Females

Area	Years N		Banded birds in June N		Previously banded birds present following year N		Survival rate per year (Per cent)	
	M	F	M	F	M	F	M	F
Old Mack Lake	9	9	29	36	17	22	59	61
Wakely Bridge Road	4	4	8	24	6	9	..	..
New Mack Lake	2	2	8	11	4	6	..	..
Total			45	71	27 *	37 *	60 *	52 *

* Actual survival may have been greater than shown if any birds escaped detection.

are not seen. Certainly there are some. Female Kirtland's Warblers are more likely to escape notice than males. On the Old Mack Lake area, for example, of 22 instances of returns a year later there were four instances of females which were not seen one year but were found the next. On the same area, which was studied intensively, no males were missed one year and found later. However, on the Wakely Bridge Road area, where it was impossible to make a thorough study of the entire populated area, of six returns of males one was missed in two intervening years.

I have two examples of females that nested at distances of almost a mile (1,350 m.) and nineteen miles (31 km.) from the previous year's nests. Ordinarily such females would not be found again. The greatest distance any male has been known to move from one year to another was about .6 mile (1,000 m.). Even a move of this distance in some areas might cause a male to be missed the next year.

I have no clear evidence of loss of adults during the nesting season, and will therefore not attempt to estimate survival rates for different parts of the year.

For the entire year, for both sexes equally, I suspect the survival rate of adults is about 60 per cent (mortality rate about 40 per cent).

Therefore, the life expectancy (longevity, or "mean after life") of an adult bird in June is about 2 years, according to the method given by Farner (1955:409, 435–438),

$$Y = \frac{1}{\text{annual mortality rate}} - (1 - \text{fraction of year survived in last year of life}).$$

This appears to be rather a long life expectancy for a passerine species, but it is not the longest on record. For the Ovenbird the comparable figure is 1.7 years (Hann, 1948:6, recalculated). The Wrentit, with an adult mortality rate of 36 per cent, has a life expectancy of 2.3 years, and the Plain Titmouse, with an adult mortality rate of 34 per cent, has a life expectancy of 2.5 years; both, however, are nonmigratory (Dixon, 1956:178).

The oldest Kirtland's Warbler in our banding records was a male, banded as an adult in June, 1941, and still present in June, 1949; that is, at least nine years old.

Survival of First-year Birds

The survival of fledglings on the nesting ground appears to be remarkably good. Here predators that pose a threat to flying birds are very scarce. In fact, I have not recorded the loss of a fledgling in many days of watching family groups, but I would not attempt to express the experience quantitatively.

I have no direct evidence from which to compute the survival rate of young birds from the time they are fledged until they return the next year as nesting adults. Of 222 nestlings banded, three have been seen as adults, but this ratio gives no clue to survival rate, since only a few nesting areas were examined in any one year.

However, from previous information about survival of adults and production of young, we can calculate the survival rate of young birds required to maintain a stationary population, as follows:

Of 100 adults, 60 survive to the next breeding season; these 100 adults produce 70 fledglings (1.4 per pair); and 40 young birds are needed the next year to replace losses of adults.

Therefore, the survival rate of young birds from the time of leaving the nest to the following June is $\frac{40}{70} = 57$ per cent (mortality rate 43 per cent) *if the population is being maintained*. This survival rate for songbirds in their first year of life is almost unbelievably high. If my calculation is applicable to the entire population, there may be serious doubts whether the Kirtland's Warbler is holding its own.

On the other hand, these data were largely gathered on a few areas, and there is a possibility that as a result of some unrecognized circumstance on the areas, or even through our own study efforts, the areas were not typical.

Now, an important question is this: What would be the production of Kirtland's Warblers if no cowbirds interfered with them? The production rate then would be 2.2 fledglings per pair, or 110 young by 100 adults. To replace the loss of 40 adults, the survival rate of young for the first year would need to be $\frac{40}{110} = 36$ per cent, a high but perhaps attainable figure.

As summarized by Lack (1954:85), the survival rate in the first year of life for many other passerine species is much lower: Song Sparrow, 21 per cent; Great Tit, 13 per cent; European Redstart, 23 per cent; European Robin, 26 per cent.

Austin (1951:173) found the survival rate in Mourning Doves for the first year of life was about 20 per cent, and about 45 per cent in each subsequent year. The nonmigratory Plain Titmouse (Dixon, 1956:179), with an unusually high adult survival rate, seems to have a first-year survival rate of only about 25 per cent.

Summary

Among Kirtland's Warbler nests lost, two-thirds are destroyed by predators. The agent of destruction has never been observed at work, but I suspect birds, particularly crows and jays, are more often responsible than mammals. Of mammals, the Red Squirrel and the Thirteen-lined Ground Squirrel are possibly the most important predators.

Reptiles and invertebrate parasites are negligible enemies.

Among Kirtland's Warbler nests lost, one-third are lost through the female's deserting the nest. These desertions may result from disturbance at the nest, flooding, death of the female, cowbird interference at the nest, and failure of eggs to hatch within a reasonable period.

Losses of nests sometimes occur during the building period, before eggs are laid, but my examples are too few to yield a numerical probability. Losses of nests during the egg-laying period, when the nest is almost completely unattended, seem to be few.

When rates of nest success without cowbird interference are presented in the customary way, the probability that nests found will hatch eggs is .64; the probability that nests with young will produce fledglings is .76; the probability that nests found with eggs will produce fledglings is .49; the probability that eggs found will hatch is .52; the probability that eggs found will produce fledglings is .40 *in the absence of cowbirds*. However, the fact that 55 per cent of the nests are parasitized by cowbirds reduces the average success to fledging of Kirtland's Warbler eggs below these figures, and certainly below the 34 per cent given by the small sample available for study by this method.

Treatment of the data in terms of exposure to the hazards of existence makes larger samples available for study, and also gives more accurate estimates of risks early in the incubation period, before most nests are found. By this means of presentation, the success of nesting is as follows: Without cowbird interference, the loss rate during incubation is .04 per nest-day, and the probability that nests will survive from the start of incubation to hatching is .56; the probability that a nest with young birds, at a loss rate of .03 per day, will survive for nine days, to fledge young, is .76; the probability that a nest will survive from the start of incubation to the fledging of young is .43; the probability that eggs will survive from the start of incubation to hatching time is .54; the probability that eggs present at hatching time will produce live nestlings through the hatching period is .78; the probability that young birds will survive the nestling period to fledging is .76; the probability that eggs at the start of incubation will produce fledglings is .32 *in the absence of cowbirds*. However, with about half the nests parasitized by cowbirds, the probability that Kirtland's Warbler eggs will produce fledglings is reduced to about .19. Thus, about 0.9 young are produced per nest at present, instead of about 1.5 per nest which would be produced without interference by cowbirds.

The production of fledglings per pair of adult Kirtland's Warblers per season at present is about 1.4; without cowbird interference it would be about 2.2.

The survival of adult Kirtland's Warblers is about 60 per cent per year, and the life expectancy of an adult is about two years.

We have no direct evidence for calculating the survival rate of Kirtland's Warblers in their first year of life. Other data suggest it would have to be more than 50 per cent—an improbable figure—to maintain the population. Hence, if the samples in this study are typical, the population has been declining in the period of this study.

16

Problems for Further Study

From time to time I have sent memoranda to a group of people known to be interested in the Kirtland's Warbler, citing questions awaiting answer. More than thirty such questions have been listed. Some of the more important are given in this section.

Observations over a Full Season

Most of the information for the present study was gathered in short periods of observation. Work over the full season in a nesting colony would throw light on many questions not answered here. For example:

What events lead up to the establishment of the pairing bond?

How do territory boundaries shift as the season progresses, and particularly when the female builds a second nest?

Do new birds join a colony after nesting is under way?

How rapidly are lost mates replaced?

Nesting Success on Large versus Small Tracts

There are theoretical grounds for believing that the Kirtland's Warbler may nest more successfully on vast burns than on small burns or plantings, where the fauna of the surrounding forest spills over into the Kirtland's habitat. This matter should be investigated.

Nesting Success in Small Colonies

The tendency of the Kirtland's Warbler to nest in colonies suggests that this habit may confer some benefit on the species. Although this question may be difficult to separate from habitat factors, it may be possible to show a difference in success between colonies of large and small size. A special study of isolated pairs would be interesting, if several could be found.

Nesting Success with One Cowbird in the Nest

Since two or more cowbirds (hatching ahead of the warblers) are invariably fatal to warbler nestlings, it becomes important to know how *one* cowbird affects the chances of survival of nestling warblers. Much more information is needed on this subject.

Control of the Cowbird

In this threatened species of warbler, the cowbird may impose an intolerable burden. Ultimately the survival of the species may depend on control of the cowbird in certain chosen areas. It would be interesting to know what problems arise in attempting to maintain a cowbird-free area during the nesting season.

Cowbird Parasitism of Neighboring Species

Very little information is available on the cowbird's use of the nests of other species than the Kirtland's Warbler in the latter's habitat. What proportion of the cowbird pressure is borne by this warbler? What species are affected before the Kirtland's Warbler starts nesting? Do certain female cowbirds specialize in certain species of hosts?

Bird Populations in Kirtland's Warbler Habitat

The few studies made of bird populations in Kirtland's Warbler areas have been conducted on very small tracts, and perhaps with a heavy influx of other species from other nearby habitats. It would be interesting to have some breeding-bird censuses on large areas, particularly of those in the midst of extensive, homogeneous tracts.

BIBLIOGRAPHY

* Indicates works mentioned in this report. Others are
references to the Kirtland's Warbler not cited here.

ABBOTT, GERARD ALAN

1915 Abbott's Collection of North American Warblers' Eggs. Oologist,
32:129–130.

ABBOTT, WALDO G.

*1954 Leaf Bathing of the Mockingbird. Condor, 56:163–164.

ADAMS, CHARLES C.

1903 Discovery of the Breeding Area of Kirtland's Warbler in Michigan.
Science, N.S., 18:217.

1904 The Migration Route of Kirtland's Warbler. Bull. Michigan Orn. Club,
5:14–21.

ALLEN, A. A.

*1937 In Henshaw and Allen. Warblers, Friends of our Forests.

ALLEN, J. A.

1880 Langdon's Ornithological Field Notes. (Review) Bull. Nuttall Orn.
Club, 5:232–233.

1903 [News note on C. C. Adams' report of the discovery of the nest of
Kirtland's Warbler.] Auk, 20:459–460.

1904 Kirtland's Warbler. (Review) Auk, 21:506–507.

AMADON, DEAN

*1944 Results of the Archbold Expeditions. No. 50. A Preliminary Life His-
tory Study of the Florida Jay, *Cyanocitta c. coerulescens*. American
Museum Novitates, No. 1252, 22 pp.

*1953 Migratory Birds of Relict Distribution: Some Inferences. Auk, 70:
461–469.

AMERICAN ORNITHOLOGISTS' UNION

1886 Check-list of North American Birds.

1895 Check-list of North American Birds. 2nd ed.

1910 Check-list of North American Birds. 3rd ed.

1931 Check-list of North American Birds. 4th ed.

*1957 Check-list of North American Birds. 5th ed.

ARLTON, ALEXANDER V.

1949 Songs and Other Sounds of Birds. Parkland, Wash. Publ. (lithoprint)
by the author, xii + 195 pp.

ARMSTRONG, EDWARD A.

*1949 Diversionary Display. Ibis, 91:88–97, 179–188.

*1956 Distraction Display and the Human Predator. Ibis, 98:641–654.

ARNOLD, EDWARD

*1904a Nesting of Kirtland's Warbler in Northern Michigan, 1904. Bull.
Michigan Orn. Club, 5:67–68.

*1904b Kirtland's Warbler. Oologist, 21:171.

1904c Another Nest of Kirtland's Warbler. Auk, 21:487–488.

*1905 The Taking of the Type Set, Nest and Four Eggs of *Dendroica kirt-landi* in Oscoda Co., Northern Michigan, June 15th, 1904, by Edward Arnold of Battle Creek. Warbler, 2nd ser., 1:1–3.

1912 A Short Summer Outing in Newfoundland, 1911. Auk, 29:72–79.

AUSTIN, OLIVER L., JR.

*1951 The Mourning Dove on Cape Cod. Bird Banding, 22:149–174.

AVERILL, C. K.

1920 Migration and Physical Proportions. A Preliminary Study. Auk, 37:572–579.

1922 A Law Governing the Elevation of the Nesting Site. Condor, 24:57–60.

AXTELL, HAROLD H.

*1938 The Song of Kirtland's Warbler. Auk, 55:481–491.

BAGG, AARON CLARK, AND SAMUEL ATKINS ELIOT, JR.

1937 Birds of the Connecticut Valley in Massachusetts. Hampshire Bookshop, Northampton, Mass., lxxiv + (20) + 813 pp., illus.

BAILEY, HAROLD H.

1925 The Birds of Florida. Publ. for author by Williams & Wilkins, Baltimore, xxi + 146 pp., 76 pls.

1930 In Memoriam (Reginald Hargreaves Bulley). Bailey Museum and Library of Natural History Bull. No. 4, April 1, 1930:4.

BAILEY, WALLACE

1955 Birds in Massachusetts: When and Where to Find Them. Publ. by the author, South Lancaster, Mass., 234 pp.

BAIRD, ROBERT L.

1905 Bird Migration at Oberlin, Ohio. Wilson Bull., 17:75–83.

BAIRD, SPENCER F., JOHN CASSIN, AND GEORGE NEWBOLD LAWRENCE

1860 The Birds of North America: The Descriptions of Species Based Chiefly on the Collections in the Museum of the Smithsonian Institution. (Vol. I, Text) Naturalist's Book Agency, Salem. (later ed. of Phila. 1860), lvi + 1005 pp.

BAIRD, S. F.

*1852 Description of a new Species of *Sylvicola*. Annals Lyc. Nat. Hist. New York, 5:217–218.

*1865 Review of American Birds. Smithsonian Misc. Collections, 181, 1864–72.

BAIRD, S. F., T. M. BREWER AND R. RIDGWAY

1905 A History of North American Birds. Land Birds. vol. 1, Little, Brown, Boston, xxviii + 596 + vi pp., 26 pls.

BALDWIN, AMY G.

1946 Kirtland's Warbler and Northern Michigan. (Illinois) Audubon Bull., No. 60, 5–8.

BANGS, OUTRAM

1900 Notes on a Collection of Bahama Birds. Auk, 17:283–293.

BARROWS, W. B.

1904 [Kirtland's Warbler (editorial)] Bull. Michigan Orn. Club, 5:70–71.

*1912 Michigan Bird Life. Special Bull. of Michigan Agric. College, Lansing, xiv + 822 pp., 70 pls.

*1921   New Nesting Areas of Kirtland's Warbler. Auk, 38:116–117.

BARTH, EDVARD K.
*1953   Calculation of Egg Volume Based on Loss of Weight During Incubation. Auk, 70:151–159.

BEER, JAMES R., LOUIS D. FRENZEL, AND NORMAN HANSEN
*1956   Minimum Space Requirements of Some Nesting Passerine Birds. Wilson Bull., 68:200–209.

BENT, ARTHUR CLEVELAND
*1953   Life Histories of North American Wood Warblers. U.S. Nat. Mus. Bull. 203, xi + 734 pp., illus.

BERGER, ANDREW J.
*1951   The Cowbird and Certain Host Species in Michigan. Wilson Bull., 63:26–34.

BIDWELL, P. W. AND J. I. FALCONER
*1925   History of Agriculture in the Northern United States 1620–1860. Carnegie Inst. of Washington.

BLACKWELDER, ELIOT
1899   A Note on Kirtland's Warbler (*Dendroica kirtlandi*). Auk, 16:359–360.

BLAIN, A. W.
1903a   [Discovery of the Nest of Kirtland's Warbler.] Bull. Michigan Orn. Club, 4:63.
1903b   [Kirtland's Warbler] Bull. Michigan Orn. Club, 4:77.

BOARDMAN, EDWARD T., AND ELIZABETH BARTO
1937   A Pictorial Guide to the Families of Birds (etc.). Cranbrook Institute of Science, Bull. 9, 48 pp.

BOGGS, I. B.
1944   Kirtland's Warbler. Redstart, 11:26.

BOND, JAMES
1940   Check-list of Birds of the West Indies. Acad. Nat. Sci. of Philadelphia, xi + 184 pp.
1945   Check-list of Birds of the West Indies. (Second Edition) Acad. Nat. Sci. of Philadelphia, xiii + 182 pp.
1947   Field Guide to Birds of the West Indies. Macmillan, New York, ix + 257 pp., illus.
1950   Check-list of Birds of the West Indies. (Third Edition) Acad. Nat. Sci. of Philadelphia, xiii + 200 pp.
1951   First Supplement to the Check-list of Birds of the West Indies (1950). Acad. Nat. Sci. of Philadelphia, 22 pp.
1956   Check-list of Birds of the West Indies. (Fourth Edition) Acad. of Nat. Sci. of Philadelphia, ix + 214 pp.

BONHOTE, J. LEWIS
1903   On a Collection of Birds from the Northern Islands of The Bahama Group. Ibis, 1903:273–315.

BORROR, DONALD J.
1950   A Check List of the Birds of Ohio, with the Migration Dates for the Birds of Central Ohio. Ohio Jour. Sci., 50:1–32.

BORROR, DONALD J., AND CARL R. REESE
*1953   The Analysis of Bird Songs by Means of a Vibralyzer. Wilson Bull., 65:271–276.

BIBLIOGRAPHY

BRACKBILL, HERVEY
*1958   Nesting Behavior of the Wood Thrush. Wilson Bull., 70:70–89.
*1959   Remating Percentage of Some Migratory Birds. Bird-Banding, 30: 123.
BRAGG, L. M.
 1912   Birds of South Carolina. Supplement. Charleston Museum Bull., 8(2): 19–25, (3): 27–33.
BRECKENRIDGE, W. J.
*1955   Comparison of the Breeding-bird Populations of Two Neighboring but Distinct Forest Habitats. Audubon Field Notes, 9:408–412.
BREWER, RICHARD
*1955   Size of home range in eight bird species in a southern Illinois swamp-thicket. Wilson Bull., 67:140–141.
BRIGHAM, EDWARD M., JR.
 1952   [Published photograph of Kirtland's Warblers.] Bull. Mass. Aud. Soc., 36(2): cover.
BRODKORB, PIERCE
*1959   Pleistocene birds from New Providence Island, Bahamas. Bull. Florida State Mus., 4:349–371.
BROOKS, MAURICE
 1944   A Check-list of West Virginia Birds. West Va. Univ. Agric. Exper. Sta. Bull. 316, 56 pp.
BROOKS, MAURICE, AND I. B. BOGGS
 1937   A Sight Record of Kirtland's Warbler in West Virginia. Redstart, 4:61.
BROWN, JOHN T.
*1940   Agriculture in Ohio, Its Beginning and Development. Ohio Dept. of Agric., Columbus.
BURNS, FRANK L.
 1921   Comparative Periods of Nestling Life of Some North American Nidicolae. (Part 3) Wilson Bull., 33:177–182.
 1924   The Philosophy of Birds' Nests and Comparative Calology in Consideration of Some Local Nidicolus Birds. (Part 3) Wilson Bull., 36: 188–200.
BUTLER, AMOS W.
 1891   A Catalogue of the Birds of Indiana. Trans. Ind. Hort. Soc. for Year 1890, Appendix C. pp. 1–135.
 1894   Notes on Indiana Birds. Proc. Ind. Acad. Sci. for 1893:116–120.
 1896   Additional Notes on Indiana Birds. Proc. Ind. Acad. Sci. for 1895:162–168.
 1898   The Birds of Indiana. 22nd Annual Rept. of Dept. of Geology and Natural Resources, 1897 (1898):515–1187, illus.
 1927   Searching for Interesting Bird Records. (Indiana) Audubon Bulletin, 1927:10–13.
 1929   Rare Birds in Cincinnati Collections. Auk, 46:196–199.
CAMPBELL, LOUIS W.
 1931   Check List. Birds of Toledo, Ohio, and Vicinity (With Migration Dates). Publ. by The Toledo Nature Study Soc., 19 pp.
*1940   Birds of Lucas County. Toledo Museum of Sci. Bull., Vol. 1, No. 1, 225 pp.

CASSIN, JOHN
   1856   Illustrations of the Birds of California, Texas, Oregon, British and Russian America. J. B. Lippincott, Philadelphia, viii + 298 pp., 50 pls.
CHAMBERLAIN, E. B.
   1936   Seasonal List of South Carolina Birds. Revised to November, 1936. Charleston Museum Leaflet No. 8:1–21.
CHANCE, EDGAR P.
  *1940   The Truth About the Cuckoo. Country Life Ltd., London, xvi + 207 pp., 38 pls.
CHAPMAN, FRANK M.
   1895   Handbook of Birds of Eastern North America. D. Appleton and Co., N.Y., xiv + 427 pp., illus.
   1898   Kirtland's Warbler (*Dendroica kirtlandi*). Auk, 15:289–293.
   1899   Further Notes on Dendroica kirtlandi. Auk, 16:81.
   1903   Color Key to North American Birds. Doubleday, Page, New York, vi + 310 pp., illus.
  *1907   The Warblers of North America. Appleton, New York, ix + 306 pp., 24 pls.
  *1908   Camps and Cruises of an Ornithologist. Appleton, New York, xvi + 432 pp., illus.
   1912   Handbook of Birds of Eastern North America. (Revised edition) Appleton, New York, xxix + 530 pp., 24 pls.
   1929   What Bird Is That? Appleton, New York, xxiv + (2) + 144 pp., 8 pls.
   1932   Handbook of Birds of Eastern North America. (2nd revised ed.) Appleton, New York, xxxvi + 581 pp., 29 pls.
CHILDS, JOHN LEWIS
   1904   Eggs of Kirtland's Warbler Taken. Warbler (ser. 1), vol. 2:60.
   1906   Ornithological Collection of John Lewis Childs, Floral Park, N.Y., Warbler (ser. 2), vol. 2:66–106.
CHRISTY, BAYARD H.
  *1936   Kirtland Marginalia. Cardinal, 4:77–89.
CHUBB, H. E.
   1880   Spring Field Notes. Forest and Stream, 14:307.
COOK, A. J.
   1893   Birds of Michigan. Michigan Agri. College Bull. (94) April, 148 pp.
   1893   Birds of Michigan. Michigan Agri. College Bull. (94) (2nd ed.), Sept., 168 pp.
COOKE, MAY THACHER
   1921   Birds of the Washington Region. Proc. Biol. Soc. Wash., 34:1–22.
   1929   Birds of the Washington, D.C., Region. Proc. Biol. Soc. Wash., 42:1–80.
COOKE, W. W.
   1888   Report on Bird Migration in the Mississippi Valley in the Years 1884 and 1885. U.S. Dept. Agric., Div. Econ. Orn. Bull. No. 2, 313 pp.
   1904a Distribution and Migration of North American Warblers. U.S. Dept. Agri., Div. Biol. Surv. Bull. 18, 142 pp.
   1904b The Migration of Warblers Seventh Paper. Bird-Lore, 6:199–200.
   1905a An Untenable Theory of Bird Migration. Condor, 7:8–9.
   1905b The Winter Ranges of the Warblers (*Mniotiltidae*). Auk, 22:296–299.

CORY, CHARLES B.
*1879 Capture of Kirtland's Warbler (*Dendroica kirtlandi*) in the Bahama Islands. Bull. Nuttall Orn. Club, 4:118.
1880 Birds of the Bahama Islands. Publ. by the author, Boston, 250 pp., 8 pls.
1885 A List of the Birds of the West Indies, including the Bahama Islands and the Greater and Lesser Antilles, excepting the islands of Tobago and Trinidad. Estes & Lauriat, Boston, 33 pp.
1886 The Birds of the West Indies, Including the Bahama Islands, the Greater and the Lesser Antilles, excepting the Islands of Tobago and Trinidad. Auk 3:1–59.
1890 The Birds of the Bahama Islands, containing many birds new to the Islands, and a number of undescribed winter plumages of North American birds. (Revised ed.) Estes & Lauriat, Boston, 250 pp., 8 pls.
1891a A List of Birds taken and observed in Cuba and the Bahama Islands, during March and April, 1891. Auk, 8:292–296.
1891b List of the Birds collected by C. L. Winch in the Caicos Islands and Inagua, Bahamas, during January and February, and in Abaco, in March, 1891. Auk, 8:296–298.
1892 Catalogue of West Indian Birds. Published by the author, Boston, 163 pp.
1896 A List of the Birds of Eastern North America. Bradley Whidden, Boston, 42 pp.
1898 Kirtland's Warbler (*Dendroica kirtlandi*) in Florida. Auk, 15:331.
1899 The Birds of Eastern North America known to occur east of the ninetieth meridian. Published by the author, Boston. 2 vols. Vol. 1, viii, 1–142; Vol. 2, ix, 131–387.
1900 The Birds of Eastern North America Known to Occur East of the Ninetieth Meridian. Boston, Bay State Publ. Co. Parts 1 and 2 (separately paged).
COUES, ELLIOTT
1878 Birds of the Colorado Valley. U. S. Geol. Surv. of the Terr., Misc. Publ. No. 11, xvi + 807 pp., illus.
1880 Description of the Female *Dendroeca kirtlandi*. Bull. Nuttall Orn. Club, 5:49–50.
1903 Key to North American Birds. Dana Eates, Boston. 5th ed. 2 vols. Vol. 1, xli, 1–535; Vol. 2, vi, 537–1152, illus.
Coulson, J. C.
*1958 Letter to the Editor. Bird-Banding. 29:134–135.
COVERT, A. B.
1876 Birds of Lower Michigan. Forest & Stream, March–Dec., 1876, 6:99. 7:276.
1881 Natural History. Birds of Washtenaw County. History of Washtenaw County, Michigan. Chicago, 1881:173–194.
1903 Remarks on the Recent Capture of a Kirtland's Warbler in Michigan. Bull. Michigan Orn. Club, 4:47–49.
CRAIGHILL, FRANCIS H.
*1942 Craighill's Last Letter about North Carolina Birds. Chat, 6:25–26.

CRUICKSHANK, A. D., R. T. PETERSON, JOSEPH CADBURY, ROLAND CLEMENT
*1942–1954 Aud. Mag., Sec. 2, Breeding Bird Census. Climax Red and White Spruce Forest.
1942, Sept.–Oct.:30; 1946, Nov.–Dec.:133; 1947, Audubon Field Notes, 1:220; 1949, 3:256–257; 1950, 4:295; 1951, 5:317; 1952, 6:319–320; 1953, 7:356; 1954, 8:381.

CURTIS, GEORGE M.
1941 Jared Potter Kirtland, M. D. Ohio State Medical Jour., 37:971–977.

DALL, WILLIAM HEALEY
*1915 Spencer Fullerton Baird, A Biography. Lippincott, Philadelphia, xvi + 462 pp.

DARLING, F. FRASER
*1938 Bird Flocks and the Breeding Cycle. Cambridge University Press, London, x + 124 pp.

DARNELL, MRS. M.
1956 Kirtland's Warbler. Migrant, 27:53.

DAVIE, OLIVER
1898 Nests and Eggs of North American Birds. (5th ed.) 2 parts, (8) + 509; 18 + xxi pp., illus. Columbus, The Langdon Press.

DAVIES, L. M.
*1906 The Birds of Cleveland, Ohio, and Vicinity. Wilson Bull., 18:110–120.

DAVIS, CHARLES M.
*1936 The High Plains of Michigan. Papers Mich. Acad. Sci., Arts, & Letters, 21:303–341.

DAVIS, DAVID E.
*1952 Definitions for the Analysis of Survival of Nestlings. Auk, 69:316–320.
*1959 Observations on Territorial Behavior of Least Flycatchers. Wilson Bull., 71:73–85.

DAWSON, WILLIAM LEON
*1903 The Birds of Ohio. The Wheaton Publ. Co., Columbus, Ohio, xlvii + 671 pp., 80 pls.

DENNIS, D. W.
1905 Capture of the Kirtland Warbler near Richmond, Ind. Auk, 22:314.

DENTON, J. FRED, AND B. R. CHAMBERLAIN
*1950 Southern Atlantic Region. Audubon Field Notes, 4:9–11.

DIXON, KEITH L.
*1956 Territoriality and Survival in the Plain Titmouse. Condor, 58:169–182.

DOUGLASS, DONALD W.
1951 Kirtland's Warbler. Michigan Conservation, 20, No. 3, May–June, 1951:33. (Reprinted in Roberts and Messner, 1952, with the addition of a photo by Brigham and map from Van Tyne.)
1959 Kirtland's Warbler. P. 5, *in* Enjoying Birds in Michigan, 2nd ed., edited by Haven H. Spencer, Michigan Audubon Soc., 66 pp., illus.

DU BOIS, A. D.
*1956 A Cowbird Incident. Auk, 73:286.

EARDLEY, A. J.
*1951 Structural Geology of North America. Harper, New York, xiv + 624 pp.

EATON, STEPHEN W.

*1957 A Life History Study of *Seiurus noveboracensis*. Science Studies, Centennial Celebration Issue. St. Bonaventure University, St. Bonaventure, New York, 19:7–36.

*1958 A Life History Study of the Louisiana Waterthrush. Wilson Bull., 70:211–236.

ELLIS, J. B.

1915 Migratory Notes taken Fall 1915 by J. B. Ellis, Chokoloskee, Fla. Oologist, 32:207, 209.

ESTEN, SIDNEY R.

1938 Etta Wilson's Marion County Migration Records. Indiana Audubon Soc. Yearbook, 16:41–47.

FARGO, WILLIAM G.

1934 Walter John Hoxie. Wilson Bull., 46:169–196.

FARNER, DONALD S.

*1955 Birdbanding in the Study of Population Dynamics. Pp. 397–449, *in* Recent Studies in Avian Biology, Univ. Illinois Press, Urbana, ix + 479 pp.

FAVER, ANNIE RIVERS

1949 Kirtland's Warbler seen at Eastover, Richland County, S.C. Chat, 13:79–80.

FIGGINS, JESSE DADE

1945 Birds of Kentucky. University of Kentucky Press, Lexington. 366 pp.

FLEMING, JAMES H.

1907 Birds of Toronto, Canada. Part II, Land Birds. Auk, 24:71–89.

1913 Birds of the Toronto Region, Ontario. Chap. 16 (pp. 212–237). The Natural History of the Toronto Region, Ontario, Canada. Toronto.

FORBUSH, EDWARD HOWE

1929 Birds of Massachusetts and Other New England States. Vol. 3, xlviii + 466 pp., pls. 63–93.

FORBUSH, EDWARD HOWE, AND JOHN BICHARD MAY

*1939 See May, John Bichard

FORD, EDWARD R.

1931 Note on Kirtland's Warbler. Auk, 48:276.

1956 Birds of the Chicago Region. Chicago Acad. Sci., Spec. Publ. No. 12, vii + 117 pp.

FORD, EDWARD R., COLIN C. SANBORN, AND C. BLAIR COURSEN

1934 Birds of the Chicago Region. Program of Activities of The Chicago Academy of Sciences, 5:19–80.

FREEMAN, F. J.

*1950 Display of Oven-birds, *Seiurus aurocapillus*. Auk, 67:521.

FREY, EDWARD SNIVELY

1943 The Centennial Check-list of the Birds of Cumberland County, Pennsylvania and Her Borders. 1840–1943. Publ. by the author, Lemoyne, Pa., 68 pp.

FRIEDMANN, HERBERT

*1929 The Cowbirds. A Study in the Biology of Social Parasitism. Charles C Thomas, Springfield, Ill., xvii + 421 pp., illus.

FROTHINGHAM, EARL H.
*1903   Another Kirtland's Warbler from Michigan. Bull. Mich. Orn. Club, 4:61.
 1906   Notes on The Birds of the Michigan Forest Reserve. Eighth Rept. Michigan Acad. Sci., 1906:157–161.

GANIER, ALBERT F.
 1933   A Distributional List of the Birds of Tennessee. Tennessee Avifauna No. 1.

GAULT, B. T.
 1894   Kirtland's Warbler in Northeastern Illinois. Auk, 11:258.
 1922   Check List of the Birds of Illinois. Illinois Audubon Society, Chicago, 80 pp., 1 map.

GIBBS, MORRIS
 1879   Annotated List of the Birds of Michigan. Bull. U.S. Geol. and Geogr. Survey of the Territories, 5:481–497.
 1885   The Birds of Michigan. Forest & Stream, 23 to 25, Jan. 15 to July 30, 1885:483–485.
 1898   Additions to the Avifauna of Kalamazoo County, Michigan. Bull. Michigan Orn. Club, 2:7.

GOODPASTER, WOODROW
 1941   Birds of Southwestern Ohio. Jour. Cincinnati Soc. Nat. Hist., 22, No. 3:6–40.

GREENE, EARLE R., WILLIAM W. GRIFFIN, EUGENE P. ODUM, HERBERT L. STOD-DARD, AND IVAN R. TOMKINS
 1945   Birds of Georgia/A Preliminary Check-List and Bibliography of Georgia Ornithology. Univ. of Georgia Press, Athens, Ga., 111 pp., 1 fig., 1 map.

GREENE, ROY FARRELL
 1902   A Successful Collector (Willis W. Worthington). The American Society of Curio Collectors' Year Book for 1902, pp. 64–65.

GROSS, MARGARET E.
 1937   Michigan—Bird Student's Paradise. Jack-Pine Warbler, 15 (No. 4): 5–12.
 1938   Kirtland Warbler on Migration. Jack-Pine Warbler, 16 (No. 3):28–29.
 1938   The Bird that Adopted Michigan. Nature Magazine, 31:301–302.

GUILFORD, H. M.
 1893   *Dendroica kirtlandi* in Minnesota. Auk, 10:86.

HAARTMAN, LARS VON
*1958   The Incubation Rhythm of the Female Pied Flycatcher (*Ficedula hypoleuca*) in the Presence and Absence of the Male. Ornis Fennica, 35:71–76. (Seen only in review by O. L. Austin, Jr., in Bird-Banding, 30:54.)

HANN, HARRY W.
*1937   Life History of the Oven-bird in Southern Michigan. Wilson Bull., 49:145–237.
*1940   Polyandry in the Oven-bird. Wilson Bull., 52:69–72.
*1941   The Cowbird at the Nest. Wilson Bull., 53:211–221.

*1947   An Oven-bird incubates a record number of eggs. Wilson Bull., 59:173–174.
*1948   Longevity of the Oven-bird. Bird-Banding, 19:5–12.

HARRINGTON, PAUL
*1939   Kirtland's Warbler in Ontario. Jack-Pine Warbler, 17:95–97.

HARRISON, HAL H.
1948   American Birds in Color. Wm. H. Wise & Co., Inc., New York, xxiv + 486 pp., illus.

HASTINGS, WALTER
See Preble, E. A., 1930 (photo of Kirtland's Warbler).

HAUSMAN, LEON AUGUSTUS
1944   The Illustrated Encyclopedia of American Birds. Halcyon House, New York, xix + 541 pp.

HAVERSCHMIDT, F.
*1953   Notes on the Yellow Warbler in Surinam. Auk, 70:369–370.

HELME, A. H.
1904   The Ipswich Sparrow, Kirtland's Warbler, and Sprague's Pipit in Georgia. Auk, 21:291.

HELLMAYR, CHARLES E.
1935   Catalogue of Birds of the Americas and the Adjacent Islands. Field Mus. Nat. Hist., Zool. Ser., 13, part 8.

HENNINGER, W. F.
*1906   A Preliminary List of the Birds of Seneca County, Ohio. Wilson Bull., 18:47–60.
1908   Bird Notes from Middle Western Ohio. Wilson Bull., 20:208–210.
1910   [Kirtland Warbler at Catawba, Ohio.] Wilson Bull., 22:128.
1912   Notes from the Tri-reservoir Region in Ohio. Wilson Bull., 24:155–156.

HENNINGER, W. F., AND G. A. KUENNING
1908   All Day with the Birds. New Bremen, Ohio, May 14, 1908. Wilson Bull., 20:96–98.

HENSHAW, HENRY W., AND A. A. ALLEN
*1937   Warblers, Friends of Our Forests. In The Book of Birds, Vol. 2:179–207. Nat. Geogr. Soc., Washington, D.C.

HERRICK, FRANCIS H.
1939   The Individual vs. the Species in Behavior Studies. Auk, 56:244–249.

HICKEY, JOSEPH J.
*1940   Territorial Aspects of the American Redstart. Auk, 57:255–256.

HICKS, LAWRENCE E.
*1934   A Summary of Cowbird Host Species in Ohio. Auk, 51:385–386.

HOFSLUND, P. B.
*1957   Cowbird Parasitism of the Northern Yellow-throat. Auk, 74:42–48.

HORBERG, LELAND
*1955   Radiocarbon Dates and Pleistocene Chronological Problems in the Mississippi Valley Region. Jour. of Geology, 63:278–286.

HOWELL, ARTHUR H.
1924   Birds of Alabama. Dept. Game and Fisheries of Alabama, Montgomery, Ala., 384 pp., illus.

*1932   Florida Bird Life. Fla. Dept. of Game and Fresh Water Fish. Coward-McCann, New York, xxiv + 579 pp., 58 pls., 72 figs.

HOXIE, WALTER

*1886   Kirtland's Warbler on St. Helena Island, South Carolina. Auk, 3:412–413.

HUSSONG, CLARA

1956   Kirtland's Warbler in Door County [Wisconsin]. Passenger Pigeon, 18(3):122–123.

HUXLEY, J. S.

*1927   On the Relation Between Egg-weight and Body-weight in Birds. Jour. Linn. Soc., London, 36:457–466.

INGERSOLL, ERNEST

1882   A History of Nests and Eggs of American Birds. Parts 6 and 7. George A. Bates, Salem, Mass.

JASPER, THEODORE

1881   Studer's Popular Ornithology. The Birds of North America. Jacob H. Studer & Co., New York and Columbus, Ohio.

JENNESS, P. M.

*1925   Kirtland's Warbler in North [South] Carolina. Bird Lore, 27:252–253.

JENNINGS, A. H.

1888   List of Birds Observed at New Providence, Bahama Islands, March–June, 1887. Johns Hopkins Univ. Circulars, 7, No. 63:39.

JOHNSTON, BETTE J.

*1957   A Technique for Trapping Cowbirds. Wilson Bull., 69:278.

JONES, J. M.

1880   Spring Field Notes. Cleveland, Ohio, May 5. Forest & Stream, 14:307.

JONES, LYNDS

1895   Record of the Work of the Wilson Chapter for 1893 and 1894, on the Mniotiltidae. Wilson Bull., 7(4):1–21.

1900a   Warbler Songs. [Mniotiltidae.] Wilson Bull., 12(1):1–57.

1900b   Kirtland's Warbler (*Dendroica kirtlandi*) at Oberlin, Ohio. Wilson Bull., 12(3):1–2.

1902   Kirtland's Warbler (*Dendroica kirtlandi*) Again in Ohio. Wilson Bull., 14(3):104–105.

*1903a   The Birds of Ohio. A Revised Catalogue. Ohio State Academy of Science, Special Papers No. 6, 241 pp.

*1903b   Kirtland Warbler (*Dendroica kirtlandi*) Found Breeding. Wilson Bull., 15(3):101.

1904a   All Day With the Birds [Oberlin section]. Wilson Bull., 16(2):37–42.

1904b   Oberlin All Day With the Birds. 1904. Wilson Bull., 16(2):43–50.

1904c   Spring Migration in Lorain County, O., 1904. Wilson Bull., 16(2):55–57.

1906   Some Noteworthy Lorain County Records for 1906. Wilson Bull., 18(2):74–75.

1910   The Birds of Cedar Point and Vicinity [2nd part]. Wilson Bull., 22(2):97–115.

1914   Nineteen Years of Bird Migration at Oberlin, Ohio. Wilson Bull., 26(4):198–205.

1917   A Season of Abundance of Birds in Central Ohio. Wilson Bull., 29(3): 166.

KEELER, CHARLES A.
1893   Evolution of the Colors of North American Land Birds. Occ. Papers California Acad. Sci., 3, xii + 361 pp., 19 pls.

KELLS, W. L.
1901   Two Warblers New to Canada. Ottawa Naturalist, 14:230–234.

KEMSIES, EMERSON, AND WORTH RANDLE
1953   Birds of Southwestern Ohio. Privately published, xii + 74 pp., illus.

KENDEIGH, S. CHARLES
*1941   Territorial and Mating Behavior of the House Wren. Illinois Biological Monog. 18, No. 3, 120 pp., 32 figs.
*1945   Nesting Behavior of Wood Warblers. Wilson Bull., 57:145–164.
*1947   Bird Population Studies in the Coniferous Forest Biome during a Spruce Budworm Outbreak. Biol. Bull. No. 1, Dept. of Lands and Forests, Ontario, 100 pp., 32 figs.
*1948   Bird Populations and Biotic Communities in Northern Lower Michigan. Ecology, 29:101–114.
*1951   Review of "On the Concept of 'Incubation Period,'" by P. O. Swanberg. Bird-Banding, 22:37–38.
*1956   A Trail Census of Birds at Itasca State Park, Minnesota. Flicker, 28: 90–104.

KEYSER, LEANDER
1891   Bird-dom. Lothrop Co., Boston.

KIRKPATRICK, JOHN
1860   Kirtland's Warbler. Ohio Farmer, 9, June 9, 1860:179.

KIRKWOOD, F. C.
1895   A List of the Birds of Maryland. Trans. Maryland Acad. Sci. 2:241–382.

KIRTLAND, J. P.
*1838   Report on the Zoology of Ohio. Second Annual Report on the Geological Survey of the State of Ohio, by W. W. Mather. Samuel Medary, Printer to the State, Columbus.
1883   [Letter to H. A. Purdie, dated May 22, 1876.] Bull. Nuttall Orn. Club, 8:126–127.

KUMLIEN, L., AND N. HOLLISTER
1903   The Birds of Wisconsin. Bull. Wisc. Nat. Hist. Soc., 2 [3] (New Series): iv + 143 pp.
1951   The Birds of Wisconsin. With revisions by A. W. Schorger. Wisconsin Society for Ornithology, Madison, vi + 122 pp. Reprinted from The Passenger Pigeon, 1948, vol. 10:11–24; 59–68; 107–113; 142–148. 1949, vol. 11:36–40; 74–79; 114–124; 157–166. 1950, vol. 12:21–30; 76–84; 117–127; 161–168. 1951, vol. 13:19–21; 69; 108; 133–135.

LACK, DAVID
*1940   Courtship Feeding in Birds. Auk, 57:169–178.
*1943   The Life of the Robin. H. F. G. Witherby Ltd., London, 200 pp., 6 pls., 3 figs.
*1944   Ecological Aspects of Species-formation in Passerine Birds. Ibis, 86: 260–286.

*1954   The Natural Regulation of Animal Numbers. Oxford University Press, London. vii + 343 pp., 1 pl., 52 figs.

LACK, DAVID, AND ELIZABETH LACK
*1951   Further Changes in Bird-life Caused by Afforestation. Jour. of Animal Ecology, 20:173–179.

LANGDON, FRANK W.
1877   A Catalogue of the Birds of the Vicinity of Cincinnati, With Notes. The Naturalist's Agency, Salem, Mass., 18 pp.

1879   A Revised List of Cincinnati Birds. Jour. Cinn. Soc. Nat. Hist., 1:167–193.

1880   Ornithological Field Notes, with Five Additions to the Cincinnati Avian Fauna. Jour. Cincinnati Soc. Nat. Hist., 3:121–127.

LANGILLE, REV. J. HIBBERT
1892   Our Birds in Their Haunts: A Popular Treatise on the Birds of Eastern North America. Orange Judd Co., New York, 630 pp.

LASKEY, AMELIA R.
*1950   Cowbird Behavior. Wilson Bull., 62:157–174.

LAWRENCE, LOUISE DE KIRILINE
*1948   Comparative Study of the Nesting Behavior of Chestnut-sided and Nashville Warblers. Auk, 65:204–219.

*1953a Nesting Life and Behaviour of the Red-eyed Vireo. Canadian Field-Naturalist, 67:47–77.

*1953b Notes on the Nesting Behavior of the Blackburnian Warbler. Wilson Bull., 65:135–144.

*1954   The Voluble Singer of the Treetops. Aud. Mag., 56:109–111.

LEATHERS, CARL L.
*   Incubating American Robin Repels Female Brown-headed Cowbird. Wilson Bull., 68:68.

LEOPOLD, N. F., JR.
*1924   The Kirtland's Warbler in Its Summer Home. Auk, 41:44–58.

LEWY, ALFRED, AND KARL E. BARTEL
1943   Seney National Wildlife Refuge. The [Illinois] Audubon Bull., 48:11–16.

LOOMIS, LEVERETT M.
1889   A Rare Bird in Chester Co., South Carolina. Auk, 6:74–75.

1891, 1892, 1894   A Further Review of the Avian Fauna of Chester County, South Carolina. Auk, 8:49–59, 167–173; 9:28–39; 11:26–39, 94–117.

LUPIENT, MARY
1951   Seasonal Report. Flicker, 23:50–53.

MACKENZIE, J. M. D.
*1950   Nestling Mortality Amongst Tits on Tentsmuir, 1949 and 1950. British Birds, 43:393–398.

MACNEIL, F. STEARNS
*1950   Pleistocene Shorelines in Florida and Georgia. U.S. Geological Survey Professional Paper 221-F, p. 104.

MACOUN, JOHN
1900–1904   Catalogue of Canadian Birds. Geological Survey of Canada. 1 vol. in 3 pts: (pt. 1) i–vii, 1–218; (pt. 2) i–iv, 219–413; (pt. 3) i–iv, 415–733, i–xxiii.

MAIN, ANGIE KUMLIEN
  1925 Bird Companions. Richard G. Badger, Boston.

MARKS, CHARLES F., AND HOWARD F. WRIGHT
  1950 Spring Flight. Indiana Audubon Quarterly, 28:64–76.

MARTIN, JOHN WILLIAM
  1901a Two Warblers New to Canada. The Petrel (Palestine, Ore.), 1:9.
  1901b Kirtland's Warbler. The Petrel (Palestine, Ore.), 1:15.

MASLOWSKI, KARL, AND RALPH DURY
  1931 Catalogue of the Charles Dury Collection of North American Birds. Proc. Junior Soc. Nat. Sciences, 2 (4):67–107.

MAY, JOHN BICHARD
  *1939 P. 438 *in* Forbush, Edward Howe, and John Bichard May. Natural History of the Birds of Eastern and Central North America. Houghton Mifflin, Boston, xxv + 554 pp., 97 pls.

MAYFIELD, HAROLD
  *1953 A Census of the Kirtland's Warbler. Auk, 70:17–20.

MAYNARD, C. J.
  1881 The Birds of Eastern North America; (Rev. ed.) C. J. Maynard & Co., Newtonville, Mass., iv + 532 pp., 32 pls.
  1885 A New Catalogue of Birds' Skins, Nests, and Eggs Obtained on the Bahamas by C. J. Maynard.
  *1889–96 The Birds of Eastern North America; (Rev. ed.) C. J. Maynard & Co., Newtonville, Mass., 721 pp., 40 pls.
  1890 Eggs of North American Birds. De Wolfe, Fiske & Co., Boston, iv + 159 pp., 10 pls.
  1899 American Warblers. Nature Study in Schools, 1 (4):85–92.
  1906 An Atlas of Plates for the Directory to the Birds of Eastern North America. C. J. Maynard, West Newton, Mass.
  1907 Directory to the Birds of Eastern North America. C. J. Maynard, West Newton, Mass.
  1916 A Field Ornithology of the Birds of Eastern North America. C. J. Maynard, West Newton, Mass., 550 pp., illus.
  1917 Kirtland Warbler in Massachusetts [Written by Julia W. Sherman.] *In* Records of Walks and Talks with Nature, 9:8–9.
  1918 Directory to the Birds of Eastern North America. Publ. by the author. West Newton, Mass., vi + 326, frontis. + 23 pls.

MCATEE, W. L.
  *1920 Notes on the Jack Pine Plains of Michigan. Bulletin of the Torrey Botanical Club, 47:187–190.

MCCLANAHAN, ROBERT C.
  1935 Fifty Years After. Florida Nat. 8:53–59; 9:1–6.
  1937 Annotated List of the Birds of Alachua County, Florida. Proc. Florida Acad. Sci. (for 1936), 1:91–102.

MERRIAM, C. HART
  1885 Kirtland's Warbler from the Straits of Mackinac. Auk, 2:376.

MILLER, ALDEN H.
  *1942 Shower Bathing of a Spotted Towhee. Condor, 44:232.

MOYER, LOUISE B.
  1908 Song of Kirtland's Warbler. Bird Lore, 10:264.

MUMFORD, RUSSELL E.
*1959   Cowbird Parasitizes Nest Containing Young. Auk, 76:367–368.
MONK, J. F.
*1954   The Breeding Biology of the Greenfinch. Bird Study, 1:2–14.
MUNNS, E. N.
*1938   The Distribution of Important Forest Trees of the United States. USDA Misc. Publ. 287, U.S. Printing Office, Washington.
MURRAY, JOSEPH JAMES
1952   A Check-list of the Birds of Virginia. Virginia Society of Ornithology, 113 pp.
MUSSELMAN, T. E.
1921   A History of the Birds of Illinois. Jour. Illinois State Hist. Soc., 14: 1–73.
NASH, C. W.
1905   Check List of the Vertebrates of Ontario and Catalogue of Specimens in the Biological Section of the Provincial Museum. Birds. Dept. of Education, Toronto, 82 pp.
NEHRLING, HENRY
1893   Our Native Birds of Song and Beauty. Geo. Brumder, Milwaukee, Wis., Vol. 1:1 + 371 pp., 18 pls.
NERO, ROBERT W.
*1956   A Behavior Study of the Red-winged Blackbird. I. Mating and Nesting Activities. Wilson Bull., 68:5–37.
NICE, MARGARET M.
*1937   Studies in the Life History of the Song Sparrow I. A Population Study of the Song Sparrow. Trans. Linn. Soc. New York, Vol. 4, vi + 247 pp.
*1943   Studies in the Life History of the Song Sparrow II. The Behavior of the Song Sparrow and Other Passerines. Trans. Linn. Soc. New York, Vol. 6, viii + 328 pp.
*1947   At the Nest of a Barn Swallow. Bird-Banding, 18:174–175. (Review of Auprès du Nid d'Hirondelle *Hirundo rustica rustica* Linné, by L. De Braey in Le Gerfaut, 36:133–198).
*1949   The Laying Rhythm of Cowbirds. Wilson Bull., 61:231–234.
*1954   Problems of Incubation Periods in North American Birds. Condor, 56: 173–197.
*1957   Nesting Success in Altricial Birds. Auk, 74:305–321.
NICE, MARGARET M., AND W. E. SCHANTZ
*1932   A Study of Two Nests of the Black-throated Green Warbler. Bird-Banding, 3:95–105, 157–172.
NICE, MARGARET M. AND W. E. SCHANTZ
*1959   Head-scratching Movements in Birds. Auk, 76:339–342.
NICHOLS, L. NELSON
1936   Kirtland's Warbler. *In* Pearson, T. Gilbert, *et al.* Birds of America. Pt. 3, pp. 146–147.
NOLAN, VAL, JR.
*1955   Invertebrate Nest Associates of the Prairie Warbler. Auk, 72:55–61.
*1958   Anticipatory Food-bringing in the Prairie Warbler. Auk, 75:263–278.

NORRIS, RUSSELL T.
*1944   Notes on a Cowbird Parasitizing a Song Sparrow. Wilson Bull., 56: 129–132.
*1947   The Cowbirds of Preston Frith. Wilson Bull., 59:83–103.
OBERHOLSER, HARRY C.
1929   *In* David Starr Jordan, Manual of Vertebrate Animals of the Northeastern United States Inclusive of Marine Species. World Book Co., New York.
ODUM, EUGENE P.
*1945   The Concept of the Biome as Applied to the Distribution of North American Birds. Wilson Bull., 57:191–201.
ODUM, EUGENE P., AND EDWARD J. KUENZLER
*1955   Measurement of Territory and Home Range Size in Birds. Auk, 72: 128–137.
PALMER, T. S.
1928   Notes on Persons Whose Names Appear in the Nomenclature of California Birds. A Contribution to the History of West Coast Ornithology. Condor, 30:261–307.
PEARSON, T. GILBERT, C. S. BRIMLEY, AND H. H. BRIMLEY
1919   Birds of North Carolina. North Carolina Geological and Economic Survey, xxiii + 380, 24 pls.
1942   Birds of North Carolina. North Carolina Department of Agriculture, xxxii + 416 pp., 37 pls.
PEARSON, T. GILBERT, *et al.*
1936   (See L. Nelson Nichols)
PETERSON, ROGER TORY
1934   A Field Guide to the Birds, giving field marks of all species found in eastern North America. Houghton Mifflin, Boston, xxi + 167 pp., illus.
1939   A Field Guide to the Birds, giving field marks of all species found east of the Rockies. Houghton Mifflin, Boston, xx + 180 pp., illus.
1948   Birds Over America. Dodd, Mead, New York, xiii + 342 pp., illus.
PETERSON, MRS. THEODORE
1941   Getting One's Share of Michigan Warblers. Jack-Pine Warbler, 19:49–58.
PETRY, LOREN C.
1909   Records of Kirtland's Warbler. Bird-Lore, 11:177.
PETTINGILL, OLIN SEAWALL, JR.
1951   A Guide to Bird Finding East of the Mississippi. Oxford Univ. Press, New York.
PICKENS, A. L.
1928   Birds of Upper South Carolina: A Study in Geographical Distribution. Wilson Bull., 40:182–191; 238–246.
PITELKA, FRANK A.
*1940   Breeding Behavior of the Black-throated Green Warbler. Wilson Bull., 52:3–18.
*1958   Timing of Molt in Steller Jays of the Queen Charlotte Islands, British Columbia. Condor, 60:38–49.

POUGH, RICHARD H.
 1946 Audubon Bird Guide: Eastern Land Birds. Doubleday & Co., Garden City, N.Y., xxxvii + 312 pp., 48 pls.
PREBLE, EDWARD A.
 1930 Birds of Hiawatha Land. Nature Mag., 15:293–296, 334.
PRESTON, F. W.
 *1948 The Cowbird (*M. ater*) and the Cuckoo (*C. canorus*). Ecology, 29: 115–116.
PURDIE, H. A.
 1879 Another Kirtland's Warbler (*Dendroeca kirtlandi*). Bull. Nuttall Orn. Club, 4:185–186.
REED, CHESTER A.
 1904 North American Birds' Eggs. New York. Doubleday, Page & Co., 356 pp., illus.
 1908 Bird Guide. Part 2. Land Birds East of the Rockies. From Parrots to Bluebirds. Worcester, Mass.
 1914 Bird Guide. Part 2. Land Birds East of the Rockies: From Parrots to Bluebirds. Doubleday, Page & Co., Garden City, N.Y.
 1951 Bird Guide. Part 2. Land Birds East of the Rockies: From Parrots to Bluebirds. (Revised by John W. Aldrich.) Doubleday, Garden City, N.Y.
RIDGWAY, ROBERT
 1881 Nomenclature of North American Birds. U.S. Nat. Mus. Bull., 21, 94 pp.
 1884 Another Kirtland's Warbler from Michigan. Auk, 1:389.
 1891 List of Birds Collected on the Bahama Islands by the Naturalists of the Fish Commission Steamer *Albatross*. Auk, 8:333–339.
 1902 The Birds of North and Middle America. U.S. Nat. Mus. Bull., 50, Pt. 2, xx + 834 pp., 22 pls.
 *1912 Color Standards and Color Nomenclature. Publ. by the author, Washington, iii + 43 pp., 53 pls.
 1914 Bird Life in Southern Illinois. I. Bird Haven. Bird-Lore, 16:409–420.
RILEY, JOSEPH H.
 1905 Birds of the Bahama Islands. Pp. 347–368 *in* The Bahama Islands, Ed. by George B. Shattuck. Macmillan, New York, xxxii + 630 pp., 93 pls.
RIVES, WM. C.
 1889–1890 A Catalogue of the Birds of the Virginias. Proc. Newport Nat. Hist. Soc., Document 7, 100 pp.
ROADS, KATIE M.
 1912 Why Birds Are So Named. Wilson Bull., 24:27–33; 130–142.
ROBBINS, SAMUEL D., JR.
 1947 1946 in Review. Passenger Pigeon, 9:48–54.
ROBERTS, THOMAS SADLER
 1919 A Review of the Ornithology of Minnesota. Research Publications of the Univ. of Minnesota, Vol. 8, No. 2, v + 100 pp., illus.
 *1932 The Birds of Minnesota. Vol. 2. Univ. of Minnesota Press, Minneapolis, xv + 821 pp., frontis. + pls. 50–90.

1934 Bird Portraits in Color: Two Hundred Ninety-five North American Species. Univ. of Minnesota Press, Minneapolis.

ROLLIN, NOBLE

*1950 Amount a Bird Sings. Dawn Song and All Day, 1:23–27.

RYVES, B. H.

*1943 An Investigation into the Roles of Males in Relation to Incubation. British Birds, 37:10–16.

SAGER, ABM.

*1839 Report of Doct. Abm. Sager, Zoologist of Geological Survey. Jour. [Mich.] H. R., Doc. No. 1, 1839:410–421.

SAMUEL, I. HUGHES

1900 List of the Rarer Birds Met with during the Spring of 1900 in the Immediate Vicinity of Toronto. Auk, 17:391–392.

SAUNDERS, ARETAS A.

*1908 Some Birds of Central Alabama. A List of the Birds Observed from March 7 to June 9, in Portions of Coosa, Clay and Talledega Counties, Alabama. Auk, 25:413–424.

SAUNDERS, W. E.

1906 Birds New to Ontario. Ottawa Naturalist, 19:205–207.

1941 Kirtland's Warbler (*Dendroica kirtlandi*). Canadian Field-Naturalist, 55:16.

SCHANTZ, ORPHEUS MOYER

1928 Birds of Illinois. Illinois Dept. Conservation, Conservation Publication No. 6, 123 pp. + 6 (index).

SCHORGER, A. W.

1931 The Birds of Dane County, Wisconsin, Part II. Trans. Wisconsin Acad. Sci., Arts, and Letters, 26:1–60.

1951 Revised edition of: Kumlien, L., and N. Hollister, 1903, The Birds of Wisconsin.

SCHRANTZ, F. G.

*1943 Nest Life of the Eastern Yellow Warbler. Auk, 60:367–387.

SCHRODER, HUGO H.

1923 Notes from Fort Pierce, Florida. Bird-Lore, 25:122–123.

SHARPE, R. BOWDLER

1885 Catalogue of the Birds in the British Museum, Vol. 10, London, Printed by order of the Trustees, xiii + 682 pp., 12 pls.

SHORT, ERNEST H.

1904 The Discovery of the First Known Nest of Kirtland's Warbler. Oologist, 21:53–55.

SICK, HELMUT, AND JOHANN OTTOW

*1958 The Shiny Cowbird and Its Hosts, Especially the Rufous-collared Sparrow. Seen only in review by M. M. Nice, Bird-Banding, 30:190–191. Originally publ. in Bonner Zoologische Beiträge, 1(9):40–62.

SKUTCH, ALEXANDER F.

*1953 How the Male Bird Discovers the Nestlings. Ibis, 95:1–37, 505–542.

*1954, 1955 The Parental Stratagems of Birds. Ibis, 96:544–564; 97:118–142.

SMITH, HARRY R., AND PAUL W. PARMALEE
  1955 A Distributional Check List of the Birds of Illinois. Illinois State Mus., Popular Sci. Series, vol. 4, 62 pp.

SMITH, HUGH M., AND WILLIAM PALMER
  *1888 Additions to the Avifauna of Washington and Vicinity. Auk, 5:147–148.

SMITH, WENDELL P.
  *1946–1953 White Pine–Hemlock Forest. Aud. Mag., Sec. 2, Audubon Field Notes, 1946, Nov.–Dec.:134–135; Audubon Field Notes, 1947, 1:196–197; 1948, 2:229–230; 1949, 3:257; 1950, 4:295–296; 1951, 5:318–319; 1952, 6:304–305; 1953, 7:337.

SMITHE, GENEVA
  1936 Kirtlandia. Jack-Pine Warbler, 14(3):3–9 (mimeo).

SNYDER, DANA
  *1949 Young Oak-Hickory Forest. Audubon Field Notes, 3:261–262; 1950, 4:297; 1951, 5:321–322.

SOUTHERN, WILLIAM E.
  *1958 Nesting of the Red-eyed Vireo in the Douglas Lake Region, Michigan. Jack-Pine Warbler, 36:105–130, 185–207.

SPRUNT, ALEXANDER, JR.
  1936 Some Observations on the Bird Life of Cumberland Island, Georgia. The Oriole, 1:1–6.
  1951 Golden-Cheek of the Cedar Brakes. Aud. Mag., 53, 13–16. Reference to the Kirtland Warbler on p. 16.
  1954 Florida Bird Life. Coward-McCann, Inc. and Nat. Aud. Soc., N.Y., xlii + 527 pp., 56 pls.

SPRUNT, ALEXANDER, JR., AND E. BURNHAM CHAMBERLAIN
  1931 Second Supplement to Arthur T. Wayne's Birds of South Carolina. Contributions from the Charleston Museum, VI, ix + 37 pp.
  1949 South Carolina Bird Life. Univ. of South Carolina Press, Columbia, S.C., xx + 585 pp., frontis. + 34 pls.

STENGER, JUDITH
  *1958 Food Habits and Available Food of Ovenbirds in Relation to Territory Size. Auk, 75:335–346.

STENGER, JUDITH, AND J. BRUCE FALLS
  *1959 The Utilized Territory of the Ovenbird. Wilson Bull., 71:125–140.

STERRETT, WILLIAM DENT
  1920 Jack Pine. U.S. Dept. Agric. Bull. No. 820:1–47, Plates 1–16.

STEVENS, O. A.
  1936 The First Descriptions of North American Birds. Wilson Bull., 48:203–215.

STEWART, ROBERT E.
  *1953 A Life History Study of the Yellow-throat. Wilson Bull., 65:99–115.

STONE, WITMER
  1898 *Dendroica kirtlandii* in Pennsylvania: A Correction. Auk, 15:331.

STRONG, W. A.
  1919 Curious Eggs. Oologist, 36:180–181.

STURM, LOUIS
*1945   A Study of the Nesting Activities of the American Redstart. Auk, 62: 189–206.

SUNDEVALL, CARL J.
1869   Öfversigt af fogelslägtet Dendroica. Öfversigt af Kongl. Vetenskaps-Akademiens Förhandlingar, 26:605–618.

TAVERNER, P. A.
1905   The Origin of the Kirtland's Warbler. Ontario Nat. Sci. Bull., No. 1:13–17.
1919   Birds of Eastern Canada. Memoir 104, Geol. Surv. Dept. of Mines, Canada, iii + 297 pp., 50 pls.
1934   Birds of Canada. Bull. No. 72, Nat. Mus. of Canada, Dept. of Mines, 445 pp., 87 pls.
1939   Canadian Land Birds. A pocket field guide. Musson Book Co., Ltd., Toronto, 277 pp., illus.

TAYLOR, WARNER
1917   Kirtland's Warbler in Madison, Wisconsin. Auk, 34:343.

TEALE, EDWIN WAY
1950   The Bird That Baffled a Continent. Natural History, 59:172–177.

TEST, L. A.
1939   The Amos W. Butler Collection of Birds. Indiana Audubon Soc. Yearbook, 17:54–57.

THOMAS, EDWARD S.
1926   Notes on Some Central Ohio Birds Observed during 1925. Wilson Bull., 38:118–119.

TINKER, A. D.
1908   Notes on Kirtland's Warbler at Ann Arbor, Mich. Bird-Lore, 10:81–82.
1910   The Birds of School Girl's Glen, Ann Arbor, Michigan: A Study in Local Ornithology. Michigan Geol. & Biol. Surv., Publ. 1:35–66, pls. 10–17.

TODD, W. E. CLYDE
1904   The Birds of Erie and Presque Isle, Erie County, Pennyslvania. Annals Carnegie Mus., 2:481–596, pls. 16–19.

TORDOFF, HARRISON B., AND ROBERT M. MENGEL
*1956   Studies of Birds Killed in Nocturnal Migration. University of Kansas Publications, Museum of Natural History, Vol. 10, No. 1:1–44.

TOWNSEND, CHARLES HASKINS
1927   Old Times with the Birds: Autobiographical. Condor, 29:224–232.

TRAUTMAN, MILTON B.
1940   The Birds of Buckeye Lake, Ohio. Univ. Michigan Mus. Zool. Misc. Publ., No. 44, 466 pp., 15 pls.

TWOMEY, ARTHUR C.
*1936   Climographic Studies of Certain Introduced and Migratory Birds. Ecology, 17:122–132.

ULREY, ALBERT B.
1896   Contributions to the Biological Survey of Wabash County. Proc. Indiana Acad. Sci. for 1895 (1896):147–148.

ULREY, ALBERT B., AND WILLIAM O. WALLACE
  1896 Birds of Wabash County. Proc. Indiana Acad. Sci. for 1895 (1896):148–159.
UTTER, W. T.
  *1942 The Frontier State, 1803–1825. Vol. II in The History of the State of Ohio by Carl Wittke. Ohio State Arch. & Hist. Soc., Columbus.
VAN TYNE, JOSSELYN
  1938 Check List of the Birds of Michigan. Univ. Michigan Mus. Zool. Occ. Papers, No. 379, 43 pp.
  1939 Kirtland's Warbler at Kalamazoo, Michigan. Auk, 56:480–481.
  *1947 Kirtland's Warbler. In Roger Tory Peterson, A Field Guide to the Birds, Houghton Mifflin, Boston, pp. 202–203.
  *1951 The Distribution of the Kirtland Warbler (Dendroica kirtlandii). Proc. 10th Internatl. Orn. Congress [1950], Uppsala, Sweden, 537–544.
  *1953 Dendroica kirtlandii (Baird). Kirtland's Warbler in Arthur Cleveland Bent, Life Histories of North American Wood Warblers, U.S. Nat. Mus. Bull., 203:417–428.
  *1957 Kirtland's Warbler Dendroica kirtlandii. In Ludlow Griscom and Alexander Sprunt, Jr., The Warblers of America, Devin-Adair, New York, pp. 178–181.
VAN TYNE, JOSSELYN, AND ANDREW J. BERGER
  *1959 Fundamentals of Ornithology. John Wiley & Sons, Inc., New York, xi + 624 pp., illus.
VAN TYNE, JOSSELYN, FREDERICK N. HAMERSTROM, JR., FRANCES HAMERSTROM, HAROLD MAYFIELD, AND L. D. HIETT
  *1942–1944 Aud. Mag., Sec. 2, Breeding Bird Census. Jack Pine Barrens. 1942, Sept.–Oct., 142:30; 1943, Sept.–Oct., 146:23–24; 1944, Sept.–Oct., 151:23.
WALKER, CHARLES F.
  1928 The Seasons of Birds in Central Ohio as Shown by Six Years' Migration Records. Ohio State Museum Sci. Bull., 1:9–23.
WALKINSHAW, LAWRENCE H.
  1932 With Kirtland's Warbler Among the Jack-Pines. Bird-Lore, 34:196–199.
  *1938a Nesting Studies of the Prothonotary Warbler. Bird-Banding, 9:32–46.
  *1938b Life History Studies of the Eastern Goldfinch. Jack-Pine Warbler, 16(4):3–11, 14–15.
  1939 Kirtland's Warbler or the Jack-Pine Warbler. Jack-Pine Warbler, 17:97–98.
  *1941 The Prothonotary Warbler, a Comparison of Nesting Conditions in Tennessee and Michigan. Wilson Bull., 53:3–21.
  *1944a The Eastern Chipping Sparrow in Michigan. Wilson Bull., 56:193–205.
  *1944b Clay-colored Sparrow Notes. Jack-Pine Warbler, 22:120–131.
  *1947 Brushy Field, Woodlots and Pond. Audubon Field Notes, 1:214–215.
  *1949 Twenty-five Eggs Apparently Laid by a Cowbird. Wilson Bull., 61:82–85.
  *1952 Chipping Sparrow Notes. Bird-Banding, 23:101–108.
  *1953 Life-history of the Prothonotary Warbler. Wilson Bull., 65:152–168.
WALKINSHAW, LAWRENCE H., BERNARD W. BAKER, EDWARD M. BRIGHAM, JR., EDWARD M. BRIGHAM 3RD, WILLIAM DYER, AND DALE ZIMMERMAN

*1944–1947   Aud. Mag., Sec. 2, Breeding Bird Census. Scrub Oak Area. 1944, Sept.–Oct., 151:18; 1945, Nov.–Dec.:61; 1946, Nov.–Dec.:134; 1947, Audubon Field Notes, 1:198.

WALLACE, VERA H. [VERA H. HEBERT]
*1945–1956   Aud. Mag., Sec. 2, Breeding Bird Census. Partially cut-over northern hardwood slope. 1945, Nov.–Dec.:61; 1946, Nov.–Dec.:133–134; 1947, Audubon Field Notes, 1:198–199; 1948, 2:230; 1949, 3:258–259; 1950, 4:296; 1951, 5:320; 1952, 6:305; 1953, 7:337; 1954, 8:365; 1955, 9:427; 1956, 10:431.

WARREN, B. H.
1888   Report on the Birds of Pennsylvania. Harrisburg, xii + 260 pp., 50 pls.
1890   Report on the Birds of Pennsylvania. 2nd ed. Harrisburg, xiv + 434, 100 pls.

WASHBURN, F. L.
1889   Recent Capture of Kirtland's Warbler in Michigan, and Other Notes. Auk, 6:279–280.

WAYNE, ARTHUR T.
*1904   Kirtland's Warbler (Dendroica kirtlandi) on the Coast of South Carolina. Auk, 21:83–84.
1910   Birds of South Carolina. Contrib. Charleston Mus., 1. xxi + 254 pp.
*1911   A Third Autumnal Record of Kirtland's Warbler (Dendroica kirtlandi) for South Carolina. Auk, 28:116.

WEEDEN, JUDITH STENGER, AND J. BRUCE FALLS
*1959   Differential Responses of Male Ovenbirds to Recorded Songs of Neighboring and More Distant Individuals. Auk, 76:343–351.

WETMORE, ALEXANDER
1926   The Migrations of Birds. Harvard Univ. Press, Cambridge, viii + 217 pp.

WHEATON, J. M.
1861   Catalogue of the Birds of Ohio. Ohio State Board of Agric. 15th Ann. Rept. (for 1860): 359–380.
1879   Kirtland's Warbler again in Ohio. Bull. Nuttall Orn. Club, 4:58.
*1882   Report on the Birds of Ohio. Rept. of the Geological Survey of Ohio, Vol. 4, Pt. 1, Sec. 2:187–628.

WHELAN, MARY ELIZABETH
1952   A Fall Kirtland's Warbler Observation. Jack-Pine Warbler, 30:25.

WICKSTROM, GEORGE
1952   Seasonal Records of Michigan Birds: Spring 1952. Jack-Pine Warbler, 30:79–92.

WIDMANN, OTTO
1885   Note on the capture of Coturniculus lecontei and Dendroeca kirtlandi within the city limits of St. Louis, Mo., Auk, 2:381–382.
1907   A preliminary Catalog of the Birds of Missouri. Trans. Acad. Sci. of St. Louis, 1907:1–288.

WILLIAMS, ARTHUR B.
1944   The Kirtland Warbler in the Cleveland Region. Cleveland Bird Calendar, 40:8 (mimeo).
*1947   Climax Beech-maple Forest with Some Hemlock (15 Year Summary). Audubon Field Notes, 1:205–210.

WING, LEONARD W.
*1933 Summer Warblers of Crawford County, Michigan, Uplands. Wilson Bull., 45:70–76.

WOLFSON, ALBERT
*1954 Weight and Fat Deposition in Relation to Spring Migration in Transient White-throated Sparrows. Auk, 71:413–434.

WOOD, J. CLAIRE
1908 The Kirtland and Pine Warblers in Wayne Co., Michigan. Auk, 25:480.

WOOD, NORMAN A.
1902 Capture of Kirtland's Warbler at Ann Arbor, Michigan. Auk. 19:291.
1903 Some Rare Washtenaw County Warblers. Bull. Michigan Orn. Club, 4:81.
*1904 Discovery of the Breeding Area of Kirtland's Warbler. Bull. Michigan Orn. Club, 5:3–13.
[1906] Twenty-five Years of Bird Migration at Ann Arbor, Michigan. Michigan Acad. Sci., 8th Annual Rept., for 1906:151–156.
1908 Notes on the Spring Migration (1907) at Ann Arbor, Michigan. Auk, 25:10–15.
1912 Notes on Michigan Birds. Michigan Acad. Sci., 14th Rept., 1912, pp. 159–162.
*1926 In Search of New Colonies of Kirtland Warblers. Wilson Bull., 38:11–13.
1951 The Birds of Michigan. Univ. Michigan Mus. Zool. Misc. Publ. No. 75, 559 pp., 16 pls.

WOOD, NORMAN A., and EARL H. FROTHINGHAM
*1905 Notes on the Birds of the Au Sable Valley, Michigan. Auk, 22:39–54.

WOOD, NORMAN A., and A. D. TINKER
1934 Fifty Years of Bird Migration in the Ann Arbor Region of Michigan. 1880–1930. Univ. Michigan Mus. Zool. Occ. Papers, No. 280, 56 pp.

WOODFORD, J. K.
*1959 Migrant Kirtland's Warbler Mist-Netted. Bird-Banding, 30:234.

WOODRUFF, FRANK MORLEY
1907 The Birds of the Chicago Area. Chicago Acad. Sci. Bull. No. 6, 221 pp., pls. 1–10 + 101 unnumbered pls.

YOUNG, HOWARD
*1951 Territorial Behavior in the Eastern Robin. Proceedings of the Linnaean Society of New York, 1945–50, Nos. 58–62:1–37.

ZIMMERMAN, DALE A.
*1956 The Jack Pine Association in the Lower Peninsula of Michigan: Its Structure and Composition. Ph.D. Thesis, University of Michigan.

ZIMMERMAN, DALE A., and JOSSELYN VAN TYNE
1959 A Distributional Check-list of the Birds of Michigan. Univ. Michigan Mus. Zool. Occ. Papers, No. 608, 63 pp.

ZUCHOLD, E. A.
1854 Literarische Notizen. Jour. f. Orn., 2:353–355.

INDEX OF BIRD SPECIES

SUBJECT INDEX

Abandonment of nests. *See* Desertion
Anticipatory food-bringing, 69
Anting, 66–67
Ants, not as food, 19; attack nestlings, 104–105; species, 105
Attack, reaction to danger, 63
Attentiveness, in courtship, 56, 57; during nest-site searching, 71–72
Audiospectrograms of song, 127, fig. 9
Au Sable River, 9, 13

Bahama Islands, climate, 35; wintering ground, 36; specimens, 36; area changes, 37
Baird, Spencer F., describes K. W., 5
Bands, carried away by female, 99
Barrows, Walter B., on K. W. population, 27
Basking, 67
Bathing, 67
Berger, Andrew J., on food, 19; on bathing, 67; on basking, 68; on sleeping, 68; on development of young, 107, 122, 138, 139; on tail bobbing, 117; on feeding habits of fledglings, 121; on plumage changes, 119, 120, 121, 140; on song of immature, 133; on effect of cowbird, 174
Bill wiping, 66
Birds associated with K. W., 19–22
Borror, Donald J., used play-back of song, 47; made audiospectrograms of song, 126, fig. 9
Breeding range. *See* Range

Cabot, Samuel, Jr., collected first specimen, 5
Census, in 1951, 9, 10
Chasing. *See* Play
Climate, of nesting region, 12, 13; of wintering region, 35
Clustering of nest starts, 87

Cohesiveness of family, 115–116, 118–119
Coition, 56, 57
Colonies, 52, 53
Cory, Charles B., discovers winter home, 6
Covered nests, 78
Cowbird, effect on K. W., 2–3; incubation, 91; 144–181

Dependency, period of, 120–123
Desertion of nests: causes, 185–187; effects of human observation, 185
Diet. *See* Food
Discovery, first specimen, 5; winter home, 6; nesting ground, 7
Display, in territory defense, 46
Distraction display, 63–65
Dockham, Verne, on forest fires, 26; on fall migration, 39; on spring migration, 44
Down, 106, 107

Ectoparasites, 185
Eggs, 81–88; failure of, 93
Eggshells, feeding of, 98

Fecal sacs, removal, 103, 104; weights of, 111
Feeding, of female, 57, 69, 94, 96, 100; eggshells, 98
Females, arrival in spring, 44
Fighting between males, 45, 46
Fire. *See* Forest fire
Fledging, hastened by hunger, 107; age at, 110–113; behavior at, 113
Food, 18–19, of no nutritive value, 68–69; experimentation, 118; of fledglings, 121, 122
Forest fire, favorable to K. W., 23; causes, 23; before 1900, 25; since 1900, 26; few barriers to, 29, 30